ION TRANSPORT
ACROSS MEMBRANES

ION TRANSPORT
ACROSS MEMBRANES

Incorporating
Papers Presented at a Symposium
Held at the College of Physicians & Surgeons
Columbia University
October, 1953

HANS T. CLARKE, *Editor*
DAVID NACHMANSOHN, *Associate Editor*

1954
ACADEMIC PRESS INC., Publishers
NEW YORK, N. Y.

Dedicated to the memory of
JACQUES LOEB

Contributors

J. J. BLUM, *U. S. Naval Medical Research Institute, Bethesda, Maryland.*

SHELDON DRAY, *National Institute of Arthritis and Metabolic Diseases, National Institutes of Health, Bethesda, Maryland.*

P. DEBYE, *Department of Chemistry, Cornell University, Ithaca, New York.*

JOHN T. EDSALL, *University Laboratory of Physical Chemistry Related to Medicine and Public Health, Harvard University, Boston, Massachusetts.*

HENRY EYRING, *Department of Chemistry, University of Utah, Salt Lake City, Utah.*

S. L. FRIESS, *U. S. Naval Medical Research Institute, Bethesda, Maryland.*

EUGENE GRIM, *National Institute of Arthritis and Metabolic Diseases, National Institutes of Health, Bethesda, Maryland.*

FRANK R. N. GURD, *University Laboratory of Physical Chemistry Related to Medicine and Public Health, Harvard University, Boston, Massachusetts.*

TERRELL L. HILL, *U. S. Naval Medical Research Institute, Bethesda, Maryland.*

J. F. HOFFMAN, *Department of Biology, Princeton University, Princeton, New Jersey.*

A. F. HUXLEY, *Physiological Laboratory, University of Cambridge, England.*

JOHN G. KIRKWOOD, *Sterling Chemistry Laboratory, Yale University, New Haven, Connecticut.*

M. F. MORALES, *U. S. Naval Medical Research Institute, Bethesda, Maryland.*

GILBERT H. MUDGE, *Department of Medicine, College of Physicians & Surgeons, Columbia University, New York.*

DAVID NACHMANSOHN, *Department of Neurology, College of Physicians & Surgeons, Columbia University, New York.*

REX NEIHOF, *National Institute of Arthritis and Metabolic Diseases, National Institutes of Health, Bethesda, Maryland.*

W. J. V. OSTERHOUT, *Rockefeller Institute for Medical Research, New York.*

RANSOM B. PARLIN, *Department of Chemistry, University of Utah, Salt Lake City, Utah.*

A. K. PARPART, *Department of Biology, Princeton University, Princeton, New Jersey.*

GEORGE SCATCHARD, *Department of Chemistry, Massachusetts Institute of Technology, Cambridge, Massachusetts.*

KARL SOLLNER, *National Institute of Arthritis and Metabolic Diseases, National Institutes of Health, Bethesda, Maryland.*

HANS H. USSING, *Zoophysiological Laboratory, University of Copenhagen, Copenhagen, Denmark.*

IRWIN B. WILSON, *Department of Neurology, College of Physicians & Surgeons, Columbia University, New York.*

Preface

The collection of papers in this volume is based upon a Symposium on The Role of Proteins in Ion Transport across Membranes, sponsored by the National Science Foundation and held at the College of Physicians & Surgeons, Columbia University, on October 2 and 3, 1953.

The problem of ion transport across cell membranes has long attracted the attention of biologists in various fields. It is of prime importance for an understanding of the mechanism of bioelectric currents and the conduction of the nerve impulses; it has also played an important role in other studies such as the functions of the kidney and of red blood cells. The recent advances of biochemistry, especially in protein and enzyme chemistry, and the availability of isotopic tracers have made possible rapid progress in the area here under consideration. The problem is reaching a stage where the molecular forces involved have become a subject of more than speculative interest.

Now that experimental biology is approaching the molecular level, active cooperation between biologists, physical chemists, and protein chemists should lead to significant developments in basic theory. History records many such cases of cross-fertilization of ideas. For example, the membrane theory which is still the basis of all modern concepts of nerve impulse conduction was built upon the fundamental work of Ostwald, Nernst, Planck, and other physical chemists and physicists. The plan of this Symposium was not, as is the usual procedure, to bring together investigators working in similar areas for the discussion of limited, specific problems. It was planned, rather, to bring together a small group of physicochemically minded biologists working on ion transport and the role of proteins in this process, with a small group of distinguished physical chemists and protein chemists who are or may become interested in this borderline problem. The study of ion transport across membranes and the interaction between ions and proteins transcends the field of biology and has always been a domain in which physical chemists were interested.

At the suggestion of Dean Willard C. Rappleye a committee was organized, consisting of Robert F. Loeb, H. Houston Merritt, and David Rittenberg, with David Nachmansohn and Hans T. Clarke as organizing secretary and chairman, respectively. This committee decided to limit the number of participants to about fifty in order to ensure an

ix

atmosphere favorable to the exchange of ideas, by informal discussion and personal contacts, between the two groups. As the Symposium was held during only two days, the program was limited to eight papers, given by Drs. Ussing, Wilson, Eyring, Kirkwood, Scatchard, Debye, Sollner and Edsall. Drs. Rittenberg, Louis P. Hammett, I. I. Rabi, and Raymond M. Fuoss served as the chairman at each of the four sessions.

The Symposium was held on the eve of the 25th anniversary of the Columbia-Presbyterian Medical Center. As stated by Dean Rappleye in his opening address, Columbia University is proud to have been host to so many distinguished scientists. The Symposium was an appropriate expression of the spirit of research prevailing at the Center.

The present volume contains the substance of the various addresses, together with six invited articles on allied topics, contributed by various investigators who could not be represented on the program. The organizing committee expresses its gratitude to all the authors of the chapters here assembled. The book is dedicated to the memory of Jacques Loeb, pioneer in the application of the principles of physical chemistry to biological problems, whose intensive studies of ion transport across cell membranes are still bearing fruit, as pointed out by Dr. Osterhout, his associate through many years.

Contents

Note on the Work of Jacques Loeb

W. J. V. OSTERHOUT

It is a pleasure to respond to the suggestion of the Editorial Committee to say something about the pioneer work of Jacques Loeb[a] in applying physical chemistry to biology.

Loeb was one of the first to see the importance to biology of the dissociation theory of Arrhenius, and he applied it with conspicuous success. A few examples will suffice to show the nature of his work.

Loeb's point of view may be illustrated by his experiments with eggs of the fish *Fundulus*, which develop in distilled water as well as in sea water. In a solution of sodium chloride isotonic with sea water, the eggs soon die. This also happens in an isotonic solution of zinc sulfate, but when these two solutions are mixed in suitable proportions normal embryos are produced. From this he concluded that sodium and zinc ions antagonize each other. He found that, in general, the toxic effects of univalent cations could be counteracted by the addition of small amounts of bivalent cations and by still smaller amounts of tervalent cations. It was a novel and important idea that the physiological effects of ions could be predicted by knowing their electrical charges, and it gave a great stimulus to the application of physical chemistry to biology.

Loeb suggested that these effects were due to the action of ions on the permeability of the membrane surrounding the egg. The antagonistic action is quite different as soon as the embryo escapes from the covering. He thus directed attention to the importance of the study of permeability.

A deep interest in the changes which occur in the egg after union with the sperm led him to attempt to analyze and control these by using the techniques of physical chemistry. His first task was to induce development in the absence of sperm (artificial parthenogenesis). This he soon accomplished by varying osmotic pressure, pH, surface tension, and other factors. These experiments aroused great interest and stimulated extensive research which still continues. Loeb concluded

[a] For a fuller account, see the Memorial Volume, *J. Gen. Physiol.* **8**, (1925–1928).

1

that the first step is a change at the surface of the egg whereby the normal structure begins to break down (cytolysis). If this continues too long, death occurs, but, if stopped at the right time, it is followed by cell division and development.

In the course of Loeb's experiments it became clear that in many cases a knowledge of the properties of colloids is important. The whole subject was at that time in a state of confusion and he sought to clarify it by using the methods of physical chemistry. He therefore began experiments on the colloidal properties of gelatin. An important aspect of this work was his study of the effects of pH. McBain[b] speaks of the invaluable services of Loeb in pointing out the predominant role of pH on amphoteric basic and acidic colloids. In this field his scientific imagination and insight had a clarifying effect, as is evident in his well-known book on proteins and the theory of colloidal behavior.

These examples may suffice to illustrate the character of his work, in all of which he sought, with notable success, to apply the methods of the exact sciences.

In many cases Loeb was able to replace obscure biological ideas by clear-cut, mechanistic conceptions and thereby opened up new fields of research of fundamental importance. His example was inspiring and his influence was great. For this we owe him a debt of gratitude.

[b] J. W. McBain, "Colloid Science," p. 215. D. C. Heath & Co., Boston, 1950.

Ion Transport Across Biological Membranes

HANS H. USSING

DIFFUSION THROUGH BIOLOGICAL MEMBRANES

At the outset it might be worth while to define briefly what we experimental biologists mean by a biological membrane. I think most of us can agree upon a formulation like this: Whenever we meet, in a living organism or part thereof, a boundary that presents a diffusion resistance to solutes higher than that of the phases separated by the boundary, it is called a membrane. The membrane is often, but not always, anatomically discernible.

The objects we study under the name of biological membranes are extremely diverse. Thus we have membranes on the multicellular level like the gastric mucosa or the frog skin epithelium. Then there are the cell membranes like, for instance, the membranes of the nerve fiber.

Finally, the work of the last few years tends to show that even membranes on the subcellular level are highly important. Notably, the surface of the mitochondria shows membrane-like properties, such as the ability to maintain, and under certain circumstances to create, within the mitochondrium concentrations of a number of substances which differ from those of the surroundings. As an example we may take a table from a recent paper by Bartley and Davies (1952) (Table I). It is seen that the Na ion undergoes a conspicuous concentration in the mitochondria as compared to the surrounding medium.

At first sight there seems very little in common between the nerve fiber membrane and the skin of a frog, or between the tip of a plant root and the gill of a crab. Nevertheless, these different structures show many similarities in the way they handle inorganic ions. Formerly it was generally assumed that the similarities stemmed from the fact that the element determining the behavior of ions was in all cases a cell membrane, or possibly a number of cell membranes placed in series. This may still be true. With the increasing knowledge concerning the ability of mitochondria to concentrate and exclude certain ion species, one may, however, speculate as to whether some of the phenomena involving the transfer of ions across cell boundaries are actually the result of the activity of mitochondria. Discussing this problem at the

3

TABLE I

INTERNAL-TO-EXTERNAL CONCENTRATION RATIOS FOUND FOR METABOLIZING
SHEEP-KIDNEY CORTEX IN MITOCHONDRIA AT 20°C

Substance	Ratio	Concentration in medium after separation (M)
H^+	2.5	1.6×10^{-7}
Na^+	26	5.9×10^{-4}
K^+	2.0	9.0×10^{-2}
Mg^{++}	4.5	2.0×10^{-4}
Orthophosphate	6.0	1.9×10^{-4}
Adenosine polyphosphates	0.7	4.3×10^{-4}
Pyruvate	0.8	3.5×10^{-3}
Fumarate	8.0	2.8×10^{-4}
Oxaloacetate	0.1	1.8×10^{-3}
α-Ketoglutarate	1.0	6.3×10^{-2}
Citrate	0.8	1.4×10^{-2}

Water content of metabolizing mitochondria = 80%.
Water content of nonmetabolizing mitochondria = 91%.
(After Bartley and Davies, 1952)

conference on active transport at Bangor this summer, Davies pointed out that in secreting kidney cells the mitochondria are arranged longitudinally from the cell wall bordering the lumen of the tubules. During the discussion following Dr. Davies' paper, Professor Wigglesworth then mentioned that, in the salt-reabsorbing part of the Malpighian tubule in insects, the giant mitochondria actually pierce the luminal cell boundary, waving with one end in the pre-urine while having the base well within the cell body.

Alternatively one may imagine that the surface of the mitochondrium and that of the cell have in common certain properties which enable them to handle ions in a characteristic manner, and resist their free diffusion.

This brings us to the point of asking: What is the nature of the cell membrane? Or, to be more cautious, how do the biologists picture the cell membrane? Without having made use of Mr. Gallup's methods, it is probably fair to assume that the concept most widely accepted is that of the lipoid-pore membrane, as proposed by Collander (1937). It implies that the less polar substances penetrate by dissolving in the membrane phase, whereas the polar substances, notably the inorganic ions, penetrate only in so far as the ionic diameter is smaller than the pore diameter. Although the lipoid-pore theory explains a multitude of experimental facts, it has not remained unchallenged, however. Thus Davson and Danielli (1943) have proved theoretically that the experimental facts obtained by Collander and Bärlund (1933) could equally well be obtained with a nonporous membrane in which the diffusing molecules and ions dissolved. The criticism by Davson and Danielli is an important one since it poses the question of whether polar molecules, like inorganic ions, pass the membrane dissolved in the water that fills the pores or whether they dissolve in a nonwatery medium.

Recently, in the Laboratory of Zoophysiology, Copenhagen, we have approached the question of the existence of pores in cell membranes from an angle which promises some measure of success (cf. Ussing, 1952). The approach is based on the following well known facts: If water, or any substance which is insoluble in the membrane phase, is to pass a pore membrane by simple diffusion, the rate is to a first approximation proportional to the total area of the pores. If, however, water is pressed through the pores by hydrostatic pressure or osmotic pressure, the rate is determined by the shape and number of the individual pores and no longer simply by the sum of their areas. We can thus define two independent measures of water permeability, namely, 1) diffusion permeability as determined by the rate of diffusion of isotopic water, and 2) filtration or osmotic permeability determined by the rate of flow induced by a difference in osmotic or hydrostatic pressure. Obviously the difference between the two water permeabilities vanishes if pores are absent so that all water molecules pass by dissolving in the membrane phase.

Thus, by determining both water permeabilities on the same membrane, one can decide whether it has pores or not. Furthermore, the relative magnitudes of the two permeabilities allows an estimate of the pore sizes.

As early as 1935, Hevesy, Hofer, and Krogh (1935) found the osmotic permeability of the frog skin to be 3–5 times greater than the diffusion permeability as determined with heavy water. This has been confirmed by Capraro and Bernini (1952), and the phenomenon has been found to be even more pronounced in the isolated skin of the toad (Koefoed-Johnsen and Ussing, 1953). Prescott and Zeuthen (1953) have determined diffusion and osmotic permeability to water in a number of eggs of fishes and amphibians (Table II).

It is seen that if both permeabilities are expressed in the same units, say μ/sec, the osmotic permeability is always higher than the dif-

TABLE II
PERMEABILITY TO WATER OF DIFFERENT EGGS

Cell type	P_d (μ/sec)	P_f (μ/sec)	P_f/P_d
Frog ovarian egg	1.28	89.1	69
Zebra fish ovarian egg	0.68	29.3	43
Xenopus body cavity egg	0.90	1.59	1.8
Frog body cavity egg	0.75	1.30	1.7
Zebra fish shed, nondeveloping	0.36	0.45	1.3

Diffusion permeability coefficient: P_d.
Filtration permeability coefficient: P_f.
(After Prescott and Zeuthen, 1953)

fusion permeability. In the ovarian eggs the difference is very striking indeed, indicating the presence of large pores. Krogh and Ussing (1937), on the other hand, demonstrated that during the first days of development the trout egg is absolutely impermeable to heavy water. This may suggest that the membrane substance, even between the pores of the membranes of other eggs, is also tight, so that all water penetration takes place through pores.

Egg membranes, however, are probably very specialized, and it would be desirable to get information concerning the two water permeabilities, even in other types of living membranes.

We shall also have to face another criticism of the simple membrane concept, a criticism which was voiced by Krogh (1937a) during a Faraday Society Discussion. Commenting on the proper use of the word membrane he said: "Active transport of a substance is brought about by some kind of dynamic machinery working within the cells, which may in turn be bounded by membranes allowing certain substances to pass and holding others back. I maintain that such membranes are, in the present state of our knowledge, definitely unsuitable for the study of membrane properties, because it is too difficult to distinguish the membrane from the cell of which it is an integral and perhaps variable part."

At that time the importance of active transport as distinct from simple diffusion was not so generally accepted as it is now, and I have heard the comment that Krogh tried to revive the old vitalistic views concerning the processes of life. But the difficulties of studying simple permeation in the presence of simultaneous active transport processes have proved real enough. If we want to study the passage of ions through cell membranes, then what we need first of all is means to decide which ions are actively transported and which are not.

Apparently the easiest case to deal with is that of a cell in equilibrium or steady state with its surroundings. Under these conditions any ion which is not subject to active transport must obey the simple condition $\bar{\mu}_o = \bar{\mu}_i$ where $\bar{\mu}_o$ is its electrochemical potential in the cell interior and $\bar{\mu}_i$ that of the ion in the bathing solution.

If we had at our disposal reversible electrodes for all ions concerned which could be inserted in the cells, the problem would be easily answered. Unfortunately this is not the case. We therefore have no better choice than to calculate the electrochemical potentials from the concentrations and the electric potential difference across the membrane, as determined with internal microelectrodes, usually making the more or less well justified assumption that the activity coefficients are the same in both phases. Crude as this method may be, it has led to rather consistent results, indicating that K and Cl are in equilibrium with the surroundings in muscle and possibly in nerve. The technique of measuring potentials by aid of microelectrodes, inserted in the cell interior, has recently been developed to a high degree of refinement, and technically it may soon be possible to measure potentials in most cell types of the body; but we are still left with a vague doubt as to whether or not the values found are always thermodynamically significant.

Even more serious is the question of the activity coefficient to be applied. Is it justifiable to treat the probably highly organized cell interior as a dilute solution? Certainly, if the ions of the cell interior are forming complexes with organic cell constituents, our estimate of the equilibrium conditions may be very far off.

It has repeatedly been claimed that myosin and hemoglobin bind potassium in preference to sodium (for references, see Stone and Shapiro, 1948, and Steinbach, 1950). However, work with pure hemoglobin and preparations of muscle particulate matter (Steinbach, 1950) showed no evidence for selective K binding. Rather, in the case of the muscle preparation, there was a distinct preference for sodium.

Thus, unless the spatial arrangement of the protein molecules within the cells changes their ion binding properties profoundly, there is reason to believe that the K ions are free in the popular sense of the word. This is also borne out by the fact that intracellular K has the same mobility in the direction of the fiber axis as has K in free watery solution (Hodgkin and Keynes, 1950).

The analysis, along the lines outlined here, of the equilibrium conditions for the more important inorganic ions has so far been performed for muscle and nerve only. It would have been tempting to extrapolate the result that K is in electrochemical equilibrium with the surroundings even in other types of animal cells with high K content, if it had not been for the fact that the erythrocytes of most animals also have a high concentration of K relative to the blood plasma. Even though the internal potential of red cells cannot be measured directly, a fair estimate of it can be obtained from the distribution of the freely diffusible ions Cl^- and H^+ between cells and surroundings. This estimate indicates strongly that the electrochemical potential of intracellular K is much higher than that of extracellular K. Thus even in the case of the K ion—which is one of those most carefully studied—it is still largely unknown whether or not it is subject to active transport in most animal cell types.

The equilibrium method for distinguishing between passive diffusion and actively transported ions clearly has its limitations. In the first place, one must know whether the ion species under study is at all able to penetrate the membrane. The introduction of isotopic tracers in biological work has, however, largely overcome this difficulty, since it is possible, without altering the chemical composition of the system, to study the rate of ion exchange across the membranes. A more serious objection to the equilibrium method is that our experimental objects are often far from the equilibrium state. Some membranes, like the frog skin and the gastric mucosa, are continuously transporting certain ions from one boundary to the other. Even single cells in the isolated state usually show continuous changes in ionic composition. It would therefore be desirable if, from the kinetics of ion permeation, one could draw conclusions as to whether a given ion species diffuses passively or whether it is subject to active transport.

The problem of passive diffusion through living membranes can be approached along two lines, different in principle.

In the first place one may integrate the general differential equation for the diffusion of charged particles, making certain *a priori* assumptions as to conditions within the membrane phase. The method was first applied by Goldman (1943) and has recently been developed further by Teorell (1951).

Teorell also tested his equation on collodion membranes and found good agreement between experiment and theory.

The integration depends, however, on the assumption that the membrane is uniform throughout—an assumption which is not even likely in the case of living membranes. If an ion does not behave according to the integrated equation, it can always be blamed upon structural peculiarities of the membrane. It can easily be shown, however, that there is one characteristic function of the permeability to a free passive ion which depends solely on the electrochemical potential difference, being independent of any assumptions as to the membrane structure. This characteristic is in the flux ratio, i.e., the ratio between the total diffusion stream of the ion passing the membrane in one direction and that passing in the opposite direction. If we denote by M_{in} the flux of the ion going inward and by M_{out} that going outward, we have

$$RT \ln (M_{in}/M_{out}) = \bar{\mu}_o - \bar{\mu}_i \qquad (1)$$

where $\bar{\mu}_o$ and $\bar{\mu}_i$ are the electrochemical potentials of the ion in the outside and inside phases, respectively. This relationship has been derived by Teorell (1949) and myself (1949) independently and seems also to be implicit in Eyring's theory of rate processes as applied to diffusion. (Zwolinski, Eyring, and Reese, 1949) In many cases the flux values can be obtained easily from experiments with isotopic tracers.

As an example we may consider the passage of chloride ions through the isolated frog skin. As is well known, the isolated frog skin, when in contact with suitable salt solutions, maintains for many hours an electric potential difference across itself, the inside solution being positive relative to the outside. Some twenty years ago another surprising property of the frog skin attracted the interest of physiologists. Huf (1935) found that the isolated surviving frog skin, when in contact with Ringer's solution on both sides, performs an active transport of NaCl from the outside to the inside solution. Shortly afterwards, Krogh (1937b) observed that frogs in need of salt will take up chloride ions through the skin even from solutions as dilute as 10^{-5} M with respect to NaCl.

Some years ago (Ussing, 1948) the present author advanced the hypothesis that only the Na ions are transported actively the the frog skin whereas the Cl ions follow passively owing to the electric potential difference created by the active Na transport. In order to test this

HANS H. USSING

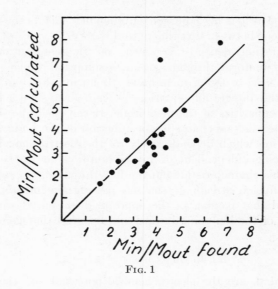

FIG. 1

hypothesis, a series of experiments were performed by my collaborators,
Drs. Valborg Koefoed-Johnsen and Hilde Levi, and myself (1952) in
which the outflux of chloride was determined by Cl^{36} added to the inside solution, whereas the difference between influx and outflux, i.e.,
the net Cl flux, was determined by chemical analysis. The spontaneous
potential difference across the skin was recorded and the mean calculated for each experimental period. Fig. 1 shows the relatively good
agreement between the flux ratios found and those calculated according
to equation 1. More recent experiments, in which influx and outflux
were determined with the two radioactive tracers Cl^{36} and Cl^{38}, are also
in agreement with the assumption of a purely passive behaviour of Cl
in the nonstimulated skin.

Linderholm (1952) in Teorell's laboratory has been able completely
to verify this finding.

Similar studies of the behavior of K ions in Cephalopod and crusta-
cean nerve have been performed by Keynes (1951) and Keynes and
Lewis (1951). Some of their results are shown in Table III. It is seen
that the agreement between the flux ratios calculated and those found
is excellent.

And that would have been a good time to stop doing experiments,
at least as far as our peace of mind is concerned. Quite recently, however, Hodgkin and Keynes (1953) have repeated the experiment on

TABLE III

INFLUX AND OUTFLUX OF K IN RESTING NERVE

	Flux ($\mu\mu$moles $cm^{-2}sec^{-1}$)		Flux ratio found (M_{in}/M_{out})	Flux ratio calculated (c_o/c_i)exp $[EF/RT]$
	Influx	Outflux		
Sepia axon	17	58	0.3	⎫
Sepia axon	11.1	33	0.35	⎬ 0.34 (Keynes, 1951)
Crab nerve	19	22	0.86	0.89 (Keynes and Lewis, 1951)

dinitrophenol poisoned Cephalopod nerve in order to have a system where active processes were blocked as far as possible. It then turned out that the above relationship between flux ratio and electrochemical potential difference for K did not apply any longer. Rather the relationship was

$$RT \ln(M_{in}/M_{out}) = 4(\bar{\mu}_o - \bar{\mu}_i) \tag{2}$$

as if during its passage through the membrane the potassium ion had 4 positive charges. This seems to imply that one of the main assumptions underlying equation 1—namely, independent movement of the ions in the membrane phase—is incorrect in this case. Hodgkin and Keynes (private communication) propose the following explanation of the phenomen: The only paths where the K ion can pass the membrane have 4 sites, each of which has always to be occupied by a K ion. Thus no K ion can leave at one boundary unless another one is taken up at the other. This means that all four of them will have to move as a unit if they are to move at all. Statistical considerations indicate that such a restriction of the free movement would lead to the relationship found by Hodgkin and Keynes. The example just discussed is by no means the only case where a presumably passive passage of an ion through a living membrane yields flux ratios that deviate from those expected, but the other cases so far known are of an entirely different nature.

As a matter of fact, the other type of deviation was predicted before any clear evidence of its existence had been found.

Commenting on the rapid exchange between intracellular and extracellular Na in isolated frog muscle, the present author pointed out (1947), that the rate found need not be a true measure of the active extrusion of Na from the fibers. Let us assume that the exchange were mediated by some carrier molecule which could not leave the membrane phase and which became completely saturated with Na at a concentration lower than that prevailing at both boundaries, whereas it did not measurably bind K or other cations. It is then obvious that the carrier could bring about the mixing of two Na isotopes across the membrane, but only in such a fashion that, for each Na ion passing in, one would have to pass out. The phenomenon was called exchange diffusion. It goes without saying that this is a limiting case. Any real carrier would show some "slip," so that sometimes a H or K ion would exchange against the Na ion. Nevertheless, an element of exchange diffusion would always tend to be present in carrier-mediated passive diffusion.

Recently, several cases have been reported in which an ion exchange shows the characteristics of exchange diffusion. As an example we may take the Na exchange of mitochondria. As mentioned earlier, Bartley and Davies (1952) have found kidney mitochondria to concentrate Na ions very appreciably. This mitochondrium Na undergoes a steady exchange with that of the medium, and this exchange shows a highly positive correlation with temperature and with the addition of substrate. So far it looks like an "ordinary" active transport. But on closer study he found that, at zero degrees, 4000 Na ions more were taken up and given off for each extra molecule of O_2 consumed after the addition of substrate. This practically rules out any stoichiometrical relationship between metabolism and Na exchange. Davies finds it more likely that the addition of substrate leads to the formation of carrier molecules, which in turn give rise to the exchange diffusion.

Summing up then: Even if we consider only the cases in which ions move passively through living membranes, we may find the following relationships

$|RT \ln(M_{in}/M_{out})| = |\bar{\mu}_o - \bar{\mu}_i|$ (Chloride in frog skin)
$|RT \ln(M_{in}/M_{out})| > |\bar{\mu}_o - \bar{\mu}_i|$ (K in DNP poisoned nerve)
$|RT \ln(M_{in}/M_{out})| < |\bar{\mu}_o - \bar{\mu}_i|$ (Na in mitochondria, over and above the active Na transport)

It is thus seen that behavior according to equation 1 strongly indicates that the ion in question moves passively. Deviations from that relationship do not *exclude* passive behavior, but they do indicate that some restriction is imposed upon the independent movements of the ions. But are the explanations outlined above the only possible ones, or can the phenomena arise through mechanisms we have so far not thought of? Is it possible to indicate ways and means to find out which explanations are the more likely ones? These are some of the questions I should like to ask the experts who are present here.

ACTIVE TRANSPORT

Although, as has been demonstrated above, penetration through living membranes often shows characteristics of passive diffusion, we are left with a number of cases where very definitely the transfer requires work on the part of the cells (or the mitochondria). Such transfer is termed active transport. As a matter of fact, if we go through the literature there seems hardly any inorganic constituent of the organism which is not transported actively in one organ or another. In spite of this we shall usually find, in the animal organs at least, that the transport in the individual organ or cell type shows a high degree of specificity.

It is of course possible that what we consider under the name of active transport processes is a thoroughly heterogeneous group, bringing together phenomena that have no natural interrelationships. However, the human mind tends to make the simplest possible assumption first, and personally I favor the hypothesis that we are dealing with a limited number of mechanisms, each concerned with the transport of one or limited number of related ions.

One of the ions whose transport has been studied most extensively in recent years is the sodium ion, and I want to use the rest of the time allotted to me to discuss the active transport of this ion species.

We have already heard about the ability of kidney mitochondria to concentrate this ion, a feature which is even more remarkable because the kidney cells themselves, like almost all animal cells, have a low Na and a high K concentration. Whereas it is still a matter of dispute to what extent the high cellular K of most cells represents a Donnan distribution, it is generally agreed that Na is kept out of the cells by a continuous active extrusion. The alternatives would be either impermeability to Na (*cf.* Boyle and Conway, 1941), which can be readily disproved by tracer experiments, or an activity coefficient for Na in the cell interior several times higher than unity.

The latter alternative is advocated by Ling (1951) who assumes that the ionic selectivity of muscle is not a membrane property but "rather a result of the difference in magnitude of coulombic forces exerted upon various hydrated ions by spatially fixed charges."

Fortunately, one may say, for the concept of active Na transport, there are systems like the kidney tubule and the frog skin in which the existence of such transport can be demonstrated beyond any doubt. The isolated frog skin in particular is well suited for studying the properties of the transport mechanism because no other active transport process is normally going on in this preparation. This can be demonstrated most conclusively by the short-circuiting technique.

Since the frog skin maintains a potential difference across itself it must be possible to draw current from it by connecting the two bathing solutions. This was first demonstrated by Francis (1933), who found that the partially short-circuited skin would give off electric current for many hours. Later, Stapp (1941) and Lund and Stapp (1947) improved the technique, using electrodes of low resistance to bring about a nearly total short circuit of the skin. These workers did not correlate the current with ionic movements. It is clear, however, that any active transport of an ion species that is not balanced by an equally large transfer of other charged particles must contribute to the short-circuit current. Ultimately, since the aqueous salt solutions used cannot accept or give off electrons, the short-circuit current must arise from the movements of ions. And a chemical analysis of the system before and after a period of short circuiting should suffice to demonstrate the origin of the current. Even though the amounts of ions transferred are too small to be measured precisely by ordinary chemical methods, the analysis is easily performed by aid of isotopic tracers.

Figure 2 shows the apparatus used by us (Ussing and Zerahn, 1951) for the simultaneous determination of ion transport and short-circuit current.

The skin, S, is placed between two celluloid (now Lucite) chambers, C, containing Ringer's solution. The potential difference across the skin is read on a tube potentiometer, P, which is connected through calomel electrodes to two agar-Ringer bridges, opening close to the skin. Another pair of bridges, B and B_1, are connected through silver-silver chloride electrodes with a microammeter, M, and a battery, D. The current in this circuit is now adjusted by aid of the variable resistance, W, so that the potential drop across the skin is zero.

It is obvious that this accomplishes a total short circuit of the skin. The current generated is read on the microammeter.

Simultaneously with the current measurement, the flux through the skin of one or more ion species can be measured by adding radioactive tracers on one side and making activity measurements on samples taken on the other side at suitable intervals. For chloride, for example, one can measure influx with Cl^{36} and outflux with Cl^{38}, so that, by dif-

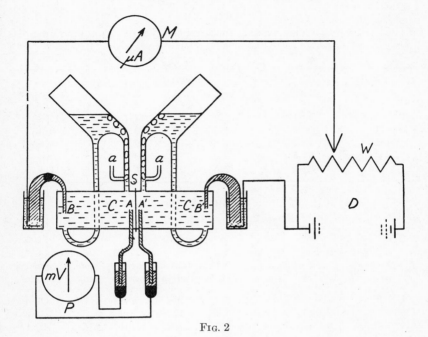

FIG. 2

ference, one gets the net transfer rate of chloride ions. Similarly in the
case of sodium we use the isotopes Na^{24} and Na^{22}.

The outcome of the experiment with chloride was, as one would expect from the passive nature of the chloride ion, that influx and outflux
were equal.

In the case of the sodium ion the result of the experiment is simpler
than one has the right to expect from a biological experiment. The net
flux of sodium ions, which is the amount actively transported, is exactly equal to the short-circuit current generated by the skin. This is
clearly seen from Table IV.

The equality between active Na transport and current holds true
whether the transport is stimulated by, for instance, posterior lobe
hormones or atropine, or whether it is inhibited by, say, dinitrophenol
or narcotics.

The transport is highly specific to Na. Of all the cations so far tested,
only Li is also transported, but nevertheless it cannot totally replace
Na in the system. Table V shows the results of some experiments performed by Dr. Zerahn, in which part of the Na in the bathing solutions

TABLE IV

SHORT-CIRCUIT CURRENT AND SODIUM FLUX VALUES FOR A NUMBER
OF SHORT-CIRCUITED FROG SKINS (*Rana temporaria*) (RINGER'S
SOLUTION ON BOTH SIDES)

	$\mu amps/cm^2$			
	Na in	*Na out*	*ΔNa*	*Current*
I	20.1	2.4	17.7	17.8
II	11.1	1.5	9.6	9.9
III	40.1	0.89	39.2	38.6
IV	62.5	2.2	60.3	56.8
V	47.9	2.5	45.4	44.3

TABLE V

EFFECT OF PARTIAL REPLACEMENT OF Na^+ BY Li^+

	(Li/Na) $\times$ 100 in solutions	*Influx ($\mu eq.$ Na/hr)*	*Outflux ($\mu eq.$ Na/hr)*	*ΔNa ($\mu eq./hr$)*	*ΔNa (μamp)*	*Total current (μamp)*	*"Li current" (μamp)*	*"Li current" (per cent of total)*
I	21.2	8.5	0.7	7.7	206	284	78	27.4
	21.2	7.0	0.6	6.4	171	249	78	31.3
II	33.3	6.0	0.4	5.6	150	194	44	22.7
	33.3	3.7	0.5	3.2	86	131	45	34.3
III	52.0	2.81	0.40	2.41	65	107	42	39.2
	52.0	2.17	0.69	1.48	40	91	51	56.0
IV	80.5	1.62	0.25	1.37	37	104	67	64.0
	80.5	0.85	0.37	0.48	13	44	31	71.0

When part of the Na in solutions bathing the short-circuited frog skin is replaced by Li, the latter ion carries a corresponding part of the current.
Area of skin: 7.1 cm^2.

was replaced by Li. It is seen that under these conditions there is an
extra current over and above that accounted for by the net Na transport. This extra current makes up very nearly the same fraction of the
total as does the Li concentration of the total cation. So it can be stated
with some degree of certainty that Li is transported.

If a similar experiment is performed in which a fraction of the total
Na of the Ringer's solution is replaced by K, the result is entirely different. As shown in Table VI, even when 35 % of the cation is K, there
is no current other than that accounted for by the active transport of Na.

Without going into detail it might be worth while to summarize the

TABLE VI

EFFECT OF PARTIAL REPLACEMENT OF Na^+ BY K^+

	(K/Na) $\times 100$ in solutions	Influx $(\mu eq.Na/hr)$	Outflux $(\mu eq.Na/hr)$	Na $(\mu eq./hr)$	Na current $(\mu amp.)$	Total current $(\mu amp.)$
I	35.0	13.2	0.58	12.6	339	289
	"	9.4	0.81	8.6	230	236
II	"	5.80	0.38	5.42	145	157
	"	6.13	0.35	5.78	155	154
	"	5.50	0.41	5.09	136	143
III	"	4.05	1.04	3.01	81	85
	"	5.30	1.06	4.24	114	116
	"	5.35	0.94	4.41	118	121

Even when as much as one-third of the Na^+ in the bathing solution is replaced by K^+, the total current generated by the short-circuited frog skin is carried by the Na ions.

Area of skin: 7.1 cm².

properties of the Na transport mechanism as found by the method just mentioned.

The transport is inhibited by lack of oxygen and by cyanide, etc. Moreover, it is completely and reversibly inhibited by dinitrophenol, indicating the participation of energy-rich phosphate bonds in the transport process.

It is inhibited completely and reversibly by 5 % CO_2 in the oxygen or the air used for mixing.

It is inhibited by the addition of anticholinesterases such as tetra-ethyl pyrophosphate, procaine, and eserine to the inside solution (Kirschner, 1953). As is the case with the esterases, the inhibition with eserine is reversible, whereas that with TEPP is not. This certainly suggests the participation of the acetyl choline-cholinesterase system in the transport process.

A strong inhibition can also be produced by those sulfa drugs that are known to be strong inhibitors of carbonic anhydrase (Fuhrman, 1952).

A very pronounced reduction of the transport is brought about in the absence of K ions (Table VII). Thus, although the mechanism does not transport K measurably, it can not work well without this ion (Koefoed-Johnsen, unpublished; cf. also Huf and Wills, 1951).

A stimulation of the transport is brought about by a whole series of

TABLE VII

EFFECT OF K-CONCENTRATION IN BATHING SOLUTIONS ON SHORT-CIRCUIT CURRENT
AND Na FLUX VALUES OF SHORT-CIRCUITED FROG SKIN (*Rana temporaria*)

	$\mu amps/cm^2$			
	Na in	*Na out*	ΔNa	*Current*
Control	47.0	2.4	44.6	43.5
K-free Ringer	11.9	4.7	7.2	6.5
K-free Ringer	6.8	3.7	3.1	2.3
33⅓% K Ringer	12.0	2.1	9.9	10.2
33⅓% K Ringer	12.8	1.8	11.0	10.5

pharmacologically diverse drugs such as atropine, several curares, histamine, and pilocarpine. Moreover, a strong and fully reversible stimulation is induced by neurohypophyseal extracts. Simultaneously with the increased Na transport, a corresponding increase in the osmotic permeability to water is observed with the neurohypophyseal extracts (*cf.* Koefoed-Johnsen and Ussing, 1953), whereas the diffusion permeability to water remains practically the same. Such an effect can be explained most easily if we assume that the hormone increases the size of the individual pores at some high-diffusion-resistance layer of the skin without increasing the total area available to water diffusion. But this implies also that the Na ions (or the Na compound concerned in the transport) pass this layer by way of the pores and not by dissolving in the membrane.

After having summarized the properties of the Na transport mechanism as it is in the frog skin, it might be of interest to compare it with the peculiarities of the Na transfer in some of the organs and cell types in which active Na transport is also assumed to be at work.

Table VIII shows the Na flux through different membranes which, presumably, transport this ion actively. In erythrocytes, nerve, and muscle, Na influx and outflux are not very different, the active transport, as it were, being largely balanced by back diffusion. The first value given for the frog skin is obtained when the influx and outflux are made equal by a counter potential balancing the active transport force. It is seen that the rates in the frog skin, nerve fiber, and muscle fiber are of the same order, whereas the red cells show an exchange which is two orders of magnitude less.

The table also includes an estimate of the net Na flux through the kidney tubules of man, assuming a total surface of 50,000 cm² (Rehberg, 1926).

TABLE VIII

TENTATIVE VALUES FOR INFLUX, OUTFLUX, AND NET FLUX OF SODIUM IONS
ACROSS DIFFERENT LIVING MEMBRANES ($\mu\mu$moles/cm²/sec)

	Influx	Outflux	Net Flux	Reference
Erythrocyte, human	0.15	0.15	—	Solomon (1952)
Muscle				
sartorius	—	14	—	Levi and Ussing (1948)
sartorius	16	—	—	Harris and Burn (1949)
adductor, long	12	—	—	Keynes (1951)
Nerve, *Sepia axon*	61	31	30	Keynes (1951)
Frog skin				
with counter potential	115	115	—	Ussing and Zerahn (1951)
short circuited	500	20	480	Ussing and Zerahn (1951)
Kidney tubule, human	—	—	3000	Rehberg (1926)

The Na transport in the red cell differs in many respects from that in the frog skin. In the first place, the red cell mechanism is insensitive to HCN and lack of oxygen. On the other hand, it is blocked by agents that inhibit anaerobic glycolysis (*cf.* Maizels, 1951).

Little appears to be known as to how far the active Na transport in muscle and nerve is affected by lack of oxygen. We know that the resting potential of nerve is depressed during anoxia (Gerard, 1932; Ling and Gerard, 1949). Frog muscle, on the other hand, shows little depression of the potential under similar conditions, unless it is also treated with iodoacetate. Ling and Gerard's A fraction of the resting potential was directly proportional to the concentration of phosphocreatine, and it was therefore suggested that phosphate bond energy may be directly concerned with the maintenance of the membrane potential. Assuming that this again depends on the functioning of the active Na transport, we are back to the energy-rich phosphate bonds as being directly concerned with the Na transport, in muscle as in frog skin. There seem, however, to be cases of active Na transport where this is not the case. Thus Koch (1953) has demonstrated that the NaCl uptake through the gills of the crab *Eriocheir sinensis* is not at all sensitive to DNP (whereas it is blocked by methylene blue). Whether this animal produces ATP by a route that is insensitive to DNP or whether the transport is energized by a different mechanism remains to be found out.

In the red cells at least, and possibly in some or all of the cells showing active Na extrusion, there is a simultaneous active uptake of K. With respect to the interdependence of Na extrusion and K uptake in erythrocytes there are rather sharp differences in opinion between the workers in the field. To take just two of the more recent discussions of the problem, Solomon (1952) considers the Na transport and the K transport to be brought about by independent mechanisms, whereas Harris (1953) assumes the transport to take place in such a way that the carrier bringing Na out is changed on arrival at the outside surface into a carrier that prefers K. The latter carrier in turn is transformed into the Na carrier by a chemical reaction taking place at the inner boundary. Both authors agree, however, that at low temperatures, where there is no active transport going on, the exchange of K and Na proceeds as if the membrane contained a carrier allowing exchange diffusion between K and Na, but showing no preference to either ion.

According to Harris' hypothesis, the only difference between the passive exchange taking place in the cold and the active transport going on at higher temperatures is that the carrier undergoes cyclic transformations between the "Na form" and the "K form" in the latter case and not in the former one.

Although this view is still largely hypothetical, it gains increased interest because Hodgkin and Keynes (1953) have recently found indications of a similar "forced exchange" of K against Na in the cephalopod nerve during recovery. Thus the Na transport does not function in the absence of K in the outer medium. One might therefore ask whether there is always a compulsory transport of K in the direction opposite to that of the Na transport.

There is, however, still no evidence of such a process in muscle and frog skin and in the isolated gill of *Eriocheir* Na ions and K ions are transported inward indiscriminately.

With respect to the mechanism of the active transport, not very much can be said at present. The fact that the transport is specific and is able to distinguish between as closely related ions as Na and K, leaves little doubt that specific chemical binding is involved. This is perhaps not as astonishing as it seemed a few years ago, since it is now known that K and Na have specific and often antagonistic effects on a number of enzymes. Thus it may not be too audacious to assume that both ions form more or less specific complexes with the enzyme proteins.

In most of the hypotheses so far advanced to explain the active transport, a complexing organic molecule is assumed to act as carrier for the ion transported, as discussed above in connection with the erythrocytes.

As I see it, the carrier hypothesis has played an enormous role as a pedagogical means of convincing the scientific public that active transport is thermodynamically possible and not at all mysterious. It is still probably the most well founded hypothesis. But we should not be content with a model just because it is not inherently nonsensical. Other possibilities, should also be considered with an open mind.

REFERENCES

BARTLEY, W., and DAVIES, R. E. (1952). *Biochem. J.* **52**, xx.
BOYLE, J., and CONWAY, E. J. (1941). *J. Physiol.* **100**, 1.
CAPRARO, V., and BERNINI, G. (1952). *Nature* **169**, 454.
COLLANDER, R. (1937). *Trans. Faraday Soc.* **33**, 985.
COLLANDER, R., and BÄRLUND, H. (1933). *Acta botan. fenn.* **11**, 1.
DAVSON, H., and DANIELLI, J. F. (1943). The Permeability of Natural Membranes. Cambridge University Press.
FRANCIS, W. L. (1933). *Nature* **131**, 805.
FUHRMAN, F. A. (1952). *Am. J. Physiol.* **171**, 266.
GERARD, R. W. (1932). *Am. J. Physiol.* **92**, 498.
GOLDMAN, D. E. (1943). *J. Gen. Physiol.* **27**, 37.
HARRIS, E. J., and BURN, G. P. (1949). *Trans. Faraday Soc.* **45**, 508.
HARRIS, E. J. (1953). Symposium on Secretion and Active Transport. Society for Experimental Biology (In press).
HEVESY, G., HOFER, E., and KROGH, A. (1935). *Skand. Arch. Physiol.* **72**, 199.
HODGKIN, A. L., and KEYNES, R. D. (1950). *Abstr. Communs. 18th Intern. Physiol. Congr., Copenhagen* p. 258.
HODGKIN, A. L., and KEYNES, R. D. (1953). Symposium on Secretion and Active Transport. Society for Experimental Biology (In press).
HUF, E. G. (1935). *Pflüger's Arch. ges. Physiol.* **235**, 655.
HUF, E. G., and WILLS, J. (1951). *Am. J. Physiol.* **167**, 255.
KEYNES, R. D. (1951). *J. Physiol.* **113**, 99.
KEYNES, R. D., and LEWIS, P. R. (1951). *J. Physiol.* **113**, 73.
KIRSCHNER, L. (1953). *Nature* **172**, 348.
KOCH, H. (1953). International Zoology Congress, Copenhagen (In press).
KOEFOED-JOHNSEN, V., AND USSING, H. H. (1953). *Acta Physiol. Scand.* **28**, 60.
KOEFOED-JOHNSEN, V., LEVI, H., and USSING, H. H. (1952). *Acta Physiol. Scand.* **25**, 150.
KROGH, A. (1937a). *Trans. Faraday Soc.* **33**, 912.
KROGH, A. (1937b). *Skand. Arch. Physiol.* **76**, 60.
KROGH, A., and USSING, H. H. (1937). *J. Exptl. Biol.* **14**, 35.
LEVI, H. and USSING, H. H. (1948). *Acta Physiol. Scand.* **16**, 232.
LINDERHOLM, H. (1952). *Acta Physiol. Scand.* **27**, Suppl. p. 97.
LING, G. (1951). *Am. J. Physiol.* **167**, 806.
LING, G. and GERARD, R. W. (1949). *J. Cellular Comp. Physiol.* **34**, 413.
LUND, E. J., and STAPP, P. (1947). *In* "Bioelectric Fields and Growth" (E. J. Lund, ed.). University Coop. Society, Austin, Texas p. 235.
MAIZELS, M. (1951). *J. Physiol.* **112**, 59.

PRESCOTT, D. M., and ZEUTHEN, E. (1953). *Acta Physiol. Scand.* **28**, 77.

REHBERG, P. B. (1926). *Biochem. J.* **20**, 461.

SOLOMON, A. K. (1952). *J. Gen. Physiol.* **36**, 57.

STAPP, P. (1941). *Proc. Soc. Exptl. Biol. Med.* **46**, 382.

STEINBACH, H. B. (1950). *Am. J. Physiol.* **163**, 236.

STONE, D., and SHAPIRO, S. (1948). *Am. J. Physiol.* **155**, 41.

TEORELL, T. (1949). *Arch. Sci. Physiol.* **3**, 205.

TEORELL, T. (1951). *Z. Elektrochem.* **55**, 460.

USSING, H. H. (1947). *Nature* **160**, 262.

USSING, H. H. (1948). *Cold Spring Harbor Symposia Quant. Biol.* **13**, 193.

USSING, H. H. (1949). *Acta Physiol. Scand.* **19**, 43.

USSING, H. H. (1952). *Advances in Enzymol.* **13**, 21.

USSING, H. H. and ZERAHN, K. (1951). *Acta Physiol. Scand.* **23**, 110.

ZWOLINSKI, B. J., EYRING, H. and REESE, C. E. (1949). *J. Phys. and Colloid Chem.* **53**, 1426.

Electrical Processes in Nerve Conduction

A. F. HUXLEY

This article is intended not for specialists in electrophysiology, nor even for physiologists of other brands, but for physicists, physical chemists, and biochemists who may take an interest in their own aspects of the many problems that remain to be solved in the activity of excitable living structures. In it I shall present a picture of the electrical aspects of the mechanism of impulse conduction which has been built up by the efforts of many workers during the last fifty years or so. As far as the events can be described in terms of electric currents and the movements of various species of ions, the picture is a fairly coherent one, but there are many questions about which it tells us nothing: for instance, how metabolic energy is utilized to keep the ionic storage battery charged, and what is the molecular mechanism of the striking changes in permeability of the nerve membrane to sodium and potassium ions which take place during the impulse.

This picture will be presented as a description of the "giant axon" of the squid, a nerve fiber which by its great size—its diameter is about half a millimeter—has made possible many of the recent experiments which have contributed to our present outlook. But probably this account will apply without fundamental change to the nerve and muscle fibers of most animals. I shall not attempt to give the evidence on which my statements are based; full references will be found in the review by Hodgkin (1951) and a paper by Hodgkin and Huxley (1952).

PHYSICAL CHARACTERISTICS OF THE RESTING NERVE FIBER

The giant nerve fiber of the squid is a cylindrical rod of clear protoplasm ("axoplasm"), with the consistency of a fairly stiff jelly, enclosed in a tubular sheath. In the body it is surrounded by "body fluid" whose composition, as far as its inorganic constituents go, is very little different from sea water. In fact it is customary to use sea water as a "physiological saline" for these fibers; a length of, say, 5 cm dissected out of the animal and placed in sea water remains able to conduct impulses for many hours. But the electrolytes of the interior of the fiber are very different. The predominant cation is potassium, and the concentrations

23

of sodium and chloride are about ten times less than in the external fluid. The inorganic cations thus greatly exceed the inorganic anions; the deficit is made up chiefly by dicarboxylic amino acids, together with organic phosphates and proteins. But it is the univalent cations, not the anions, which play the important roles in the conduction of the impulse, and their concentrations (in milliequivalents per kilogram of water) in the internal and external media can be given in round figures as follows:

	Na	K
External medium (sea water)	450	10
Internal medium (axoplasm)	50	400

The specific resistance of sea water is about 20 Ω-cm, and that of the axoplasm is only a little higher, say 30 Ω-cm. This suggests that the small ions in the axoplasm are freely mobile, an assumption which is confirmed by an elegant experiment of Hodgkin and Keynes (1953) in which the internal potassium in a short stretch of a fiber (actually from the cuttlefish, not the squid) was labeled with K^{42} and was found to move along the fiber in an applied electric field with a mobility indistinguishable, within the limits of error, from that in free solution.

Most of the sheath which surrounds the axoplasm consists of fibrous connective tissue which gives mechanical strength to the whole structure. This part is permeated by the external fluid and is of little significance for the conduction of the impulse. But the sheath also contains the "membrane" which separates the external medium from the internal. This membrane has not yet been located with certainty under the microscope, but there is no doubt of its existence. It is generally thought to consist of a thin (perhaps bimolecular) layer of mixed phospholipids and cholesterol, supported on a protein framework. At any rate, most substances are prevented from diffusing freely between external and internal media. There are three classes of substances which can penetrate in significant amounts: (1) substances of very low molecular weight, (2) substances which are soluble in non-polar liquids, and (3) certain substances of physiological importance. Presumably the membrane has specially developed mechanisms for letting through substances in the third group, and in many cases there is direct evidence that these do not enter the cell by a straightforward process of diffusion. Sodium and potassium belong to this group, and the very special features of their passage through the membrane—to be described later—are the essence of the mechanism of impulse conduction.

This membrane has a high electrical resistance, corresponding to its finite but small permeability to ions, and a high electrical capacity, corresponding to its thinness. The nerve is therefore a concentric cable, and it is found to obey Kelvin's equations very satisfactorily so long as the applied current does not change the potential difference across the membrane by more than a few millivolts. Inductance of the kind that is important in a submarine cable is altogether negligible in the nerve, but the resistance and capacity of the membrane can be deduced from the time course of the potential difference across it at a series of points near the electrode by which current is fed to the external fluid. Each square centimeter of nerve membrane is found to have a resistance of the order of 1000 Ω—it varies considerably between different animals— and a capacity which is very uniform at about 1 μf. These are the values that would be given by a layer 27 Å thick of a material with dielectric constant 3 and specific resistance 4×10^9 Ω-cm, so that it is not unreasonable to attribute them to a bimolecular layer of lipids very nearly impenetrable to ions, the lipid acting as the dielectric of a cylindrical capacitor whose plates are the relatively freely conducting aqueous phases in contact with its inner and outer surfaces.

The potential difference across the membrane can be measured by inserting a micropipette filled with sea water or with concentrated KCl. In the squid giant fiber, dissected free from the animal, the interior is found to be about 50 mv negative to the outside. Almost certainly the potential difference is larger in a living fiber *in situ*; probably it lies between 70 and 100 mv in the excitable tissues of most animals. The existence of this potential difference (although not its exact magnitude) has been known for a long time, and, in 1902, Bernstein put forward the theory that it arises from the tendency of the positively charged K ions to diffuse out of the axoplasm, in which they are many times more concentrated than in the external fluid. In some sense this idea is certainly right, but we are not yet clear about the relation between this mechanism and the chemical energy provided by the metabolism of the fiber, which must be the ultimate source of the emf. It is probably best to regard the K concentration cell as a storage battery (with a small leak corresponding to the permeability of the membrane to ions such as Na) which is kept charged during life by processes deriving their energy from metabolism. Even when metabolic energy is cut off, the potential difference can be maintained for several hours at something approaching its normal value by the concentration cell drawing on the reserve of K ions stored inside the fiber.

VOLTAGE-CURRENT RELATIONS IN THE MEMBRANE

The properties of the resting fiber which have so far been described are remarkable, but they do not suffice for conveying messages over long distances. The nerve impulse is a transient change in the potential difference across the membrane; the inside, initially at, say, -50 mv relative to the exterior, goes to $+50$ mv for a period of the order of 1 msec, and this alteration travels along the fiber as a wave without change of shape or size, and with a velocity in the squid giant fiber of about 25 meters/sec. It is true that the cable properties cause any change in membrane potential difference to spread along the fiber, but the membrane leak restricts this spread to a few millimeters from the point where the pulse is generated. The work of Keith Lucas and Adrian, shortly before and after the first world war, showed that the size of the impulse is maintained by energy released at each point on the fiber as the impulse arrives. This raises two questions: the immediate source of this energy, and how its release is controlled.

These questions have been largely answered by studies of the current through the membrane as a function of membrane potential difference and time. This is the point where the giant fiber of the squid has been of the greatest value to the experimentalist: it is possible to insert a pair of long, silver-wire electrodes down the inside of one of these fibers and pass current through one while recording potential changes with the other—a procedure which would be impracticable in a smaller structure. A feed-back amplifier adjusts the current—all of which must cross the membrane—in such a way that the membrane potential difference undergoes a predetermined sequence of changes, usually a step to a new value followed by a return to the resting level a few milliseconds later. In spite of the high resistance of the membrane in the resting state, currents of several milliamperes per square centimeter can pass when the potential difference is reduced or reversed. The time course of the current at a given membrane potential is greatly affected by the composition of the external fluid, especially its sodium concentration. The sequence of events described in the next paragraph is deduced from these effects of ionic concentrations on the membrane current in the squid fiber.

In the resting state, the membrane is slightly permeable to potassium ions. This permeability can be expressed as a conductance, since the *instantaneous* change in current carried by K ions is proportional to the change in membrane potential difference; the resting K conductance is perhaps 0.5 mmho/cm². In addition there may be a still smaller conductance contributed by the movement of Na ions across the membrane (perhaps 0.01 mmho/cm²), and also by other ions, so that the resting potential difference is smaller than the equilibrium potential for K ions. If the potential difference is increased (inside made more negative), the conductances due both to K and to Na fall during the first few milliseconds and remain less than they are in the resting state. The currents carried by these ions through the membrane therefore remain small. If, however, the membrane potential difference is reduced (say, from its resting 50 mv to zero), both conductances undergo characteristic increases. That for Na ions rises in one or two tenths of a millisecond to perhaps 15 mmho/cm², and then falls to a low value with a time constant of about 1 msec. That for K ions does not change noticeably at first, but rises along an S-shaped curve, becoming appreciable as the Na conductance falls from its peak, and eventually flattening out and remaining at about 20 mmho/cm² as long as the membrane potential difference is held at zero. When the membrane potential difference is restored to its ordinary resting value, the K conductance returns to its resting value along an exponential decay curve, without an S-shaped start. The Na conductance remains low, but the "inactivation" which caused it to fall after its peak during the period at zero membrane potential difference persists, decaying exponentially with about the same time constant as the K conductance. Its persistence shows up if the membrane potential difference is again reduced, when the peak reached by the Na conductance is smaller than it was the first time. This sequence of events is illustrated in Fig. 1.

The state of the membrane is thus defined by three parameters: first, the degree to which the Na permeability is "turned on," second, the degree to which the Na permeability is "inactivated," and third, the degree to which the K permeability is "turned on." Each of these increases when the membrane potential difference is reduced from its resting value, the first quickly, the other two slowly. All these changes are graded and reversible; that is to say, the extent to which each parameter changes, and the rapidity of the change, depend in a continuous manner on the amount by which the membrane potential difference is reduced, and the changes are reversed even when the potential difference is restored before the parameters have reached their new steady values. There is no sign of anything like a "trigger action" in the effect of the potential difference on the membrane properties. If the potential difference is taken through any sequence of changes, the time course of each of the three parameters is described by a single differential equa-

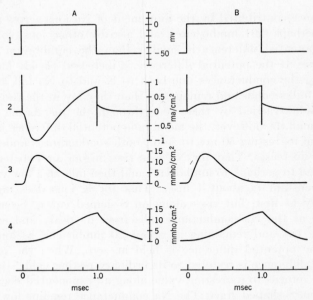

FIG. 1. Diagram showing time course of permeability changes of nerve membrane to Na and K ions when potential difference across the membrane is changed. A: Fiber immersed in sea water. B: Fiber immersed in a sodium-free medium. Abscissa: time (same scale for all drawings). 1: Potential of interior of fiber relative to external fluid. 2: Current through membrane, outward current plotted upward. 3: Component of membrane conductance due to movement of Na$^+$. 4: Component of membrane conductance due to movement of K$^+$.

The conductance changes are identical in A and B, but the current carried by sodium ions is reversed in the sodium-free solution since the electrochemical gradient for Na$^+$ is then directed outwards instead of inwards. The time scale is appropriate to a temperature of about 20° C.

tion in which the coefficients are continuous functions of the potential difference and of nothing else.

A combination of the first two factors ("turning on" and "inactivation") gives the permeability of the membrane to Na ions, measured as a conductance. The current carried by Na ions at any instant is the product of this conductance and the difference of the membrane p. d. from the value at which Na ions would be in equilibrium. This "Na potential" is given by

$$\frac{RT}{F} \ln \frac{[\text{Na}]_{\text{out}}}{[\text{Na}]_{\text{in}}}$$

which can be controlled experimentally by altering $[Na]_{out}$, the concentration of sodium in the external fluid. The value of the membrane potential difference at which the early phase of current, attributable to Na movement, reverses its direction (Fig. 1B) is found to vary with $[Na]_{out}$ quantitatively as predicted by this expression. This is excellent evidence that the driving force for the sodium component of the membrane current is the resultant of the difference of concentration and the difference of electrical potential on the two sides of the membrane. The ions move down their electrochemical gradient.

The current carried by K ions appears to be determined in a similar manner, although the experimental evidence is less good, as the high internal K concentration cannot readily be varied.

The Sequence of Events in a Nerve Impulse

We are now in a position to describe the events which occur at each point on a nerve fiber as an impulse passes.

Initially, the interior is, say, 50 mv negative to the exterior, and the membrane is slightly permeable to potassium ions and almost impermeable to sodium ions. A nearby point on the fiber is already active, and its interior is at about $+50$ mv. Current flows along the interior of the fiber from the active region, the circuit being completed mostly through the capacity of the membrane in the resting region and finally through the external fluid. The potential difference across the resting membrane is therefore reduced. The permeability to sodium rises, and Na ions enter the fiber under the combined influence of their concentration gradient and the electrical potential difference. They carry positive charge into the interior of the fiber, reducing still further, and eventually reversing, the charge on the membrane capacity. The potential difference generated by sodium entry at this point on the fiber both completes the permeability change initiated by cable action from the nearby active region and causes current to flow forwards inside the fiber to the next part, bringing it into activity in the same way.

Meantime, the slower effects of the changed membrane potential difference are making themselves evident. The Na permeability falls because of "inactivation," and the K permeability rises. Na ions are thus less able to hold the potential difference near their equilibrium potential, while K ions are allowed to diffuse out, carrying positive charge out of the fiber, until the resting potential (inside, 50 mv negative) is again reached. But the fiber is not yet in its resting state: the degree of inactivation of the sodium permeability mechanism, and the potassium permeability, are both high, and these revert only slowly to their ordinary values. During this process, the fiber is "refractory": at first it cannot be made to conduct another impulse, however hard it is stimulated; later it will conduct, but at less than the normal velocity, and it needs a stronger stimulus than normal to set it off.

At each point on the fiber there is therefore a regenerative process, which is indicated diagrammatically in Fig. 2. So long as the potential change is only a few millivolts, the rise in inward Na current is less than the purely passive rise which takes place immediately in the outward K current, and the situation is stable. But the Na permeability rises exponentially with the change in potential, so that, as the potential difference is reduced further, the Na current overtakes the linear rise in K current (the K permeability being assumed to change too slowly for its increase to affect the situation). As soon as this happens, the situation is unstable, and the potential difference is pushed by the regenerative cycle nearly to the Na potential. Thus there is a "trigger action" in each segment of the fiber; this does not show up in the voltage-permeability relations since the regenerative cycle is broken at the point indicated by the dotted line in Fig. 2 when the membrane potential difference is kept under control.

Myelinated Nerve Fibers

In the giant fiber of the squid, the processes which have just been described take place continuously at every point on the fiber, the whole sequence of potential and permeability changes moving along the fiber in a wave-like fashion. This is true of almost all the nerve fibers of invertebrates, and also of the smallest ("unmyelinated") nerve fibers of

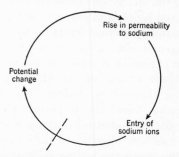

Fig. 2. Diagram of the cycle of events through which a reduction of the potential difference across the membrane of a nerve fiber continues itself regeneratively.

vertebrates. But in the larger, myelinated fibers of the vertebrates there is a further specialization. For almost the whole of its length, the sheath of one of these fibers is a thick coat of myelin, a material containing a high proportion of lipid. In a fiber of 15 μ outside diameter, this coat is about 2 μ thick, against the 30 Å (0.003 μ) or so that is probably the thickness of the membrane of the squid fiber. This coat acts simply as an insulator, and the parts of the fiber which possess it behave as straightforward concentric cables. The only places on the fiber where this coat is lacking are the "nodes of Ranvier." These are spaced regularly along the fiber; in a large fiber of a mammal (15 μ diameter) they are about 1 mm apart. At each node, there is a narrow gap between the myelin coats of the adjacent internodal segments, and here the interior of the fiber is separated from the external fluid by a membrane more or less similar to that which covers the whole of the squid fiber. Conduction takes place by the same process as in the squid fiber, but the sequence of permeability changes, and the entry of Na ions and exit of K take place only at these nodes. The internodes act as cables conducting the potential change generated at one node to stimulate the next. The whole structure is a telegraph cable with a relay station every millimeter along its length.

The advantages of this arrangement over the continuous system in the squid fiber arise from the small average capacity between interior and external fluid. Because of the thickness of the myelin coat, this is perhaps 400 times smaller than in a nonmyelinated fiber of the same diameter (15 μ). The quantities of ions that must enter or leave the fiber to produce the potential changes (which have about the same amplitude) are reduced in proportion. Not only is there an economy from the point of view of energy requirements, but the conduction velocity is greatly increased, since the longitudinal currents by which one point on the fiber stimulates the regions ahead of it need only flow for a correspondingly shorter time to produce the critical amount of potential change necessary to initiate the regenerative sodium entry.

OVER-ALL CHANGES IN AN IMPULSE

According to this picture, an element of excitable membrane (squid fiber membrane, or membrane from a node of Ranvier in a myelinated fiber) can be represented by the diagram in Fig. 3. In parallel with the electrostatic capacity of the thin lipid layer are two batteries, which are concentration cells acting one with Na, the other with K ions. They are oppositely directed, since Na is more concentrated outside the fiber

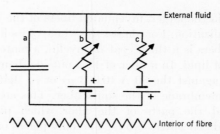

FIG. 3. Diagram of an element of the excitable membrane of a nerve fiber. *a:* constant capacity; *b:* channel for K^+; *c:* channel for Na^+.

than inside, whereas the reverse is true of K. The resistance in series with each battery represents the permeability (or rather, the reciprocal of the permeability) of the membrane to the ion in question. Both are drawn as variable resistances since they change when the potential difference across the element of membrane changes.

These batteries are the immediate source of the energy needed for conducting the impulse; the energy therefore comes from a reduction of the concentration differences of Na and K between the inside and the outside of the fiber. The smallest amount of Na and K exchange which could produce the observed potential changes can easily be calculated; it is the product of membrane capacity and potential change, divided by the Faraday. This comes out to be a very small fraction of the potassium content of the fiber, but detectable changes would be expected when a fiber is made to conduct a large number of impulses. This has been found experimentally, both by means of tracers and by other methods. The amount of the exchange per impulse is always greater—a few times—than the theoretical minimum needed to produce the potential change; this is to be expected since the periods of Na entry and K exit overlap so that an appreciable amount of unprofitable exchange takes place.

GAPS IN THE SCHEME

It was pointed out at the beginning of this article that the picture to be presented would leave two major questions untouched: how metabolic energy is utilized, and what is the mechanism of the permeability changes. As to the first, all we can say is that, over a long period of time, metabolic energy must be used to recharge the Na and K concentration cells, i.e., the fiber must pump out the Na which has entered and replace it by K. How this is done is immaterial from the point of view of the mechanism of conduction; conversely, a knowledge of the processes involved in conduction does not help us to understand the equally necessary restorative activities of the fiber.

As to the mechanism of the control of permeability, a few very general statements can be made. In the first place, the permeabilities to Na and K are very sharply separable; it has not yet been possible to detect K ions passing through the membrane by the mechanism whose function is to transmit Na, or vice versa. The methods available are not highly sensitive, so it might be that each channel allows the other ion to pass 1 % as freely as its own. But, in any case, there is a high degree of specificity, and it is difficult to imagine that a purely physical (as opposed to chemical) mechanism, depending perhaps on "pore size," could achieve such specificity first in favor of Na and a millisecond later in favor of K.

The fact that it is the potential difference across the membrane which governs these permeabilities suggests strongly that charged molecules, or parts of molecules, in the membrane must be involved. Movements of such particles under the electric field might affect directly the freedom of an ion to move, or might influence chemical reactions which culminate in the permeability change.

The change of permeability with potential difference is very steep; in both the Na and the K systems an e-fold change in conductance is produced by a 4–6-mv change in membrane potential difference. In most processes involving a single electronic charge per event studied, an e-fold effect occurs with a potential change equal to kT/e, which is 25 mv. The much greater steepness of the observed permeability changes suggests that either the relevant particle is multiply charged or else that several singly charged particles are involved at each site where ions can go through.

This is probably all that can safely be deduced about the permeability mechanisms from what is known of current flow and ionic movements. For instance, studies on the effects of substances which interfere with acetylcholine metabolism have not yet reached the point where they can tell us which of the electrical events is linked to the release of that substance, either as cause or as effect. Again, it is easy to suggest hypotheses for the mode of action of narcotics, but these have not yet been put to the test of experiment. Fascinating fields are open here for the physicist or chemist interested in biological processes on the molecular scale.

REFERENCES

BERNSTEIN, J. (1902). Untersuchungen zur Thermodynamik der bioelektrischen Ströme. I. *Pflügers Arch. ges. Physiol.* **92**, 521–562.

HODGKIN, A. L. (1951). The ionic basis of electrical activity in nerve and muscle. *Biol. Revs.* **26**, 339–409.

HODGKIN, A. L., and HUXLEY, A. F. (1952). A quantitative description of membrane current and its application to conduction and excitation in nerve. *J. Physiol.* **117**, 500–544.

HODGKIN, A. L., and KEYNES, R. D. (1953). The mobility and diffusion coefficient of potassium in giant axons from *Sepia*. *J. Physiol.* **119**, 513–528.

The Generation of Bioelectric Potentials[a]

IRWIN B. WILSON AND DAVID NACHMANSOHN

In spite of the great diversity of biological membranes, referred to by Ussing at this Conference[1] the concentration of electrolytes in most cells differs from the outer environment in a similar way. For example, most cells have higher potassium and lower sodium ion concentrations than do the external fluids. It therefore appears *a priori* likely that, in spite of their great differences in structure and function, cell boundaries are endowed with certain similar properties which enable them to maintain the uneven electrolyte distribution so essential for life. The generality of the phenomenon supports the assumption that most of the chemical forces acting in these processes are similar. The last 30 years have offered abundant evidence for the correctness of the idea of the biochemical unity of life, a notion greatly cherished by Louis Pasteur and Otto Meyerhof, two leaders in the development of cellular physiology. The problems of ion transport in general, as discussed by Ussing, may then be considered as applicable to a large extent to most cells.

It is, however, not unusual to find that some cells modify common cellular properties and adapt them for their specific requirements. It has long been suspected that ionic concentration gradients and ionic movements are essential in the generation of the bioelectric potentials known to be closely associated with the conduction of nerve impulse. Our presentation will be limited to this particular problem and, even within this restricted area, special attention will be paid to the possible role of proteins in the movements of ions connected with the generation of bioelectric potentials.

Membrane theory. In raising this problem before an audience in which so many distinguished physicochemists are present, it appears appropriate to recall that physicochemists laid the groundwork for all theories upon which our concepts of the conduction of nerve impulses are based.

[a] This review is based on work supported by Grants from the United States Public Health Service, Division of Research Grants and Fellowships of the National Institutes of Health, by the Research and Development Division, Office of the Surgeon General, Department of the Army, and by the Atomic Energy Commission.

When, in the later part of the 19th century, the large potential differences produced by semipermeable membranes became known, their theory was developed by Traube, Ostwald, Planck, Nernst, and other physicochemists. Their ideas led to the so-called "membrane theory" which is still the basis of all modern concepts of conduction. This theory, best formulated by Bernstein and Tschermak, assumes that the nerve fiber is surrounded by a polarized membrane not readily permeable to certain ion species and charged positively on the outside and negatively on the inside. During activity, the ionic permeability of the active region increases, with a corresponding decline in electrical resistance. This leads to depolarization. The active region becomes negative in relation to the charged adjacent regions. Small currents are generated, stimulating the adjacent region, and the same process is repeated there. In this way successive parts of the membrane are activated and the impulses propagated along the axon.

A modification of the theory resulted from observations of Cole and Curtis[2] and Hodgkin and Huxley.[3] When an electrode is inserted into the interior of a nerve axon and the transmembrane potential is measured, the charge in the active region is not simply abolished, but reversed; the inside becomes positive during the passage of the impulse. Due to this "overshoot," the spike potentials are about twice as great as the resting potential.

Experimental evidence that there is a change in membrane permeability during the passage of the impulse had first been demonstrated in 1939 by Cole and Curtis.[4] On the basis of measurements of impedance changes they calculated that, during activity, the resistance of the membrane decreases from about 1000 to about 40 ohms-cm^2.

Ion movements. During the last few years the movements of ions across nerve membranes in rest and during activity have been analyzed in various laboratories. Particularly revealing in this respect were the studies of Hodgkin and Huxley and their associates at Cambridge.[5] Their results, discussed by Huxley in a separate paper of this volume,[6] suggest that the action potential depends on a specific rapid increase in sodium permeability which allows sodium ions to move from the outside of the fiber to the inside. The permeability to sodium during activity was estimated by Hodgkin and Huxley to be about 500 times as high as in rest. This movement of charge makes the inside of the fiber positive and provides a satisfactory explanation for the rising phase of the spike. The falling phase and the subsequent repolarization probably depend on outflow of potassium ions and may be accelerated by a process which increases the potassium permeability after the action potential has reached its crest. A still more detailed analysis of the ion movements during the various phases of electrical activity was carried out by Hodgkin and Huxley with a new experimental method developed on the basis of that described by Cole and Marmont. The results indicate that the current carried by sodium ions rises rapidly to a peak and then decays rapidly to a low value. The current carried by potassium ions rises much more slowly along an S-shaped curve, reaching a plateau which is maintained with little change until the membrane is restored to its resting state.

The investigations described support the view that ionic concentration gradients are the source of the electromotive force (emf) of the action potentials. This raises the fundamental question: By what mechanism does the potential source of emf inactive in rest become suddenly effective? The membrane theory postulated a change in permeability, but the process by which this change was achieved was not considered. There must be a process in the membrane responsible for the sudden, transient change in resistance and the increase of permeability to sodium.

A sharp distinction must be made between the activity and recovery phases. The entrance of sodium and leakage of potassium during activity occur *with* the concentration gradients and tend, therefore, to eliminate the gradients. Their restoration requires extrusion of sodium and uptake of potassium *against* the concentration gradient. These latter processes require a considerable amount of energy in excess of that necessary for maintaining the resting condition. Most of the heat produced during nerve activity is developed after the electrical changes and is presumably associated with the restoration of the electrolyte distribution. For this active ion transport we may admit chemical processes common to most cells. Although very little experimental basis is available as yet, it appears justifiable to assume participation of some of the most widely used cellular sources of energy. Since oxidation provides large amounts of ATP (15 moles per mole of pyruvic acid oxidized via the citric acid cycle) it appears likely that ATP, as in so many other cellular functions, plays an important part in these processes. The formation of H^+ and OH^- ions in the cytochrome-cytochrome oxidase system may be of importance in this energy-requiring exchange of ions across the membrane. Carbonic anhydrase may play in this osmotic work a role similar to that proposed by Davies and Ogston[7] for the HCl formation in the stomach. These mechanisms are probably not specific for the nerve cell but may be similar to other mechanisms of ion exchange across cellular membranes.

Fundamentally different is the situation in respect to the ion movements during nerve activity. Here the movements are *with* the concentration gradients. The suddenly increased rate of flow for the extremely short period of time may require very little energy if there occurs a transient change in permeability.

Problem of permeability change. The first hypothesis concerning the nature of the process responsible for the change in ion permeability required for the generation of bioelectric potentials was proposed by Kurt H. Meyer in 1937.[8] On the basis of his extensive studies of ion permeability across artificial membranes, Meyer postulated that every change in permeability is preceded by a chemical reaction. Membranes are formed by protein chains. Appearance of amino groups will increase anionic permeability, whereas that of carboxyl groups will increase movements of cations. The specific chemical reactions thought to be responsible for the appearance of these groups remained, however, unexplored.

The difficulty of identifying these reactions is readily recognized if two essential features of the process are kept in mind: the high speed and the small amount of energy involved. According to the impedance measurements of Cole and Curtis, the permeability change of the membrane reaches its peak within 100 μsec. A chemical reaction responsible for this change must have a comparable speed. According to the heat measurements of A. V. Hill and his associates, the heat released during nerve activity is of the order of magnitude of 10^{-11} gm-calories/cm^2 per impulse. Therefore, the metabolism of the specific compounds responsible for the permeability change must be exceedingly small.

In 1913 Otto Meyerhof, then a young Privatdozent at the University of Kiel, pointed out, in a lecture entitled "Zur Energetik der Zellvorgaenge," that the real problem in the utilization of metabolites is the question of how the energy is made useful, step by step, for function.[9] Knowledge of the sequence of energy transformations is required for the understanding of cellular mechanisms. The muscle, in which relatively large amounts of chemical energy are transformed in mechanical work, seemed to be the most favorable material for such an analysis. Meyerhof's life work was devoted to establishing the sequence of energy transformations associated with the elementary process of muscular contraction. He emphasized (1) the significance of thermodynamics for studying the sequence of reactions in intermediary metabolism; (2)

the cyclic character of the reactions taking place; and (3) the necessity of correlating chemical reactions observed *in vitro* with events in the intact cell. The analysis of cellular function in general must be based upon the same approach.

Early in this century it was discovered that acetylcholine has a powerful pharmacological action and mimics the effects of stimulation of certain nerves. The compound therefore attracted the interest of many physiologists. Studies of the last 15 years, based upon an approach fundamentally similar to that used for the analysis of muscular contraction, have shown that the action of acetylcholine is directly associated with the permeability changes to ions occurring during the passage of the impulse and forms an integral part of the elementary process by which bioelectric potentials are generated.[10-12] Before discussing the picture as it has developed, we shall factually illustrate the way in which this problem has been analyzed.

ACETYLCHOLINESTERASE

Specificity. The enzyme which inactivates the ester by hydrolysis is called acetylcholinesterase.[13] Esterases are, of course, widely distributed in animal organisms and hydrolyze a great variety of esters, but the type of esterase in conducting tissue has a number of properties by which it may readily be distinguished from other esterases. The enzyme has a rather sharply defined optimum substrate concentration. The activity-substrate concentration relationship shows a typical bell-shaped curve (Fig. 1). The hydrolysis rate is about the same when the acyl group of the substrate contains 2 or 3 carbons, but in contrast to most other esterases it drops sharply with 4 carbons.[14, 15] The Michaelis constant is small. This type of esterase is present in all types of conducting tissue throughout the animal kingdom. It occurs even in monocellular organisms endowed with ciliary movements.[16]

Localization. Another physiologically significant feature is the exclusive localization of acetylcholinesterase in the surface membranes of nerve fibers. In experiments with the giant axons of squid, all the enzyme activity was found in the sheath whereas no activity was detectable in the axoplasm.[17] Since the active membrane must be in the sheath, this peculiar localization appears pertinent, especially in connection with other findings.

Speed. The outstanding feature of the enzyme from the functional point of view is the rapidity with which it is able to hydrolyze the ester. The turnover number is about 20 million per minute,[15] i.e., the

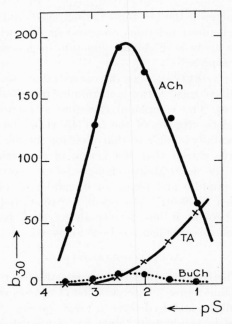

Fɪɢ. 1. Activity-pS curve of acetylcholinesterase from mammalian brain. Abscissas: pS (negative log of molar concentration of substrate). Ordinates: Activity, cubic millimeters of carbon dioxide output per 30 minutes. ●—● acetylcholine (ACh) ●···● butyrylcholine (BuCh) ✕—✕ triacetin (TA)

ester may be split in a few microseconds. This is a much higher speed than that of all other enzymes tested except catalase. The obvious prerequisite for associating a chemical reaction with electric manifestations is a comparable speed. The high speed of the esterase action satisfies this postulate and makes it possible to assume that its action is responsible for the generation of bioelectric current.

Essentiality. The features described, although suggestive, do not provide evidence that the actions of acetylcholine or cholinesterase are essential in conduction. Such an assumption requires a demonstration of a direct relationship between function and chemical reaction. One method frequently employed for testing the essentiality of an enzyme for a cellular function is to block its activity by specific inhibitors. A famous observation of this kind is Lundsgaard's classical demonstration that lactic acid formation can be blocked with iodoacetate without impairing muscular contraction. Clearly, if the esterase is essential in conduction, this function must be abolished by complete inactivation of the enzyme.

A large amount of evidence has accumulated indicating that it is impossible to dissociate conduction from acetylcholinesterase activity. This was first shown with reversible inhibitors of the enzyme which block conduction reversibly.[18] Still more conclusive evidence was obtained with an irreversible inhibitor, diisopropyl fluorophosphate (DFP), an alkyl phosphate. The famous German "nerve gases," as for instance Tabun, belong to this group; they are the most powerful chemical warfare agents known. These compounds inhibit acetylcholinesterase essentially irreversibly. Inhibitors of this type are in many respects more suitable for such investigation than are reversible inhibitors. Extensive studies with a great variety of nerve fibers exposed to DFP have shown that it is impossible to dissociate conduction of the nerve impulse from acetylcholinesterase activity.[10] To illustrate this point, one experiment may be briefly mentioned.[19] Acetylcholine is a quaternary ammonium salt and unable to penetrate into the nerve fiber, but its tertiary analogue dimethylaminoethyl acetate, which also is hydrolyzed by cholinesterase, penetrates readily. This compound permits, therefore, simultaneous measurement of conduction and acetylcholinesterase activity. On exposure to DFP, conduction fails when the enzyme activity has dropped to 20 % of the initial value (Fig. 2), in agreement with previous data.

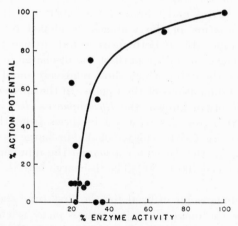

FIG. 2. The relationship between action potential and enzyme activity in nerves subjected to 5–8 mg of DFP per milliliter.

The presence of acetylcholinesterase in all types of conducting tissue, and the dependence of conduction in all those tissues upon the activity of the enzyme, permits the conclusion that the role of acetylcholine in conduction is both general and essential.

SEQUENCE OF ENERGY TRANSFORMATIONS

For a better understanding of the physiological role of acetylcholine it appeared necessary to integrate acetylcholine into the metabolic pathways of the cell and to establish the sequence of energy transformations. For this analysis the electric organ of fish proved to be an invaluable material. The most important feature of these organs is the generally accepted fact that their strong bioelectric potentials are of a nature identical with that of nerve and muscle. The electric organ is formed by compartments each containing one cell, the electric plate or electroplaque, and arranged in columns. The action potential developed by a single plate is about 0.15 volt, which is of the same order of magnitude as that found in ordinary nerve and muscle fibers. It is the arrangement of these plates in series, as in a Voltaic pile, which makes the electric discharge of these organs so powerful. Indeed, Volta recognized the analogy and called his pile an artificial electric organ. Only one face of the electric plate is innervated, and half a century ago Bernstein suggested that the arrangement in series may be explained by the change of potential at the innervated face only. Recent work on individual cells of *Electrophorus electricus* has shown that Bernstein's hypothesis was correct and that only the innervated face reverses the charge.[20, 21] Summation of the voltages developed by the individual cells would be impossible if both faces would reverse their potentials. The great differences in the strength of the discharge in various species do not depend on the units, which show relatively small variations, but on the shape and dimensions of the organs. In the species with the most powerful electric organ known, the *Electrophorus electricus* (Linnaeus), about 5000–6000 plates are arranged in series from the head to the caudal end of the organ. The voltage of the discharge is, on the average, 500 to 600 volts. In the *Torpedo marmorata* the number of elements in series does not exceed 400 to 500. The discharge here is, on the average, 40 to 50 volts.

In 1937, Nachmansohn utilized for the first time the electric organ for the study of the metabolic relationships of acetylcholine and their connection with the energy transformations involved in the generation

TABLE I

ACETYLCHOLINESTERASE CONCENTRATION IN VARIOUS TISSUES COMPARED TO
THAT OF ELECTRIC TISSUE OF *Electrophorus electricus*

Tissue	*mg ACh. split per gm/hour*
Mammalian (37° C)	
muscle	5–10
nerve fibers	10–30
brain	20–100
Frog (23° C)	
muscle	3–6
nerve fibers	5–10
brain	40–80
Electric organ of *E. electricus* at 23° C	2000–4000
Mammalian kidney	0
Mammalian liver	0

of bioelectric currents. The choice of this material was decisive for the later developments.

Direct proportionality between voltage and acetylcholinesterase. The strong electric organs of *Torpedo* and *Electrophorus electricus* have an extraordinarily high concentration of acetylcholinesterase. Two to four grams of acetylcholine are hydrolyzed per gram (wet weight) of tissue per hour. The significance of these figures becomes apparent when compared to those in other tissues (Table I). The high concentration of enzyme is even more striking in view of the high water and low protein content. The protein content is only about 2%, whereas 92% of the organ is water. The fact that organs contain amounts of enzyme capable of hydrolyzing amounts of acetylcholine equivalent to several times their own weight per hour suggests a close relationship to their highly specialized primary function, i.e., the generation of bioelectric potentials. Indeed, a striking parallelism exists between the concentration of the enzyme and the voltage and number of plates per centimeter. The electric organ of *Electrophorus electricus* is particularly suitable for the demonstration of this relationship. The number of electric plates per centimeter varies considerably with the size of the specimen and decreases, moreover, markedly from the head to the caudal end of the organ in each specimen. Since the voltage of each plate is about the same, the voltage per centimeter varies considerably. Figure 3 shows the relationship between voltage and acetylcholinesterase concentration tested on a great number of specimens of *Electrophorus electricus* of various sizes, covering a range of the action potential from 0.5 to 22 volts/cm.[22] The voltage per centimeter is plotted against acetylcholinesterase concentration. Calculated by the method of least squares, the resulting line goes through zero, indicating a direct proportionality between voltage per centimeter and the enzyme concentration. Such a direct proportionality between physical and chemical processes is rarely found in biological function. The electric organ offers, of course, a particularly favorable case for many reasons. The finding is in rather striking contrast to the even distribution and low concentration of other enzymes tested, like respiratory and glycolytic enzymes, ATPase, and others.

Phosphorylated compounds as energy source. From the studies of the intermediary metabolism associated with muscular contraction it became apparent that chemical reactions of some phosphorylated compounds constitute the most readily available source of energy for endergonic processes. The work of Meyerhof and Lohman suggested that adenosinetriphosphate (ATP) may be the primary source of energy for muscle contraction and that the adenosinediphosphate (ADP) formed is rephosphorylated from phosphocreatine, a transfer of phosphate which occurs without loss of energy. Phosphocreatine thus acts as a

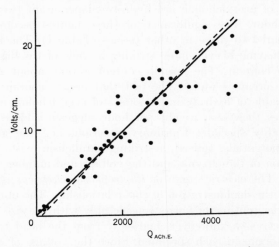

FIG. 3. Direct proportionality between voltage per centimeter and acetylcholinesterase concentration in the electric tissue of *Electrophorus electricus.* Dotted line calculated from data with the method of least squares; solid line calculated on assumption that line goes through zero point.

kind of storehouse for supplying phosphate to ADP for the rapid regeneration of ATP. The energy released by the breakdown of phosphocreatine was found to be adequate to account for the total electric energy released by the discharge.[23] In addition there is energy released by the simultaneous formation of lactic acid. It may be assumed that the energy released during lactic acid formation is used as in muscle for rephosphorylating creatine. The sum of the two reactions may therefore be used as indication of the energy supplied by the phosphorylated compounds rich in energy. This amount is more than adequate to account for the total electric energy released, but it is possible, and indeed probable, that part of the energy released is not used for the immediate process of recovery but for the restoration of the ionic concentration gradient.

It was safe to assume that, as in muscle, the breakdown of ATP during nerve activity precedes that of phosphocreatine. It is today generally accepted that ATP reacts directly with the structural muscle protein in the elementary process of contraction. It appeared, however, most unlikely, for many reasons, that ATP is responsible for the change in permeability postulated in the elementary process of conduction. On the basis of the available evidence it appeared more likely that the action of acetylcholine is directly responsible for the alterations of the membrane required for the generation of the action potential and that these reactions occur prior to the breakdown of ATP. The latter would then be a recovery process supplying the energy for the resynthesis of acetylcholine hydrolyzed during activity.

This assumption proved to be correct. In 1943, an enzyme was extracted from brain and electric tissue which, in cell-free solution, acetylates choline only in the presence of ATP.[24] The enzyme was referred to as choline acetylase. This was the first demonstration that the energy of ATP may be used outside the glycolytic cycle. Since then, during the last 10 years, a great number of endergonic reactions have been shown to utilize the energy of ATP.

Acetylation mechanisms. The observation that ATP provides the energy for the acetylation of choline opened the way for a detailed analysis of the mechanisms of acetylation in general. It was the first time that a biological acetylation was obtained in a soluble system. At that time, in the early 1940's, the paramount importance of acetate in intermediary metabolism as a building stone of many essential cell constituents had become apparent, mainly through the application of isotope techniques. During the last 10 years many investigators have studied the mechanisms of acetylation. Today it is well established that the first step is the acetylation of a coenzyme discovered in 1945 simultaneously by Lipmann and Kaplan,[25] by Lipton[26] in Barron's laboratory, and in our laboratory,[27] and called Coenzyme A (CoA). The formation of acetyl CoA is catalyzed by the enzyme acetylkinase, using the energy of ATP hydrolysis. The acetyl group is then transferred to other acceptors through the action of enzymes that are more or less specific for the acceptor. Choline acetylase transfers the acetyl group from acetyl CoA to choline.

Besides the implications for general biochemistry, the evidence that ATP provides the energy for acetylcholine synthesis supports the view that the action of acetylcholine and its hydrolysis precede the breakdown of ATP in the sequence of energy transformations. It thus became possible to integrate acetylcholine into the metabolic pathways of the cell.

The question remained, however, whether acetylcholine is itself responsible for the permeability change associated with the generation of bioelectric potentials. If this were so it should have an electrogenic action. This is indeed the case.[28] Injection of acetylcholine into the electric organ of *Torpedo* perfused with eserine generates electric potentials (Fig. 4). This electrogenic effect makes it difficult to assume that acetylcholine is required for recovery, and supports the assumption that the action of the ester is responsible for the change in permeability associated with the nerve impulse. It is true that other compounds may produce similar effects, but acetylcholine is the only compound

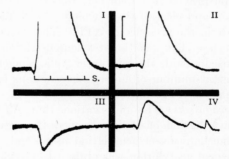

Fig. 4. Electrogenic action of acetylcholine. The potential changes are produced by intra-arterial injection of acetylcholine into the electric organ of *Torpedo marmorata* in presence of eserine. I, II, and IV correspond to the injection of 10, 5, and 2.5 μg of acetylcholine; at III only perfusion fluid was injected. 0.5 mv indicated at II. Time in seconds.

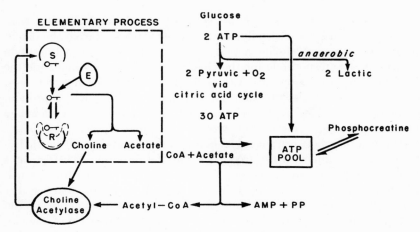

FIG. 5. Sequence of energy transformations associated with conduction and integration of the acetylcholine system into the metabolic pathways of the nerve cell. The elementary process of conduction may be tentatively pictured as follows:

(1). In resting condition, acetylcholine (OT) is bound, presumably to a storage protein (S). The membrane is polarized.

(2). ACh is released by current flow (possibly hydrogen ion movements) or any other excitatory agent. The free ester combines with the receptor (R), presumably a protein.

(3). The receptor changes its configuration (dotted line). This process increases the Na ion permeability and permits its rapid influx. This is the trigger action by which the potential primary source of emf, the ionic concentration gradient, becomes effective, and by which the action current is generated.

(4). The combination between free ester and receptor is in dynamic equilibrium; the free ester is, therefore, open to attack by acetylcholinesterase (E).

(5). The hydrolysis of the ester permits the receptor to return to its original shape. The permeability decreases and the membrane is again in its original polarized condition.

which fulfills all the requirements for such an assumption, and all the known facts are consistent with this conclusion.

The elementary process. The precise action of acetylcholine in the elementary process is still under investigation, but the picture which has emerged on the basis of all the facts available may be briefly outlined. Acetylcholine is, in resting condition, in an inactive and bound form. It may be tentatively called the storage form. It appears likely that the ester is bound to a protein or lipoprotein. No information is at present available about the nature of this storage form. During activity, as is well established experimentally, acetylcholine is released from the bound form. The free acetylcholine acts upon a receptor, and this action upon the receptor is responsible for the change of permeability and thus the generation of the potential. Although the receptor has not yet been isolated, the most likely assumption appears to be that it is a protein. Some data to be discussed later suggest that the effect of acetylcholine may be a change in configuration of the protein.

The complex between acetylcholine and the receptor will be in dynamic equilibrium with the free ester and the receptor. The free ester will be susceptible to attack by the esterase, and the hydrolysis will permit the receptor to return to its resting condition. The "barrier" for the rapid ion movements is thus established again. This action of the enzyme leads to the immediate recovery and ends the cycle of the elementary process. It is the rapidity of this inactivation process which makes rapid restoration of the membrane possible and thus permits the nerve to respond to the next stimulus within a few milliseconds. The further recovery leads to the resynthesis of acetylcholine in its bound form. Here the cyclic processes known from muscle and other cells enter the picture. The immediate precursor of the acetyl group of the acetyl CoA is not yet known. It may be acetate, but it may also be another acetyl donor. Figure 5 shows the sequence of energy transformations associated with conduction and the integration of acetylcholine into the metabolic paths of the nerve cell. It illustrates how the role of acetylcholine may be tentatively pictured in the elementary process.

The Proteins of the Acetylcholine System

We have seen that the acetylcholine system forms an integral part of the metabolic pathways of the neuron and is intrinsically associated with its primary function, the propagation of the nerve impulse. Knowledge of the forces of interaction between acetylcholine and the proteins of the system is evidently necessary for an understanding of the fundamental process. Unfortunately, only the two enzymes are available in purified aqueous solution, so that studies with the receptor must be made with intact structures, whereas nothing is known of the postulated storage protein. Fortunately, knowledge acquired with one of these proteins may aid us in understanding processes involved with the others, which at present can be approached only indirectly. Since acetylcholine has only a limited number of features which may contribute to its binding with proteins, all proteins which combine specifically with the ester must do so through much the same elementary interactions and are presumably similarly constituted at the active site. The consequences of this binding will differ from protein to protein and small differences may lead to a considerable alteration of function. The esterase is the most suitable for these studies and has been extensively investigated, but only those properties which appear to be important to the group as a whole will be presented.

The interaction of acetylcholine with the esterase falls naturally into two phases; the first is the enzyme-substrate complex and the second is the ensuing hydrolytic process.

Intermolecular Forces Between Enzyme and Substrate

The enzyme-substrate complex. The positive electrical charge of the normal substrate suggests that the enzyme might contain a suitably located negatively charged region which augments the enzymic activity by contributing to the attraction, orientation, and fixation of the substrate upon the enzyme surface.

This possibility was investigated with the aid of competitive inhibitors.[29] Figure 6 compares the inhibition of prostigmine and eserine as a function of pH. These compounds are similarly constituted and both are powerful inhibitors, but prostigmine is a quaternary ammonium salt whereas eserine is a tertiary amine ($pK_a = 8.1$). The constitution of prostigmine is consequently independent of pH, whereas eserine

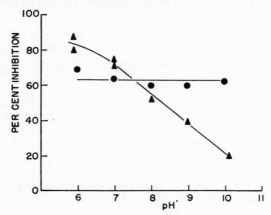

FIG. 6. Inhibition of acetylcholinesterase by prostigmine (●) and eserine (▲) as a function of pH.

exists predominately as the cationic conjugate acid below pH 8, and as the uncharged base at higher pH. Since prostigmine inhibition does not change in this pH range, the difference observed with eserine can be ascribed to a marked preference in the binding of the cationic form by a factor of 16.

Dimethylaminoethanol ammonium ion is a 30-fold better competitive inhibitor of the esterase than the structurally similar but uncharged isoamyl alcohol.[30] Similarly, nicotinamide, which exists as the uncharged base at neutral pH 7, is only one-eighth as effective an inhibitor as the positively charged N-methyl nicotinamide.[31]

Further evidence that Coulomb forces are involved in the binding is found in the marked salt effect of decreasing the inhibition caused by positively charged inhibitors.[32] The effect of charge can be analyzed, approximately, in terms of electrostatic theory. The electrical contribution to the free energy of binding F_e is given by

$$\Delta F_e = RT \ln \frac{k(\text{neutral})}{k(\text{charged})} = \sum_i \frac{Z_i \, \epsilon^2}{D_i \, r_i} \tag{1}$$

where the K's are the dissociation constants of the inhibitor enzyme complexes, Z_i is the ith charge in the protein at a distance r_i from the positive substrate charge in the complex, and D_i is the corresponding effective dielectric constant and is a function of r_i and can be estimated from work of Schwartzenbach.

These data are summarized in Table II. The value of r calculated from equation (1) assuming a single negative charge as responsible for the Coulomb effects as indicated in column 3.

Column 4 indicates calculated values of r when a term for the ionic strength of the medium is introduced using an approximate Debye-Hückel form applicable to small spherical molecules and low ionic

TABLE II

THE EFFECT OF POSITIVE ELECTRICAL CHARGE ON THE POTENCY OF INHIBITORS

	K°/K^+	$-\Delta F_e$ (Kcal/mole)	r	r (corrected for salt)
N-Methyl nicotinamide-nicotinamide	8	1.2	7.7	5.8
Eserine cation-eserine	16	1.7	6.7	5.4
Dimethylethanolammonium ion-isoamyl alcohol	30	2.0	6.3	5.0

strength on the assumption that the distance of closest approach for the salt ions is the same as r.

The calculated values agree well with what might be expected for a close fit of enzyme and inhibitor as judged from atomic radii. A methylated quaternary structure has a radius of about 3.5 Å, and the smallest distance of the negative charge from the protein surface is one unbonded atomic radius, or about 1.5 Å. The closest approach would thus be about 5.0 Å. These data show a closer approach the more nearly the structure resembles the ammonium portion of acetylcholine.

The effect of electrical charge is also demonstrable with substrates. Dimethylaminoethyl acetate (pK = 8.3) at pH below 8.3 exists predominantly in the cationic form and in uncharged form at higher pH. The hydrolytic rate relative to acetylcholine (in arbitrary units) as a function of pH (Fig. 7) reflects the change in electrical charge of the substrate, decreasing rapidly between pH 8 and 9, yet remaining constant at other pH.[29]

Similarly, isoamyl acetate has a Michaelis-Menten constant 10-fold higher than has dimethylaminoethyl acetate cation.[30] Similar conclusions have been derived by comparing 3,3-dimethylbutyl acetate with acetylcholine.[33]

The importance of alkyl groups on the cationic portion of the molecule is illustrated by methylated competitive inhibitors of the ammonia

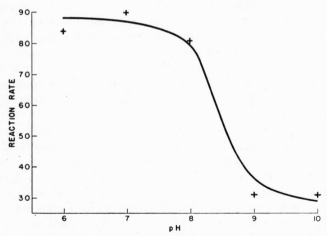

FIG. 7. Rate of hydrolysis of dimethylaminoethyl acetate relative to acetylcholine (arbitrary units) as a function of pH.

TABLE III
INHIBITORY POTENCY OF METHYLATED AMMONIUM IONS

The concentration necessary to produce 50% inhibition when the acetylcholine concentration is 4×10^{-4} M. In the hydroxyethylammonium series, the member containing n methyl groups ($n + 1$ alkyl) corresponds to the member of the simple methylammonium series containing $n + 1$ methyl groups.

Number of methyl groups (n)	$-N-$ (M)	$-N-C_2H_4OH$ (M)
4–3	0.018	0.005
3–2	0.015	0.005
2–1	0.12	0.07
1–0	0.70	0.28

and ethanolamine series (Table III).[30] All of these inhibitors are cationic at pH 7. Except for the methyl group which becomes the fourth alkyl group, each methyl group has binding properties amounting to about 1.2 kcal/mole and, on the average, increases the potency of an inhibitor 6.7-fold. If we make the reasonable assumption that neither the changes in hydration characteristics attending binding nor the entropies of binding differ very greatly for any member of the series, we may conclude that the additional binding associated with each methyl group arises from Van der Waals attraction (London dispersion forces) between the methyl group and a hydrocarbon group of the protein. The latent energy of evaporation of methane is about 2.0 kcal/mole, so that we have, in this force, energies of suitable magnitude for explaining the observed binding property of a methyl group. In accordance with expectation, larger alkyl or aryl groups improve the binding properties of ammonium ions.

It is of interest to consider why the trialkyl and tetraalkyl members are bound equally well. The explanation lies in the tetrahedral structure of the ammonium group which renders the protein unable to come into the requisite close contact simultaneously with all four alkyl groups unless the protein folds itself about the ion so as to engulf it. Apparently such a reorientation of the protein either does not occur or, if it does, the attending increase in free energy, which such a process would imply, just offsets the decrease in energy due to extra binding, so that there is no apparent difference in the binding of these quaternary and tertiary inhibitors.

Besides an anionic site there must also be an enzyme region which interacts with the ester group—an esteratic site. The carbonyl group has a marked polar character; the positive carbon and negative oxygen contribute about 50 % of the bond strength. Since this electrophilic carbon is a site of attack for basic reagents, it is of interest to compare the inhibitory properties of a series of compounds in which there is a large difference in the electrophilic character of a carbonyl carbon. The importance of an electrophilic carbon is well illustrated by a series of nicotinic acid derivatives. The order of increasing electrophilic character from nicotinic acid anion to ethyl nicotinate parallels the observed order

$$-\overset{\overset{O}{\|}}{C}-O^- \;<\; -\overset{\overset{O}{\|}}{C}-NH_2 \;<\; -\overset{\overset{O}{\|}}{C}-N(C_2H_5)_2 \;=$$

$$-\overset{\overset{O}{\|}}{C}-CH_3 \;<\; -\overset{\overset{O}{\|}}{C}-O-C_2H_5$$

of inhibition and suggests that a covalent bond is formed between the carbon and some basic group in the enzyme.[31]

Similar effects are observed with substrates, e.g., the Michaelis-Menten constant decreases rapidly in the order ethyl acetate, ethyl chloroacetate, acetic anhydride, although the maximum velocity remains about the same. Hydrogen bonding does not seem to be of importance in the enzyme substrate complex since choline and trimethylamino-propane inhibit equally.[30]

Valuable information has been obtained from the pH dependence of the enzyme catalyzed hydrolysis.[34] The activity is maximal between pH 8 and 9 but, as the constitution of acetylcholine does not change with pH, changes in activity must be attributed to changes in protein structure. These changes may be interpreted in terms of the dissociation of acidic and basic groups, represented schematically as follows

$$EH_2{}^+ \underset{inactive}{\overset{H^+}{\rightleftharpoons}} \underset{active}{EH} \overset{OH^-}{\rightleftharpoons} \underset{inactive}{E^- + H_2O}$$

where EH, the active enzyme, is arbitrarily assigned a relative net charge of zero. Either the forms $EH_2{}^+$ and E^- cannot form complexes at all or the complexes are inactive, but although the form of the deductions is the same, whichever may be the case, the calculated constants will be different. It is simpler to anticipate the presentation and merely state that although the forms represented by $EH_2{}^+$ can form complexes only with much higher dissociation constants than EH, and may therefore be neglected, the complexes of E$^-$ are of equal stability but are inactive. These concepts suggest the following equilibria and dissociation constants

$$EH_2^+ \rightleftharpoons EH + H^+; \; K_{EH_2^+}$$

$$EH \rightleftharpoons E^- + H^+; \; K_{EH}$$

$$EHS \rightleftharpoons ES^- + H^+; \; K_{EHS}$$

$$EHS + S \rightleftharpoons EHS_2; \quad \cdot \; K_2$$

and the rate equation

$$EH \; + \; S \; \underset{k_2}{\overset{k_1}{\rightleftharpoons}} \; EHS \; \xrightarrow{k_3} \; EH \; + \; products$$

where S is the substrate and EHS_2 is an inactive super complex which accounts for substrate inhibition observed at concentrations greater than $4 \times 10^{-3} \, M$.

Analysis of these relations leads to the equation for the velocity v

$$\frac{v^0}{v} = 1 + \frac{K_1}{K_{EH_2^+}\left(K_1 + (S) + \dfrac{(S)^2}{K_2}\right)} (H_+) + \frac{K_1 K_{EH} + (S)K_{EHS}}{\left(K_1 + (S) + \dfrac{(S)^2}{K_2}\right)} \frac{1}{(H^+)} \quad (2)$$

where v^0 is the reaction velocity at optimum pH, and K_1 is the apparent dissociation constant $(k_2 + k_3)/k_1$.

The prediction that v^0/v will vary linearly with H$^+$ on the acid side of the pH optimum, and linearly with OH$^-$ on the basic side, has been borne out experimentally (Fig. 8).[34]

These experimental observations are thus in agreement with the concept that certain basic and acidic groups are essential for enzyme activity and are consonant with the previous conclusion that the interaction of a basic group in the enzyme with the carbonyl carbon atom of substrates and inhibitors contributes to the binding of these compounds. The decline of enzyme activity in acid media can be attributed in part to poorer binding caused by the conversion of the basic group of the esteratic site to the conjugate acid and, in part, by a similar conversion of the negatively charged groups of the anionic site. The binding of inhibitors containing a carbonyl group as well as a methylated ammonium structure declines much more rapidly than those containing the ammonium structure alone.[35]

The decline in alkaline media is not, however, caused by poorer binding. This is indicated by the fact that noncompetitive inhibition

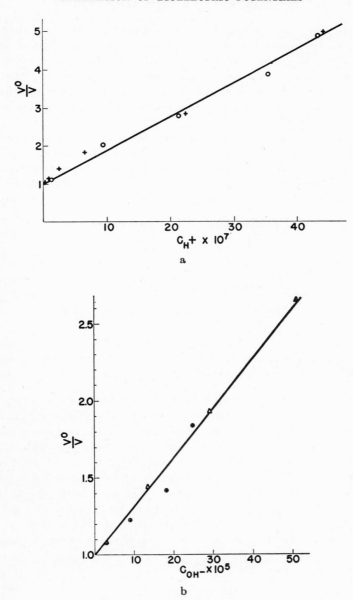

FIG. 8. A: v^0/v as a function of a hydrogen ions. B: v^0/v as a function of hydroxyl ions.

by prostigmine, although declining in acid media at precisely the same rate as acetylcholine hydrolysis, remains constant in alkaline media even to pH 11 where acetylcholine hydrolysis has fallen to 30%.[36] That the binding is just as good in alkaline media indicates that the acid group is not involved in binding and suggests that the decline in enzyme activity is due to the requirement of the acid group in the hydrolytic process.

The enzyme substrate complex (Fig. 9) is stabilized by Coulomb attraction by the anionic site, by Van der Waals-London dispersion forces, and by covalent bond formation between the carbonyl carbon and the basic group of the esteratic site. The esteratic site is here symbolized by H-G, where a dissociable hydrogen atom represents the

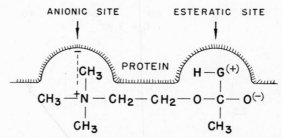

Fig. 9. Schematic presentation of interaction between the active groups of acetylcholinesterase and its substrate.

acid and the electron pair indicates the basic group. In this representation the esteratic site acquires a formal positive charge which must increase the acidity of the acid group. Moreover, the cationic substrate brings a positive charge into this region and this too would tend to increase the acidity of the esteratic site. The decline of activity in alkaline region is best attributed, therefore, to acidic dissociation of the complex rather than of the free enzyme. The dissociation constant for EH_2^+ is a combination of the constants of the anionic site and the esteratic site, but both have individual values of the same order. The constants calculated from experimental observations based on equation (2) are

$$k_1 = 2.6 \times 10^{-4}$$

$$k_{EH_2^+} \begin{cases} \text{anionic site} \\ \text{esteratic site} \end{cases} \sim 5 \times 10^{-7}$$

$$k_{EHS} = 4 \times 10^{-11}$$

$$k_2 = 3 \times 10^{-2}$$

As discussed, the value of K_{EH} is probably somewhat smaller than K_{EHS}.

The hydrolytic process. The discussions so far have described the nature of the enzyme-substrate complex. We now turn to the mechanism of the hydrolytic process and shall fix our attention upon the esteratic site. It will be convenient first to present the mechanism of hydrolysis which has been proposed[37] and then to show how this theory conforms to the observations

$$G\text{—H} + R\text{—}\overset{\overset{\displaystyle O}{\|}}{C}\text{—OR}' \rightleftharpoons R'\text{—}\overset{H\text{—}G^{(+)}}{\overset{|}{\underset{\underset{\displaystyle R}{|}}{\ddot{O}\text{—}C}}}\text{—O}^{(-)} \rightleftharpoons \overset{G^{(+)}}{\overset{\|}{\underset{\underset{\displaystyle R}{|}}{C}}}\text{—O}^{(-)} + R'\text{OH}$$

$$(A) \qquad\qquad (B)$$

$$H\text{—}\overset{H}{\underset{\ddot{}}{\ddot{O}}}: + \overset{G^{(+)}}{\overset{\|}{\underset{\underset{\displaystyle R}{|}}{C}}}\text{—O}^{(-)} \rightleftharpoons H\text{—O—}\overset{H\text{—}G^{(+)}}{\overset{|}{\underset{\underset{\displaystyle R}{|}}{C}}}\text{—O}^{(-)} \rightleftharpoons H\text{—}\underset{\ddot{}}{G} + R\text{—}\overset{\overset{\displaystyle O}{\|}}{C}\text{—OH}$$

$$(B) \qquad\qquad (C)$$

The structure symbolized by G is assumed to have electron transmitting properties as shown, for example, by a conjugate double-bond system. The mechanism is a two-step process involving the simultaneous acylation of the enzyme and the internal elimination of a small molecule, followed by the deacylation of the enzyme.

(A) is the ester-enzyme Michaelis-Menten complex, (B) is a resonance form of the acylated enzyme, and (C) is an acid-enzyme complex similar to the ester-enzyme complex.

The mechanism follows readily from the structure of the enzyme substrate complex and assigns a positive role to the enzyme in launching a combined acid-base attack. The critical complex is a ring involving a kind of hydrogen bond which helps to stabilize the complex so that a low energy of activation is possible and explains the function of the acid group.

The acyl enzyme reacts with nucleophilic reagents such as water, hydroxylamine or an alcohol, e.g. choline, to yield an acid, a hydroxamic acid, or an ester. The rate controlling step is the formation of the acyl enzyme. We may start with acids or esters, but only the undissociated acid molecules have the electrophilic carbon atom necessary for the enzyme substrate complex. Consequently, any reaction which the enzyme will catalyze involving carboxylic acids as substrates should occur much more rapidly with the corresponding esters. This was found to be the case in the comparison of the enzyme catalyzed formation of hydroxamic acids and choline esters from simple esters and the corresponding acids where reaction with the esters is about 100 times faster.[37]

This mechanism predicts that the enzyme should catalyze oxygen exchange between acids and water. This prediction has been confirmed directly[38] and in an indirect manner using thiolacetic acid.[39] In the latter case, H_2S is evolved and acetic acid formed. This reaction can be inhibited completely by prostigmine. It is of especial interest that the small cationic inhibitor trimethylammonium ion, although it inhibits ethyl acetate hydrolysis completely, can inhibit the H_2S liberation (even in enormous concentration) only by 30%. Evidently the binding of this small molecule at the anionic site does not seriously interfere with reaction by the relatively small thiolacetic acid molecule at the neighboring esteratic site. This illustrates the spatial and functional independence of the anionic and esteratic sites. On the basis of this mechanism, the irreversible inhibition caused by certain phosphate esters, such as dialkyl fluorophosphates, tetraalkyl pyrophosphates, and dialkylnitrophenylphosphates has been explained.[29, 40] Although phosphate esters in general tend to react (hydrolyze, for example) by a mechanism which involves the dissolution of a carbon-oxygen bond, thus preserving the phosphate group, these inhibitors tend to react in such a manner that a group linked to phosphorus is broken and a phosphoryl group is transferred to the attacking reagent, i.e., the reactions of these compounds tend to involve a nucleophilic attack at the electrophilic phosphorus atom. We would expect, therefore, that the enzyme attacks these substances in the same way as substrates and that a phosphorylated intermediate is formed, but that the reaction of this intermediate with water is very slow in contrast to the rapid reaction of the analogous acylated enzyme. The phosphorylation is itself an enzymatic process. It is the slowness of the water reaction which makes these compounds inhibitors rather than substrates. This would explain the apparently irreversible inhibition. It is highly significant that the pH dependence of tetraethylpyrophosphate inhibition is similar to the pH dependence of acetylcholinesterase activity. The inhibitor is most potent in just that pH range where the enzyme is most active. Moreover, if the compound contains an unesterified acid group, so that in aqueous solution the molecule is negatively charged and the electrophilic property of the phosphorus atom is largely lost, the compound does not inhibit. On the basis of this theory we should expect that the enzyme would be regenerated by prolonged standing in solution due to slow reaction with water, and this was found to be the case.[40] Nucleophilic reagents, according to the theory, should be good reactivators and, in fact compounds containing amino, pyridyl, guanidino, amidino, hydroxyl, or sulfhydryl groups, were found to be effective reactivators of diethylphosphoryl enzyme.[41] Choline and hydroxylamine are especially good. The reactivation itself is an enzymic process similar to the water reaction, showing saturation when the reactivator contains a binding group as well as a nucleophilic center (e g., choline). As with the normal enzymic hydrolytic activity, the reactivation process can be inhibited by methylated ammonium ions.

When a highly nucleophilic center is combined with a quaternary structure suitably placed in the same molecule so as to exploit the enzymic properties of the surviving anionic site of the phosphorylated enzyme, as with nicotin-hydroxamic acid methiodide, a very effective reactivator is obtained. Diisopropylphosphoryl enzyme is much more difficult to reactivate than the diethylphosphoryl enzyme, but can be completely reactivated with this hydroxamic acid.

This theory of irreversible inhibition has recently been further substantiated.[42]

The approximate values of the dissociation constants of the acidic and basic groups constitute a valuable aid in considering the chemical nature of the esteratic site. In this connection it is interesting to note that imidazole derivatives have appropriate constants, have the electron fluidity assumed for G, and would form a favorable 5- to 6-membered ring in the critical complex. However, the planar structure of the imidazole ring introduces geometrical difficulties in the proposed critical complex.

Comparative properties. In comparing the specificity characteristics of the receptor and the two enzymes, it is important to bear in mind that there are two phases of interaction with the enzymes but, in the case of the receptor, we generally observe only a complete effect and the process does not readily separate into distinct phases. We have, therefore, to consider both the binding and the catalytic specificities of the enzymes. The comparative specificity of the three proteins towards the acid group of appropriate compounds, namely Coenzyme A derivatives for the acetylase and choline derivatives for the esterase and the receptor (tested by contraction of frog's rectus abdominis muscle), are shown in Table IV.[43] It is apparent that there is a marked parallelism in the interaction pattern.

This similarity extends to the alcoholic group. In this connection it is

TABLE IV

COMPARATIVE PROPERTIES OF THE PROTEINS OF THE ACETYLCHOLINE SYSTEM
TOWARDS THE ACID GROUP OF THE REACTING COMPOUNDS

The acetyl derivatives are assigned the reference values of 100. *a* indicates catalytic efficiency, *b* indicates binding strength.

Acidic group	Acetylase		Esterase		Receptor
	a	b	a	b	
Acetyl	100	100	100	100	100
Propionyl	80–100	100	80–100	100	90–100
Butyryl	1	~200	0.7	~150	80
Benzoyl	1	—	0.05	~300	1

found that tertiary and quaternary compounds are very different where some positive action occurs, although as enzyme inhibitors there is little difference between the two groups. In the case of the esterase there is only a small difference (factor of 2) in the binding and hydrolysis of dimethylaminoethyl acetate and acetylcholine, a large factor in the case of the acetylase, and with the receptor the difference is very large indeed. Although the esterase thus appears to be out of line, there are two types of interactions with this enzyme in which the difference is very large. The first is the phenomenon of substrate inhibition which is a marked and distinctive feature of the esterase, occurring at concentrations in excess of 4×10^{-3} M when acetylcholine is a substrate, but completely lacking with the tertiary ester. The other is the reactivation of diethylphosphoryl enzyme which occurs readily with choline, but not at all with dimethylaminoethanol. The comparative specificities are shown in Table V.[43]

TABLE V

COMPARATIVE PROPERTIES OF THE PROTEINS OF THE ACETYLCHOLINE SYSTEM
TOWARDS THE EXTENT OF METHYLATION OF THE AMINO GROUP OF THE
REACTING COMPOUND

The trimethyl derivatives are assigned the reference value of 100. *a* indicates hydrolytic efficiency, *b* indicates the substrate inhibition at high concentration, and *c* indicates the reactivation of TEPP inhibited enzyme.

Extent of methylation	Acetylase	Esterase			Receptor
		a	b	c	
Trimethyl	100	100	100	100	100
Dimethyl	8	45	<5	<5	~1–0.1
Monomethyl	2	—	—	—	—

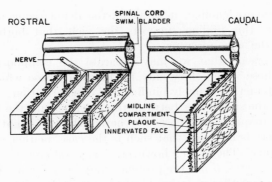

FIG. 10. Diagrams of the two types of layer preparations of the bundle of Sachs. On the left, horizontal layer; on the right, vertical layer.

Studies with the electric organ of *Electrophorus electricus* have been valuable in analyzing interactions with the acetylcholine system. Microelectrodes were introduced into a single cell. A schematic drawing of the preparation used is presented in Fig. 10. The electrical characteristics of the membrane were studied on exposure to compounds which react specifically with the acetylcholine system (Altamirano *et al.*, unpublished experiments of this laboratory). All these compounds, as expected, block the discharge. However, there are striking differences in quality and quantity.

Some of the compounds have a relatively weak action on the esterase but a high affinity to the receptor, and this has made it possible to distinguish block of conduction from enzyme inhibition. Using ethyl chloroacetate as a substrate it is possible to assay the esterase in the intact cell. With certain blocking agents, such as procaine, decamethonium, and carbaminoylcholine, the enzyme is but slightly inhibited under conditions where propagation has been eliminated. In contrast, eserine, DFP, prostigmine and its tertiary analogue produced block only under conditions where the enzyme was very strongly inhibited.

These studies have also suggested that interaction with the receptor may involve two phases analogous to the two phases of interaction with the enzymes. Quaternary compounds, for instance, have a much stronger tendency to depolarize than the tertiary analogues. Most of the tertiary compounds do not depolarize at all, even in high concentrations. Possibly they are unable to produce the change in configuration necessary for accelerated ion movements. The local anesthetic, procaine, a tertiary structure related to acetylcholine, has long been known to block conduction without depolarization. Applied to the electric cell before carbaminoylcholine, it prevents the depolarizing action of the choline ester; this finding supports the view that both compounds compete for the same receptor.

Thus it appears that we may separate the compounds into two categories, those which show only binding and those which show two aspects of interaction, namely binding and depolarization.

In view of the similarities between the receptor and the esterase, the question has frequently arisen as to whether the two might be identical. Although there is no proof that such is the case, neither is there proof of the contrary. There are, however, many differences that suggest that the active sites, if not the proteins, may be different. We have just discussed the fact that procaine blocks propagation without interfering with enzyme activity. Another example is offered by the reactions of the three compounds butyrylcholine, acetylcholine, and dimethyl-aminoethyl acetate. The first two are good stimulators of the receptor, the butyryl compound, however, being a very poor enzyme substrate; on the other hand, dimethylaminoethyl acetate is a good substrate, but acts poorly upon the receptor. Hydrolytic activity is not a prerequisite for receptor activity. Indeed, some compounds which are not esters have strong receptor activity. In this respect, at least, the situation is quite different from that encountered in the elementary process of muscular contraction, where only substrates of ATPase have contractile properties.

We have already discussed the binding of tertiary and quaternary compounds, and it appears that a fourth alkyl group can be effective only if there is a major rearrangement of the protein, so as to bring the latter into simultaneous contact with all the tetrahedrally oriented groups of the small molecule. This is the kind of phenomenon we are seeking as a possible explanation of the observed alteration of ionic permeability and the colligative changes in membrane resistance and membrane potential which, together with the underlying chemical processes, constitute the nerve impulse. Rearrangement of acidic and basic groups by folding or unfolding of the protein chains would be one possible explanation of the increased sodium permeability effected by the system.

This kind of reasoning is the basis of our present approach. Although it has aided us in formulating and interpreting experiments, we do not have a definite experiment which would indicate that this view is essentially correct. It constitutes merely a working scheme which integrates our present knowledge.

REFERENCES

1. USSING, H. H., *in* "Ion Transport across Membranes" (H. T. Clarke and D. Nachmansohn, eds.), p. 3. Academic Press, New York, 1954.
2. CURTIS, H. J., and COLE, K. S., *J. Gen. Physiol.* **22**, 649 (1939).
3. HODGKIN, A. L., and HUXLEY, A. F., *J. Physiol.* **104**, 176 (1945).
4. CURTIS, H. J., and COLE, K. S., *J. Cellular Comp. Physiol.* **19**, 135 (1942).
5. HODGKIN, A. L., *Biol. Revs.* **26**, 338 (1951).
6. HUXLEY, A. F., *in* "Ion Transport across Membranes" (H. T. Clarke and D. Nachmansohn, eds.), p. 23. Academic Press, New York, 1954.
7. DAVIES, R. E., and OGSTON, A. G., *Biochem. J.* **46**, 324 (1950).
8. MEYER, K. H., *Helv. Chim. Acta* **20**, 634 (1937).
9. MEYERHOF, O., "Zur Energetik der Zellvorgaenge." Vandenhoeck & Ruprecht, Göttingen, 1913.
10. NACHMANSOHN, D., *in* "Modern Trends of Physiology and Biochemistry" (E. S. G. Barron, ed.), 229. Academic Press, New York, 1952.
11. NACHMANSOHN, D., and WILSON, I. B., *Advances in Enzymol.*, **12**, 259 (1951).
12. NACHMANSOHN, D., *Harvey Lectures* 1953–54 (in press).
13. AUGUSTINSSON, K. V., AND NACHMANSOHN, D., *Science* **110**, 98 (1949).
14. NACHMANSOHN, D., and ROTHENBERG, M. A., *Science* **100**, 454 (1944).
15. NACHMANSOHN, D., AND ROTHENBERG, M. A., *J. Biol. Chem.* **158**, 653 (1945).
16. SEAMAN, G. R., and HOULIHAN, R. K., *J. Cellular Comp. Physiol.* **37**, 309 (1951).
17. BOELL, E. J., and NACHMANSOHN, D., *Science* **92**, 513 (1940).
18. BULLOCK, T. H., NACHMANSOHN, D., AND ROTHENBERG, M. A., *J. Neurophysiol.* **9**, 9 (1946).
19. WILSON, I. B., and COHEN, M., *Biochim. et Biophys. Acta* **11**, 147 (1953).
20. ALTAMIRANO, M., COATES, C. W., GRUNDFEST, H., AND NACHMANSOHN, D. *J. Gen. Physiol.* **37**, 91 (1953).
21. KEYNES, R. D., AND MARTINS-FERREIRA, H., *J. Physiol.* **119**, 315 (1953).
22. NACHMANSOHN, D., COATES, C. W., and ROTHENBERG, M. A., *J. Biol. Chem.* **163**, 39 (1946).
23. NACHMANSOHN, D., COX, R. T., COATES, C. W., and MACHADO, A. L., *J. Neurophysiol.* **6**, 383 (1943).
24. NACHMANSOHN, D., and MACHADO, A. L., *J. Neurophysiol.* **6**, 397 (1943).
25. LIPMANN, F., and KAPLAN, N. O., *J. Biol. Chem.* **162**, 743 (1946).
26. LIPTON, M. A., *Federation Proc.* **5**, 145 (1946).
27. NACHMANSOHN, D., and BERMAN, M., *J. Biol. Chem.* **165**, 551 (1946).
28. FELDBERG, W., FESSARD, A., and NACHMANSOHN, D., *J. Physiol.* **97**, 3P (1940).
29. WILSON, I. B. and BERGMANN, F., *J. Biol. Chem.* **185**, 479 (1950).
30. WILSON, I. B., *J. Biol. Chem.* **197**, 215 (1952).
31. BERGMANN, F., WILSON, I. B., AND NACHMANSOHN, D., *J. Biol. Chem.* **186**, 693 (1950).
32. MYERS, D. K., *Arch. Biochem.* **27**, 341 (1950).
33. ADAMS, D. H., and WHITAKER, V. P., *Biochim. et Biophys. Acta* **4**, 543 (1950).
34. WILSON, I. B., and BERGMANN, F., *J. Biol. Chem.* **186**, 683 (1950).
35. BERGMANN, F., *Biochim. et Biophys. Acta* **9**, 473 (1952).
36. WILSON, I. B., *Biochim. et Biophys. Acta* **7**, 466 (1951).

64   IRWIN B. WILSON AND DAVID NACHMANSOHN

37. Wilson, I. B., Bergmann, F., and Nachmansohn, D., *J. Biol. Chem.* **186,** 781 (1950).
38. Sprinson, D. B., and Rittenberg, D., *Nature* **167,** 484 (1951).
39. Wilson, I. B., *Biochim. et Biophys. Acta* **7,** 520 (1951).
40. Wilson, I. B., *J. Biol. Chem.* **190,** 111 (1951).
41. Wilson, I. B., *J. Biol. Chem.* **199,** 113 (1952.
42. Aldridge, W. N., and Davison, A. N., *Biochem. J.* **55,** 763 (1953).
43. Berman, R., Wilson, I. B., and Nachmansohn, D., *Biochim. et Biophys. Acta* **12,** 315 (1953).

Some Optical Observations on the Interaction Between Acetyl Cholinesterase and Its Substrate

S. L. FRIESS, J. J. BLUM, AND M. F. MORALES

In a prominent theory of conduction in nerve,[a] which attributes the variation in permeability of the membrane to K^+ and Na^+ ions to the presence of the acetyl choline-cholinesterase system, Nachmansohn and co-workers have postulated the existence of a so-called receptor protein endowed with certain special properties. Important among these is the occurrence of a reversible, large-scale structural change in this protein molecule on adsorption of acetyl choline ions, and of a local alteration in configuration of the membrane sufficient to permit the establishment of the calculated K^+ and Na^+ ion fluxes associated with the generation of the action potential. Destruction of the bound acetyl choline by immediately adjacent esterase molecules is then presumed to permit reestablishment of the resting condition of the membrane.

An intriguing variation in this scheme would be the assignment of a dual role to the single protein acetyl cholinesterase, allowing it to function as the receptor protein in addition to its catalytic action in the subsequent hydrolysis of the released acetyl choline.[b] On this assumption, it should be possible to observe a change in shape for the isolated, purified enzyme actively engaged in adsorbing and turning over its substrate, as compared to that of its normal state.

Two lines of inquiry have now been directed toward the investigation of this possible change in molecular shape of the enzyme. In the first of these, spectrophotometric measurements in the 200–400 mμ region of the spectrum have been made on the purified enzyme,[c] its sub-

---

[a] For a recent summary, see the paper by I. B. Wilson and D. Nachmansohn in this volume.

[b] This assumption that the enzyme may serve as the receptor protein has also been presented recently by A. O. Župančič, *Acta Physiol. Scand.* **29,** 63 (1953). It is also worth noting that this duality of function for acetyl cholinesterase constitutes an exact analog of the role postulated for the enzyme myosin, in its interaction with ATP, according to one recent theory.

[c] The enzyme was a highly purified preparation derived from electric eel tissue and previously described in the paper by S. L. Friess and W. J. McCarville, *J. Am. Chem. Soc.* **76,** 1363 (1954).

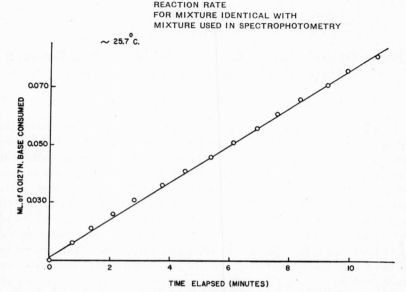

FIG. 1. Reaction rate at pH 7.4 and 25.7°C for a 3.20-ml reaction mixture initially 3.34×10^{-3} M in acetyl choline and containing 2.6×10^{-5} mg of enzyme.

strate acetyl choline, and on a mixture of the two under the conditions of a steady-state reaction at optimum substrate concentration. Typical results are shown in the sequence of Figs. 1–3. The rate plot of Fig. 1 indicates that at pH 7.4, and the same concentrations of enzyme and substrate employed in the spectrophotometric work, a steady-state reaction of at least ten minutes' duration is observed. During this time, which is sufficiently long to allow the scanning of the short spectral region for the reaction mixture, less than 10 % of the substrate is consumed. Figure 2 shows the absorption spectra for the individual components of the final reaction mixture, and curve I of Fig. 3 shows their summation. In contrast to this summation of spectra of components, curve II of Fig. 3 was obtained within a 10-min interval on a steady-state reaction mixture identical with that of Fig. 1.

Comparison of curves I and II of Fig. 3 for the region below 250 mμ shows a very marked difference between the sum of the spectra of the nonreacting enzyme and substrate, and the spectrum of the reacting mixture. The inference as to whether or not this difference is a direct reflection of an altered configuration of the enzyme upon complex formation with the substrate cannot be drawn clearly from these data; how-

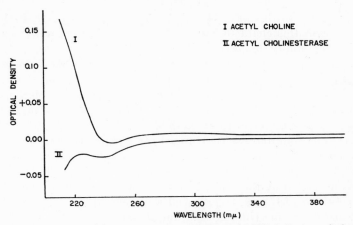

FIG. 2. Absorption spectra in phosphate buffer of pH 7.4. I: Acetyl choline at $3.34 \times 10^{-3}\ M$ concentration. II: Acetyl cholinesterase at 2.6×10^{-5} mg/3.20 ml.

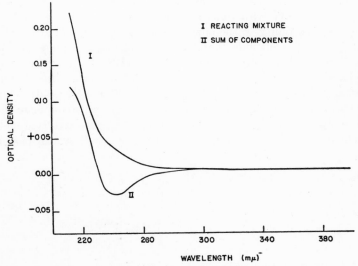

FIG. 3. Absorption spectra in phosphate buffer of pH 7.4. I: Reaction mixture identical to that of Fig. 1. II: Sum of spectra in Fig. 2.

ever, the possibility is certainly not excluded. Further, the transmittancies in excess of 100 % recorded at the lower wavelengths for the enzyme component alone, against its buffer blank, as shown in Fig. 2, would make it appear that an element of light scattering enters into the observed readings in this spectral region. Consequently, changes in density readings with this characteristic might at least in part reflect changes in scattering ability, and hence in particle shape.

A second approach to this problem of a possible change in particle shape for the enzyme was made by means of light-scattering measurements (with visible light) on more concentrated protein solutions.

A solution of the enzyme containing 0.16 mg/ml was prepared in specially filtered buffer (0.15 M phosphate, 0.1 M NaCl, 0.01 M MgCl$_2$, pH 7.4). The solution was centrifuged for 1 hour at about 15,000 g at 4°C, after which 35 ml were transferred to a light-scattering cell. As a control, 35 ml of filtered buffer were placed in another cell. The turbidity was measured at 135°, 90°, and 45° from the incident beam, whose wavelength was 547 mμ. To each cell was then added (in turn) 1 ml of 0.5 M acetyl choline chloride solution, dissolved in buffer and also filtered to remove dust. The turbidity of the enzyme solution was followed for a time greater than was required (as measured in a separate experiment) for all the acetyl choline to be hydrolyzed. There was no change in turbidity with time, and there was no significant difference[d] between the turbidity of the enzyme solution before and after addition of substrate. We conclude that by this criterion no significant change in the over-all shape of the protein occurs when its substrate is added. The change in the ultraviolet absorption spectrum may therefore result from the effect of binding of substrate onto the site. It is also conceivable that a significant local shape change may occur at or near the enzymatic site which would not be detectable by light-scattering methods but which would still be of consequence in controlling the passage of ions.

[d] The data for the enzyme solution alone, at three scattering angles, reproduce the results for the reacting mixture within the ±2% precision of the measurements.

Ion Permeability of the Red Cell

A. K. PARPART AND J. F. HOFFMAN

A considerable variety of experimental evidence is available to indicate that inorganic ions are the primary osmotically active units, both inside and outside the red cell. These ions are in as freely diffusible a state in the cytoplasm as they are in the normal environment, limited only, as far as the cytoplasm or environment is concerned, by small inequalities of distribution determined by the Donnan equilibrium conditions (Warburg, 1922; Jacobs and Parpart, 1931). Thus, there is very little trapping of cations by chemical bonding with organic molecules within the red cell. Since the plasma membrane is only slightly permeable to most of the normally occurring organic molecules within the cell (e.g., hemoglobin), any such bonding, if specific, might lead to accumulation of a particular cation. There is very little experimental evidence to indicate even moderate amounts of such combinations.

Also well established is the fact that the red cells of a number of species of vertebrates show marked inequalities in the distribution of particular cations between the environment and their cytoplasm. This is particularly true of the ions that regulate the osmotic behavior of red cells, viz., sodium and potassium. It has, therefore, been necessary to place the determinant of these inequalities of cation distribution at a limiting surface or surfaces (the plasma membrane) between the environment and the cytoplasm. For these reasons red cells have been claimed to be highly "impermeable" to cations. The osmotic behavior of the red cells, their ability to increase or decrease in volume in hypotonic or hypertonic environments in a predictable manner, is the result not only of their ready permeability to water but is chiefly due to their exceptionally low permeability to sodium and potassium ions. It is this impermeability that balances the continued osmotic influence of hemoglobin (Wilbrandt, 1941; Jacobs and Willis, 1947; Parpart and Green, 1951).

Anions, on the other hand, enter and leave red cells with great ease. The shift of bicarbonate ions out of the red cell for chloride ions entering the cell attains equilibrium in one to two seconds (Dirken and Mook, 1931). Similar rapid exchange of sulfate ions outside for chloride ions inside the red cell have been reported (Parpart, 1940). This chloride-sulfate exchange has a very high μ value (23,000 calories; $Q_{10} = 3.0$), which suggests that the exchanging anions must pass a barrier of high potential energy. This is true even though $Cl^--SO_4^=$ exchange reaches equilibrium in two to three seconds at 37° C, when the $SO_4^=$ ion is entering the cell. Sulfate ions leave the cell at a much more rapid rate. The rate of exchange of cations compared to that of anions is less by a factor of about 100,000 under optional conditions at 37° C.

Recent interesting studies on phosphate-ion permeability (measured as P^{32} in Na_2HPO_4) do not, unfortunately, give direct evidence of the rate of penetration of phosphate ions (Gourley, 1952). They do indicate a slower rate than for the previously mentioned anions. In this and related work there appears to be a confusion between the penetration of phosphate ions and the subsequent trapping of these anions in the interior of the cell in the form of organic esters. The cell membrane is only very slightly permeable to most of these esters (Hevesy and Hahn, 1940), and hence the chemically bound phosphate would not take part in the diffusion equilibrium toward which the inorganic phosphate inside and outside the cell proceeds. The net result, as long as the cell is actively glycolyzing, would be a higher concentration of total phosphate in the cell. This is a situation quite different from that for most other inorganic anions and for inorganic cations. Mueller and Hastings (1951) observed a slow rate of penetration of the phosphate ion and presented evidence that "the phosphorus crosses the red cell membrane by a process of slow diffusion."

It would thus appear that the inorganic anions enter and leave red cells rapidly by a process compatible with the concept of simple diffusion through aqueous channels whose electrochemical charge is such as to favor the negatively charged ions (Parpart and Ballentine, 1952). Such electrochemically charged channels would, at the same time, greatly impede the entrance and exit of inorganic cations, although this would not account for the selection of the type of cation that crosses.

The selection of potassium over sodium forms one possible explanation of the fact that the potassium concentration of the red cells of many animals, and of a wide variety of other plant and animal cells, is greater than the potassium concentration of the environment, whereas the cell sodium concentration is lower; this phenomenon has been labelled specific ion "accumulation."

Various mechanisms have been proposed to account for this specific ion accumulation:

1. Selection in a charged channel by virtue of the hydrated size of the ion.

2. Selective solubility in a molecular component of the plasma membrane.

3. Specific chemical combination (e.g., by salt formation or by union in nonionized form with a specific carrier or in a manner analogous to exchange resins) with a component in the membrane.

4. A "sodium pump" mechanism associated with the cytoplasm and/or plasma membrane responsible for removing sodium ions entering the cell. This also includes the idea that the plasma membrane has a low permeability to potassium ions, normally.

It can be deduced thermodynamically that any mechanism proposed must require energy for the maintenance (or the accumulation) of the cations against a concentration gradient. How this energy is coupled into the permeability for these ions is still a matter of conjecture.

The first three mechanisms can be thought of as requiring an exchange of a hydrogen ion from the interior of the cell, energy not being directly involved in the exchange. The metabolic production of acid (lactic in the case of mammalian red cells) provides a continued source of these ions. The fourth mechanism requires the direct utilization of energy and may apply to certain aspects of the third.

Any one of these mechanisms, or any combination of them that may be responsible for the accumulation of potassium in the red cells of some species of vertebrates, must be thought of as acting across a membrane about 60 Å thick (Parpart and Ballentine, 1952; Hillier and Hoffman 1953).

This thin membrane is essentially a nonconductor, with an electrical resistance of 1000 ohms/cm² (Cole, 1940). The ion-permeable region represented by this resistance is only a small portion of the total cell surface, as suggested by Cole from his measurements of the electrical capacity of the membrane (1 $\mu f/cm^2$) which would represent a large part of the surface area as ion impermeable. It is doubtful whether the surface area available for the passage of ions across the surface of a red cell can be greater than 1/1000 of the total surface area of the cell. Since there are of the order of 10^5 channels in the membrane (Parpart and Ballentine, 1952; Hillier and Hoffman, 1953) this would mean that the area of a channel could not exceed 100 Å².

The rate of efflux of potassium ions, measured as K[39] leaving the cell in exchange for Na[23] outside the cell, is of the order of 0.62 mM/l cells/hr under optimal conditions at 37° C; and of the order of 0.07 mM/l cells/hr at 7° C (Parpart *et al.*, 1947). These values are about one-third of those reported for similar conditions but measured in a steady state of K^{42} influx (Raker, *et al.*, 1950; Sheppard and Martin, 1950; Solomon, 1952). The analytical procedures involved in these two methods of approach to the problem have about the same order of reliability, although, of course, the K^{42} studies involve the distribution of a much smaller number of ions. In fact, in the studies of Raker, *et al.* (1950), the system consisted of 8 parts of medium in which 2 parts of red cells were suspended. The 8 parts of medium contained about 0.8 mc of K^{42} or about 1×10^{12} radioactive potassium particles, and the 2 parts of red cells must have had at least 1×10^{12} red cells if calculated on the basis of a 1-liter system. Considered on a per cell basis, then, there was not more than one K^{42} available per cell. Considered as a two-compartment system, the cellular compartment took up the K^{42} to approximately 20 times the external concentration, or in the same proportion as the K^{39} distribution.

The net result of these numerous *in vitro* studies, whether by K^{42} or K^{39}, on the potassium transport across the red cell membrane is that it is a relatively slow process which would require approximately eight days at 37° and 70 days at 7°C to remove all the K^{39} from the cell. The K^{39} influx data of Harris (1941) and of Ponder (1950) and the K^{42} data both suggest that the potassium content of red cells is the result of a balance between the rates of influx and efflux of this ion.

Models of the type Michaelis proposed for the pore structure of collodion membranes involving charged pores have frequently been invoked to account for the accumulation of potassium ions in cells. If aqueous channels are present in the plasma membrane of the red cell, and these channels are at the point of attachment of the phospholipid molecules with the protein that make up the membrane, then there is the possibility for a small but definite excess of positive charge in these channels. Data on the permeability to nonelectrolytes indicate that few of these channels can exceed 5 Å in diameter. The influx and efflux of anions through such channels would be rapid, whereas that of cations such as potassium and sodium would be slow. However, as mentioned before, selection of K over Na would have to be on the basis of the hydrated size of the two ions. Although this concept has frequently been proposed to account for potassium accumulation, there is little evidence available to establish or to disprove it.

One of the better models of a carrier system is that of guaiacol as proposed by Osterhout. The application of this conceptual approach to the problem of potassium accumulation in the case of the red cell runs into experimental facts that make it difficult if not impossible to apply. All of the lipid (of the total lipid, 70 % is phospholipid and 25 % cholesterol) is present in the plasma membrane of the cell, but the amount of this lipid is only sufficient to form the equivalent of a bimolecular layer. The lipid appears to be arranged primarily in parallel with the surface and to be largely concentrated in the 10^5 pores of the membrane. This arrangement might allow for a thickness comprising 4 or 5 nonpolar heads of the lipid molecules to be stacked up in the channel from outside to inside. Although there would be a large number of such stacked lipid molecules around the edge of any given pore, it is improbable that any of these known lipid components of the membrane serves as a transporting agent that is selective for potassium.

Whatever mechanism or mechanisms are eventually found to account for the accumulation of K^{39} by the red cells of some species of vertebrates, it will be necessary that the factors that influence the K^{39} exchange be taken into account. Some of the more important of these factors are as follows:

1. Temperature has an effect whose Q_{10} is about 2.2 ($\mu = 12,000$ calories). This appears to be true whether measurements are made of K^{39}-Na^{23} exchange or K^{42} flux.

2. The rate of K^{39} loss from the cell is markedly altered by pH; there is a minimum at about pH 7.0 and a marked increase on either side of this pH.

3. The rate of K^{39} loss is also reduced by the addition of glucose to the system at pH 7.0, but this effect is much less marked at higher (7.5) and lower (6.5) pH levels even though the rate of glucose utilization by the red cells is not altered. This was observed when the glucose concentration was changed from 0 to 500 mg %. K^{42} influx data indicate that, over the range of glucose concentration from 250 to 800 mg %, the rate of this influx is unaffected.

4. Lytic agents added to the environment induced an increased rate of exchange of K^{39} for Na^{23} long before the agents cause the diffusion of hemoglobin to equilibrium concentration inside and outside the cell. In the case of some lytic agents, e.g., monohydric alcohols, their action on this cation exchange can be stopped by removal of the agent.

5. The addition of potassium to the environment in the range from the normal 4 mM/l plasma to a value of 16 does not alter the K^{42} influx. Cold stored red cells returned to 37° show an increased rate of K^{39} influx as the external concentration of potassium is increased.

6. Various metabolic inhibitors have been shown to increase the rate of K^{39} exchange for Na^{23}, although to varying degree. It is probable that this effect is related to the degree of lytic action of the inhibitor.

7. It has been claimed that acetyl choline breakdown plays a part in decreasing the rate of K^{39} exchange. There is a considerable body of evidence that negates this.

8. Removal of oxygen has no effect on K^{39} exchange or K^{42} influx. Nucleated red cells are exceptions to this.

9. The red cells of various species of mammals show marked differences in the degree of potassium accumulation.

Thus any hypothesis that offers an adequate explanation of the observed potassium accumulation of red cells must take into account the normally low permeability of the cell to potassium ions; the known molecular composition of the plasma membrane; the probable organization of these molecular components; and the various factors that influence the permeability to the potassium ions in the environment and in the cytoplasm.

REFERENCES

COLE, K. S. (1940). *Cold Spring Harbor Symposia Quant. Biol.* **8**, 110.
DIRKEN, M. N. J., and MOOK, H. W. (1931). *J. Physiol.* **73**, 349.
GOURLEY, D. R. H. (1952). *Arch. Biochem. and Biophys.*, **40**, 1, 13.
HARRIS, J. E. (1941). *J. Biol. Chem.* **141**, 579.
HILLIER, J., and HOFFMAN, J. F. (1953). *J. Cellular Comp. Physiol.* **42**, 203.
HEVESEY, G., and HAHN, L. (1940). *Kgl. Danske Videnskab. Selskab. Mat.-fys. Medd.* **15**, 3.
JACOBS, M. H., and PARPART, A. K. (1931). *Biol. Bull.* **60**, 95.
JACOBS, M. H., and WILLIS, M. (1947). *Biol. Bull.* **93**, 223.
MUELLER, C. B., and HASTINGS, A. B. (1951). *J. Biol. Chem.* **189**, 869.
PARPART, A. K. (1940). *Cold Spring Harbor Symposia Quant. Biol.* **8**, 25.
PARPART, A. K., GREGG, J. R., LORENZ, P. B., PARPART, E. R., and CHASE, A. M. (1947). *J. Clin. Invest.* **26**, 641.
PARPART, A. K., and GREEN, J. W. (1951). *J. Cellular Comp. Physiol.* **38**, 347.
PARPART, A. K., and BALLENTINE, R. (1952). "Modern Trends in Physiology and Biochemistry," Academic Press, New York.
PONDER, E. (1950). *J. Gen. Physiol.* **33**, 745.
RAKER, J. W., TAYLOR, I. M., WELLER, J. M., and HASTINGS, A. B. (1950). *J. Gen. Physiol.* **33**, 691.
SHEPPARD, C. W., and MARTIN, W. R. (1950). *J. Gen. Physiol.* **33**, 703.
SOLOMON, A. K. (1952). *J. Gen. Physiol.* **36**, 57.
WARBURG, E. J. (1922). *Biochem. J.* **16**, 153.
WILBRANDT, W. (1941). *Pflüger's Arch. ges. physiol.* **245**, 22.

Renal Mechanisms of Electrolyte Transport

GILBERT H. MUDGE, M.D.

Among the many biological membranes that are concerned with the transport of electrolytes, the tubular epithelium of the mammalian kidney is of unusual physiological importance. Its transport mechanisms are so delicately balanced that extremely small deviations from normal function result in relatively enormous distortions in the volume and composition of body fluids. The kidney also represents one of the few organs in which certain aspects of electrolyte transport can be studied in normal man by techniques which are not only very accurate but, at the same time, are relatively simple. Electrolyte transport in the kidney is profoundly affected by a large number of factors such as the endocrine glands, the circulatory system, the composition of the diet, the pH of the blood, and the administration of many pharmacological agents. It is not the purpose of this paper to review these regulatory mechanisms in any systematic fashion, but rather to summarize some of the fundamental observations on electrolyte transport in as much detail as is warranted by currently available physiological studies.

It may also be pointed out that the kidney is quite different from some of the other tissues in which electrolyte transport has been extensively examined. The nervous system conducts an impulse, the muscular system lengthens and contracts, the red blood corpuscle combines reversibly with oxygen, whereas a major function of the kidney, as well as of the gastrointestinal tract, is the transport of water and solute. These tissues also differ widely in their general metabolic reactions. Metabolism in the red blood corpuscle is largely anaerobic, in muscle it is both anaerobic and aerobic, whereas in kidney aerobic reactions are of overwhelming importance. These simple generalities deserve mention only because of possible implications concerning the mechanisms of ion transport. In so far as the movement of electrolyte may be related to cell function or to metabolic reactions, it seems reasonable to anticipate that the mechanisms of ion transport may vary widely between different tissues. Although future studies may reveal reactions in common, it would at present appear unwarranted to assume universal applicability of mechanisms or to prejudice the interpretation of any single observation by extrapolation from studies on other cell types.

75

ELECTROLYTE TRANSPORT *IN VIVO*

The composition and volume of the excreted urine is determined by four separate types of renal function—filtration, reabsorption, secretion, and chemical transformation. These may be briefly described in terms of the fundamental anatomical unit of the kidney, the nephron. In normal man the two kidneys weigh about 300 gm and contain approximately two-million nephrons. Each nephron consists of two distinct parts, the relatively small glomerular tuft and the renal tubule. After the renal artery enters the kidney it divides into smaller and smaller branches, finally to form an arteriole which goes into the glomerular tuft and there divides into a network of capillaries. These, in turn, eventually merge into another single arteriole which carries blood out of the glomerulus and thence to a second network of capillaries which surrounds the epithelial portion of the nephron. As a result of this vascular arrangement, the glomerular capillaries are perfused by blood at pressures approaching the high levels of the arterial tree, and the glomerulus thus serves as a filtering device. By analogy, one can visualize a handful of macaroni (the glomerular capillaries) held together somewhat in the shape of a ball and suspended in the mouth of a funnel (the glomerular capsule), and thus separated from the funnel by a slight space (the space of Bowman). If a long piece of tubing is attached to the neck of the funnel it becomes comparable to the tubular portion of the nephron, which in reality is composed of a single layer of cells, so arranged around a central lumen that they form a long narrow tubule.

The thin walled glomerular capillaries are virtually impermeable to the passage of large molecules, and thus an ultrafiltrate of plasma, free or almost free of protein, is formed in Bowman's space. The energy for filtration is furnished by the work of the heart and is transmitted to the kidney as the arterial pressure. From the point of view of energy expenditure, the kidney itself can be considered to participate in the filtration process only by virtue of the very minute fraction of renal metabolism which is probably required to maintain the semipermeable characteristics of the glomerular membrane and also possibly in so far as local events within the kidney may modify the effective filtration pressure.

The ultrafiltrate of plasma passes down into the tubular portion of the nephron where major portions of both solvent and solute are transported back across the tubular epithelium and into the peritubular spaces, finally to re-enter the blood stream in the peritubular capillaries. In terms of water and most solutes, the urine that is finally excreted represents that small fraction of the glomerular filtrate which has escaped reabsorption. This process is relatively selective so that "waste products," notably urea, are reabsorbed less completely and therefore appear in high concentrations in the excreted urine; conversely, those substances which are in short supply tend to be more completely reabsorbed. The term reabsorption indicates only the direction of transport and does not imply any specific type of mechanism or reaction. For example, glucose is reabsorbed by an active cellular mechanism[a] which renders the urine glucose-free, whereas urea is reabsorbed by passive back diffusion as a result of the high concentration of urea established in the urine by the reabsorption of other solutes and water.

A third process, tubular secretion, may be defined as the sum of those reactions which transfer a substance from the extracellular fluid of the peritubular spaces, across the tubular epithelium, and into the tubular lumen. Secretion is thus tubular transport in a direction opposite to that of reabsorption. As a result of the secretory process, certain substances may appear in the excreted urine without having been filtered at the glomerulus. In the past, tubular secretion has been of interest because of a limited number of organic acids which are transported by this route.[b] However, within recent years it has been shown that this general type of reaction is of considerable importance in the transport of inorganic ions; this aspect will be discussed more fully below.

The fourth type of renal mechanism may be called chemical transformation and may be regarded as the synthesis of excretory products by the cells of the renal tubule, with their subsequent discharge into

[a] The term active transport has a number of different meanings in the physiological literature and is sometimes a source of confusion. One of the most exact definitions, proposed by Ussing,[1] is that of transport against a chemical potential gradient. The term is also widely used to indicate movement against just a concentration gradient. It is also employed in a much more general sense to denote transport which depends on "some special activity on the part of the cells."[2] This latter concept not only calls attention to the metabolic aspects of the problem but also emphasizes our present inability to describe many of the biological phenomena in terms of the simplifying laws of physics and chemistry. Some of the inconsistencies resulting from excessively rigid definitions are illustrated by the tubular transport of phenol red. As pointed out by Shannon,[3] the cellular mechanism which facilitates the transport of this compound against a concentration gradient is also capable of limiting its rate of transport in the direction of the gradient. In the present paper, active transport is used in a very general sense to denote transport across biological membranes which appears to be directly related to local metabolic events.

[b] The tubular transport of foreign organic acids is considered beyond the scope of this paper; the subject has been extensively reviewed elsewhere.[4, 5]

the tubular urine. A classical example is the formation of ammonia from nitrogenous precursors.

Many of our current concepts of renal function are based on the theories proposed by Cushny. These have been greatly amplified in recent years by the micropuncture studies of individual nephrons carried out by A. N. Richards and his associates. The measurements of renal function in intact animals and in man have been accomplished by the clearance techniques, developed in large part in the laboratory of H. W. Smith, and very completely described by him in a recent and excellent monograph.[4] As a result of these studies, many of the specific functions of the kidney can now be measured rather easily and also with considerable accuracy. The following values for normal man serve to define both the nature and magnitude of the various processes. The normal cardiac output is approximately 5 liters of blood per minute and, of this, about 1.2 liters per minute flow through the kidneys, an extremely high rate of flow in view of their relatively small size. Correcting for the percentage of blood which is composed of red blood corpuscles, the renal plasma flow is found to be about 700 ml per minute. Of this, approximately 130 ml are filtered across the glomerular membrane each minute, and this comparatively large volume of fluid enters the proximal ends of the renal tubules. Since the amount of urine actually excreted is about 1 ml/min, it follows that all but a very small fraction of the glomerular filtrate undergoes reabsorption. As a first approximation, the amounts reabsorbed each minute by the renal tubules in man are: sodium, 18 meq; bicarbonate, 3 meq; chloride, 14 meq; potassium, about 0.6 meq; and water, 129 ml. One direct consequence of the magnitude of the reabsorptive process warrants emphasis. By simple calculation, if 99 % of the filtered sodium is normally reabsorbed and 1 % is excreted, then a decrease in reabsorption to only 98 %, i.e., a change of about 1 %, would increase the amount excreted to 2 % of the glomerular filtrate, but this would constitute a two-fold increase in the sodium content of the urine finally elaborated. Such an arithmetical relationship poses an overwhelming problem for the physiologist in attempting to study small fluctuations in tubular reabsorptive activity; it also emphasizes the precision with which tubular function is apparently regulated.

The renal tubule is a nonhomogeneous structure, both structurally and functionally. It consists of three well-defined parts—the proximal convoluted segment, the thin intermediate segment (the loop of Henle), and the distal convoluted segment. Each nephron terminates in a collecting tubule which joins with those from other nephrons to form a system of ducts which carry the urine to the pelvis of the kidney and thence to the ureters and bladder. It had been generally held that the collecting ducts do not modify the volume or composition of the urine, and thus the processes of urine formation may initially be considered in terms of the three portions of the nephron itself.

It may be of interest to estimate the area available for the reabsorptive process. As a very crude approximation, made on the basis of available measurements[6] and on the assumption that the various segments are simple, smooth-walled tubes, the surface which constitutes the apparent interphase between tubular lumen and tubular cell can be calculated to be about 2.6 m², whereas the area between tubular cells and peritubular fluid is 7.5 m². That such a calculation may be a gross underestimate is clearly indicated by a number of factors, of which the most important is probably the fact that it completely ignores the presence of the "brush border" of the proximal tubule. As observed by light microscopy, this is made up of extremely fine filaments projecting from the tubular cells into the lumen; it might well play an important role in reabsorption in association with the enormous increase in surface area thus obtained. Re-examination of its functional significance may be anticipated in view of the recent advances in electron microscopy. The studies of Sjöstrand and Rhodin[7] suggest that this border consists of tightly packed cylindrical ducts which have closed ends and which share adjacent walls in common, so that there still exists a more or less continuous membrane parallel to the cell border. Although this would not increase the surface area as such, it would result in a great increase of the reactive surface immediately subjacent to the anatomical border. However, a final interpretation of the structure of this border must wait upon additional studies. Since the proximal tubule reabsorbs a wide variety of solutes—for example, glucose, amino acids, sodium, and chloride—no specific correlation can be made at present between its structure and the transport of specific substances. By histochemical techniques, the area of the brush border is found to be rich in phosphatase activity.[8] Although this enzyme has been implicated in the reabsorption of glucose, the evidence is inconclusive.[9] The exact role of phosphatase in reabsorptive processes remains to be determined.

Some of the functions of the proximal tubule in reabsorbing electrolytes may be briefly summarized. According to the micropuncture studies, the urine within the proximal segment remains essentially isosmotic with plasma.[10] Since the volume becomes progressively reduced as the urine flows down the tubule, it follows that considerable quantities of solute as well as of water must be reabsorbed. Glucose virtually disappears from the urine within the proximal tubule and is generally believed to be reabsorbed exclusively in this segment. From the same studies it is clear that major portions of the filtered sodium and chloride are also reabsorbed proximally. Variable amounts may be reabsorbed more distally, as will be discussed below. The isosmotic nature of the proximal urine indicates that solvent and solute are reabsorbed in approximately proportional amounts, and thus electrolyte concentration gradients are normally not established. During osmotic diuresis, the normal relationship of electrolyte to water reabsorption is altered. In this type of experiment a brisk diuresis is produced by the administration of large amounts of compounds such as mannitol or urea which are reabsorbed to only a limited degree. As a result, there remains within the tubular urine a large quantity of unreabsorbed solute which, by virtue of its osmotic effect, prevents the back diffusion of water. This results in an increase in the volume of the voided urine which may rise to as high as 75 % of the glomerular filtrate under conditions of extreme osmotic loading. The urine is characterized by an osmotic pressure approximately equal to that of plasma, by a concentration of sodium and chloride significantly less than that of plasma, and by a pH of about 7.0.[11, 12] It can be readily calculated that the low sodium and chloride concentrations of the voided urine must result from the reabsorption of these ions against a concentration gradient, either the gradient from tubular urine to peritubular fluid, or the greater gradient from tubular urine to the hypothetical "reabsorbate."[c] Under normal circumstances the rate of urine flow in the proximal portion of the tubule is quite high, approaching the rate of glomerular filtration, whereas the distal rate is low, approaching the rate of excretion of urine into the bladder. During osmotic diuresis, the more distal portions of the nephron are therefore virtually flooded with an enormous volume of tubular urine. The magnitude of this exceptional load has made it reasonable to believe that under these circumstances the total contribution of the distal segments in modifying the composition of the urine must be relatively small. The experiments on osmotic diuresis clearly demonstrate the primary reabsorption of electrolyte (particularly sodium and chloride) with the secondary back diffusion of water in response to the osmotic gradients thus established. In view of the

[c] Although calculations of concentrations in the reabsorbate may at times be useful, it should be remembered that this is an hypothetical fluid. As far as is known, the reabsorbed fluid is readily mixed with the intracellular fluid of the tubular cells.

results obtained from the micropuncture studies as well as the considerations outlined above, it is reasonable to believe that this mechanism characterizes the reabsorptive process in the proximal tubule.

The studies of Pitts[13] on the mechanisms of acidification showed that the amount of hydrogen ion excreted in the urine can not be accounted for by the process of glomerular filtration; he therefore concluded that hydrogen ions are secreted by the tubular cells, presumably in exchange for sodium. With the use of the rather ineffective carbonic anhydrase inhibitors that were at that time available, it was originally thought that this process was limited to the distal tubule, but recent studies with more powerful inhibitors have shown that the same fundamental reactions occur in the proximal segment as well.[14] One of the initial effects of replacing sodium ions in the tubular urine by hydrogen ions is to convert bicarbonate to carbonic acid and thence to carbon dioxide and water, both of which may readily diffuse back across the tubular epithelium. The secretion of hydrogen ions can therefore be regarded as the mechanism by which the reabsorption of bicarbonate is accomplished.

The secretion of hydrogen ions modifies the composition of the urine in at least four different respects: (1). It leads to the reabsorption of bicarbonate. (2). It lowers the pH of the urine to a minimal value of about 4.5. (3). If the tubular urine contains an adequate concentration of buffer anion, there is an increase in the titratable acidity. (4). If ammonia is being rapidly synthesized by the tubular cells, the secreted hydrogen ions may be accounted for in the final urine as ammonium ions. Marked changes in pH and in ammonium concentration occur in the distal segment of amphibia.[15, 16] The pH of the proximal urine is less clearly defined, but a limited number of micropuncture studies suggest slight proximal acidification;[10, 17] slightly acid urines are also obtained during extreme osmotic diuresis. There are no observations reported on the pH of the tubular urine when the excreted urine is alkaline.

The renal mechanisms regulating the excretion of potassium are more complex and involve the three processes of filtration, reabsorption, and secretion.[d] Under conditions of normal intake, the amount of potassium excreted in the urine is equivalent to about 10 % of the amount filtered at the glomerulus, and this relationship had led to the belief that potassium excretion involved just filtration and reabsorption. However, it

[d] Thiosulfate is the only other inorganic ion which is known to be both reabsorbed and secreted by the renal tubule; on the basis of pharmacological evidence, its transport system can be distinguished from that involved in the transport of organic anions.[18]

has been shown that under some circumstances the amount excreted could be greater than that filtered, and this observation has implicated a third renal process, that of tubular secretion.[19, 20] It was originally proposed by Mudge, et al.,[20] on the basis of the indirect evidence obtained by the administration of mercurial diuretics, that most or all of the filtered potassium was reabsorbed and that tubular secretion accounted for the potassium actually excreted in the urine. Further evidence in support of this concept was obtained by Berliner et al.[21] in their studies on the combined effect of both mercurials and carbonic anhydrase inhibitors. It has also been postulated that reabsorption occurred in the proximal tubule, and secretion at a more distant site. The validity of these hypotheses has been greatly increased by the definitive micropuncture studies reported by Bott.[17] In the *Necturus* kidney it was found that potassium virtually disappeared from the urine of the proximal tubule, to reappear in samples taken from the distal segment. Although still in a preliminary stage, these studies are of fundamental importance and it now seems quite reasonable to believe that virtually all of the filtered potassium is reabsorbed and that all the excreted potassium results from distal secretion. Virtually nothing is known about the nature of the reabsorptive process. The mechanism of secretion has been characterized as a cationic exchange for sodium.[19] Thus, in a sense, the tubular secretion of potassium constitutes one of the renal mechanisms of sodium reabsorption. Tubular secretion is enhanced by cellular dehydration,[22] an increased intracellular potassium concentration,[19] and a rise in urinary pH.[14]

In each of the instances cited above, sodium ions are reabsorbed in the process of hydrogen ion secretion, and these exchange reactions therefore constitute mechanisms by which a portion of the filtered sodium is reabsorbed. Another mechanism involves the net exchange of sodium for the potassium secreted by the distal tubule. But by far the major portion of the filtered sodium must be reabsorbed by yet another type of reaction, namely the reabsorption of sodium with equivalent amounts of fixed anion, mostly chloride (Fig. 1). Certain aspects of this type of electrolyte transport have been previously considered in terms of proximal reabsorption, but the nature of the cellular mechanism remains unknown except for the evidence indicating primary transport of electrolyte. In this respect, the mechanism seems quite similar to that directly observed in the gastrointestinal tract.[23] One may postulate ion exchange reactions, involving cation and/or anion and also possibly related to carrier complexes within the cell, but there is no direct evidence

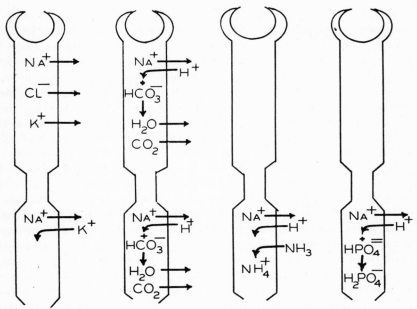

Fig. 1. Schematic diagram of tubular mechanisms of electrolyte reabsorption and secretion. The diagrammatic nephrons show the glomerulus at the top, then the proximal, thin, and distal segments of the tubule. See text for discussion of the separate mechanisms of sodium reabsorption.

on the nature of the fundamental processes involved. It has been recently reported that the movement of sodium across the tubular epithelium of the frog is not unidirectional, but that sodium from the peritubular capillaries can exchange with that of the tubular urine.[23] Since these studies demonstrate only an exchange of sodium and not a net movement in a secretory direction, they do not modify the concept of the reabsorptive process as depicted above. However, they may be of basic importance in future attempts to analyze the detailed mechanisms of sodium transport.

Pharmacological agents are of great value in attempting to define physiological mechanisms. The mercurial diuretics increase the renal excretion of both sodium and chloride. There is both clinical[24] and experimental[25] evidence to suggest that the primary action is on chloride reabsorption and that this in turn leads to an obligatory increase in sodium excretion. The mercurials do not depress ammonia production or inhibit acidification of the urine. Their effect on potassium excretion is variable, but the results indicate rather complete inhibition of the secretory process; any clear cut effect on reabsorption is masked by the simultaneous changes in anion excretion. The tubular reabsorption of lithium,[26] nitrate,[25] phosphate, and sulfate[27] are not affected by the mercurials. The xanthine diuretics produce a transient increase in sodium and chloride excretion; they do not inhibit potassium secretion.[e] Some of the adrenal steroids have a marked effect in enhancing the mechanisms of sodium conservation and this is, at least in part, mediated by a direct tubular action. It is not known, however, which of the processes of sodium reabsorption is critically sensitive to these agents. Adrenal insufficiency is characterized by the loss of both sodium and chloride, whereas the administration of excessive amounts of adrenal hormone is associated with a loss of potassium and a systemic alkalosis. This latter effect suggests an action on the cation exchange mechanism of the distal tubule. However, the relative change in tubular activity is too small to permit localization of steroid action or to distinguish between primary and secondary effects on different tubular functions.

Factors regulating the rate of sodium and chloride reabsorption are extraordinarily difficult to define in quantitative terms. Some of these have been referred to above. In addition, transport is related to the filtered load. That the amount reabsorbed can not exceed that which is filtered is self-evident. In the case of acute experiments, changes in the electrolyte load tend to be reflected by proportional changes in the total amount reabsorbed, but attempts to describe an exact relationship between these two processes have been unsuccessful. In chronic studies, no such relationship can be ascertained. The effect of nervous stimuli on ion transport has been examined, but with conflicting and inconclusive results.[28, 29]

One of the characteristics of tubular function is the existence of maximal rates of transport, of T_m. Historically, this concept dates from the studies on glucose reabsorption and the secretion of certain organic acids. With these compounds it can be readily shown that the transport mechanisms are of limited and relatively fixed capacity. In the case of glucose, when the load presented for reabsorption exceeds the maximal rate of transport, or T_m, the excess is quantitatively rejected and appears in the excreted urine. Attempts have been made to define the

---

[e] The limitations imposed by dosage in pharmacological studies of this type are illustrated by the effect of the xanthines and the nitrophenols which are inactive with the doses tolerated *in vivo* but which have a marked effect on potassium transport when higher concentrations are employed *in vitro*.[46]

regulatory mechanisms of electrolyte reabsorption in terms of the T_m concept. In the case of sodium, for instance, a distal T_m has been postulated.[4] However, there are many difficulties which prevent acceptance of this concept. Sodium is normally excreted in the urine despite the fact that the amount reabsorbed is considerably less than capacity, as can be readily shown by acute elevations of the filtered load (cf. ref. 30). The concept is also complicated by the multiple mechanisms of cation exchange which involve sodium and which, to a certain extent, appear to be independently regulated. Changes in anion reabsorption represent another inescapable variable. Calculations of a T_m confined to a given segment are contingent on the assumption that reabsorption in other portions of the tubule can be quantitatively estimated. At present there is no proof that either a constant amount or a constant fraction of the sodium is reabsorbed by any single portion of the nephron, especially in the face of changing filtered loads. A definitive examination of the problem is also handicapped by quantitative considerations similar to those that obtain for water reabsorption (see below). In contrast to organic compounds, therefore, maximal rates of tubular transport have not been established for electrolytes, with the exception of sulfate[31] and possibly phosphate.[32] In the case of sodium and chloride, the rate of transport, and hence the absolute amount reabsorbed, appears not to be limited by a fixed cellular component, but is apparently conditioned by other factors, as yet not understood. The rate of flow of the tubular urine and its concentration of electrolyte may influence the amount of electrolyte reabsorbed, especially during osmotic diuresis or following sudden changes in filtered load. Under conditions of unusual loading with uni- or multivalent anions, the rate of chloride reabsorption may be modified by interionic effects.[33] However, it can not be ascertained to what extent any of these factors play a regulatory role under normal conditions.

The rate of sodium reabsorption is partially determined by the tubular secretion of hydrogen ions, and some of the factors which regulate this process have been defined. Pitts[13] showed that the amount of hydrogen ion secreted is limited by the gradient for hydrogen ions established between tubular cells and urine. One determinant of this gradient is the pH of the urine. Another is the availability of hydrogen ions from the carbonic acid within the tubular cells, and this may be influenced either by the partial pressure of carbon dioxide or by the activity of carbonic anhydrase.[34, 35] The processes of acidification affect sodium reabsorption not only by the direct exchange of sodium for hydrogen ions but also by secondary actions on other tubular functions. Thus, the pH of the urine is one of the factors controlling the release of ammonia from the tubular cells. Also, potassium secretion is partially dependent on pH; a type of competition between hydrogen and potassium for exchange with sodium has been described by Berliner et al.[21]

Quantitative studies on the tubular mechanisms of electrolyte transport are further complicated by the heterogeneous nature of the nephron population. Although it is popular to consider all nephrons as identical, such is not the case. Anatomically, the greatest discrepancies are to be found in the lengths of the thin segment.[36] Functional evidence of heterogeneity has also been obtained from several types of studies—the titration curves of tubular transport capacity,[4] certain features of urinary acidification,[37] and the nature of the so-called renal delay time.[38]

The regulation of water excretion represents a complex problem. In response to general physiological demands, the kidney shows unusual versatility in varying the composition of the urine over a wide range of osmotic pressures. Although hemodynamic and hormonal factors play a major role, it is apparent that their effects must eventually be mediated through tubular mechanisms, some of which have already been referred to. In an effort to define these more precisely, a vast number of clearance experiments have been performed within recent years. On the basis of currently accepted concepts, the clearance technique in most instances permits the accurate determination of the amount of a substance filtered, the amount appearing in the voided urine, and, by difference, the total amount reabsorbed throughout the entire length of the tubule. Attempts to measure other attributes of the reabsorptive process must be necessarily indirect and often dependent on implicit assumptions. In this category may be included the efforts to describe water reabsorption quantitatively in terms of segmental functions. Some have considered the proximal reabsorption of water to be isosmotic and have postulated at least two separate distal processes,[39] whereas others, on the basis of slightly different assumptions, have been lead to consider the possibility of distal secretion of water.[40] By the same token, it would be entirely possible, although perhaps less popular, to interpret many of the experimental findings in terms of a homogeneous tubule without any segmental specialization for this particular function. It is doubtful if problems of this nature can be resolved by clearance studies alone.

It has been suggested that changes in the osmotic pressure of the urine might occur within the loop of Henle. Many of the difficulties in accepting this concept have been summarized by Smith.[4] One of the most pertinent criticisms is based on the comparative study of structure and function in different species. This aspect of the problem has been critically reviewed by Sperber.[41] It has also been proposed that concentration of the urine might occur within the collecting ducts, and many authors include these structures along with the distal convoluted tubule in discussing "distal" sites of water reabsorption. However, in mammals there is no quantitative evidence on this point.

In this connection, certain limitations of the micropuncture technique warrant emphasis. These are a consequence of the truism that the more proximal the site of the puncture, the more the urine must resemble the glomerular filtrate, and the more distal the sample, the more it must resemble the voided specimen. This relationship does not pose any particular obstacle when there is a large difference between the concentration in plasma and in tubular urine, such as in the case of glucose or diodrast, and apparently also potassium. But, for example, consider the problem of the reabsorption of water leading to the formation of a hypertonic urine. One may assume a filtration rate of 100 ml and a urine volume of 1 ml/min, and that the concentration of total solute in the urine is twice that of plasma. The formation of such a urine may be described as the reabsorption of 98 ml of isosmotic fluid plus 1 ml of water without solute (negative free-water clearance[f]). The reabsorption of this 1 ml could occur at some particular site along the tubule; it could also result from the uniform reabsorption of a homogeneous fluid containing 98% of the filtered solute and 99% of the filtered water. If, under these conditions, a sample of urine were obtained from that point along the nephron at which one-half of the water of the glomerular filtrate had been reabsorbed, its osmotic pressure relative to that of plasma would be as follows. If, as is generally believed, reabsorption were isosmotic proximal to the point of sampling, and the urine became concentrated solely in the distal segment, the osmotic ratio would be 1.00. If the localization of these functions were completely reversed, the

---

[f] The free-water clearance is a very useful concept; it relates both the volume and osmotic pressure of the urine to the osmotic pressure of the plasma. If the voided urine is isosmotic, the free-water clearance is zero. If the urine is hyperosmotic to plasma, the clearance is negative and represents the calculated volume of water that is reabsorbed without solute. If the urine is hypo-osmotic to plasma, the clearance is positive and is calculated as the volume of water in the excreted urine which contains no solute. For example, 15 ml of urine with an osmotic pressure one-third that of plasma is equivalent to 5 ml of isosmotic urine plus 10 ml of water (positive free-water clearance: 10 ml).

ratio would be 1.02. In this situation, reabsorption of water without solute would occur high in the proximal tubule, and reabsorption for the rest of the nephron would be isosmotic with respect to plasma. In a third situation, that of a process which is uniform in terms of the composition of the reabsorbate and for which there is no segmental specialization, the osmotic ratio at the mid-point would be 1.01. Thus, due to the relative magnitudes of the volumes of the urine and of the reabsorbate, extreme differences of tubular localization would result, in this example, in only 2 % variation in the composition of the tubular urine at the site sampled. On a theoretical basis, the problem might be further complicated by the kinetics of solute and water reabsorption. Even if the process were fundamentally isosmotic in character, the back diffusion of water might lag behind the primary transport of solute sufficiently to dilute the urine slightly. Such a phenomenon has been described for the intestine;[23] the dilute urines occasionally observed during forced osmotic diuresis might be explained by such a mechanism.

In contrast to the low rates of hypertonic urine flow, a very dilute urine can be excreted in large volumes, especially when elaboration of the antidiuretic principle of the posterior pituitary is completely inhibited. Under these conditions, the relative magnitude of the volume of urine and of reabsorbate would be more favorable for the detection of early changes in the composition of the tubular urine. However, no micropuncture studies during water diuresis have as yet been reported in mammals. In experiments performed under conditions which were presumably associated with the production of antidiuretic hormone, the proximal urine was considered to be isosmotic with plasma.[10] As a result of these studies it has been widely held that dilution and concentration occur exclusively in the distal segment and that the antidiuretic principle acts there.

Although it is granted that most of the observations are consistent with the functions of the proximal and distal tubules as outlined above, it is emphasized that much of the evidence is indirect in nature. For example, the maximal values calculated for both negative[12] and positive[39] free-water clearances have been found to be relatively independent of the rate of urine flow. This has been cited as evidence for two discrete distal processes, although, as an independent finding, it could equally well be considered an indication of separate proximal and distal functions. On a teleological basis it might be reasonable to consider the formation of a concentrated urine as a distal mechanism. In view of the known actions of the antidiuretic hormone[42] and the magnitude of proximal reabsorption, it would be equally reasonable to consider dilution as a proximal function. But, regardless of the segments involved, it is evident that the renal tubule is capable of varying the proportion of water to solute that is reabsorbed. The cellular mechanisms are unknown. In addition to the antidiuretic hormone, steroids of adrenal origin, notably cortisone, are involved in the production of a dilute urine.[43] Wirz and his associates[44] have attempted to consider water transport in terms of a physical model, that of a countercurrent system provided by the loop of Henle. The significance of their observations can not at present be evaluated. In this connection, the comparative anatomy of the thin loop is worthy of note since this structure is very poorly developed in some species which can elaborate a highly concentrated urine.[41]

Despite the complexities of the many separate mechanisms of tubular transport, many attempts are still made to estimate the energy expended by the kidney in the formation of the urine. In general, these treatments consider only the concentration of the various constituents in the plasma and urine. Although it is readily possible to obtain a mathematical solution in conformity with thermodynamic concepts, the significance of the answer almost defies the imagination. Such estimates of renal work have virtually no meaning in terms of what little is known about renal function at the physiological level. If reasonable estimates of the energy requirements are to be obtained, they must be based upon a greater knowledge of the cellular mechanisms involved in the transport of each of the constituents under consideration.

ELECTROLYTE TRANSPORT *IN VITRO*

In vitro studies of cellular function are uniquely suitable for an examination of metabolic correlations. Although considerable insight into the nature of ion transport has been obtained in the intact animal, it is immediately apparent that an isolated system must be employed if the role of cellular metabolism is to be explored by the more rigorous procedures available to the experimental biologist. In the past, many studies have been made on electrolyte transport in unicellular organisms, invertebrates, amphibia, and in the mammalian erythrocyte. Within more recent years, there have been a number of reports on other mammalian tissues, the examination of which has been made possible by techniques adapted, for the most part, from the field of cellular biochemistry. The principal virtue of an *in vitro* study is to be found in the almost endless number of experimental variables which can be explored; uniformly reproducible results can be consistently obtained under a variety of controlled conditions. But it should be emphasized, even though self-evident, that the results obtained are directly dependent on the immediate experimental conditions, so much so, that interpretations should be extended beyond the limits of direct observation only tentatively and with caution.

When kidney slices or isolated tubules are examined *in vitro*, the functions of the nephron are examined in the absence of their normal blood supply and in the absence of the process of glomerular filtration. Because of the complexity of the tubular processes of ion transport, one may well wonder which of these normal mechanisms is susceptible to examination by the *in vitro* techniques. Many of the results obtained with the kidney are qualitatively similar to those obtained with other organs which are nontubular in nature. It therefore is probable that the reactions which are observed in kidney slices involve the equilibria between tubular cell and peritubular fluid. The following questions have been examined: What correlations can be made between metabolic activity and the ability of the cell to accumulate potassium against a concentration gradient? What is the dynamic status of intracellular potassium as determined with isotopes? How does the behavior of sodium compare with that of potassium? How is the degree of cellular hydration related to metabolic functions? And finally, to what extent can the phenomena of electrolyte transport be examined in a cell-free system? Independent studies on many of these problems have been reported by Mudge,[45–47] Aebi,[48, 49] and Davies;[50, 51] the results are in general agreement despite minor variations in experimental procedures.

The renal cortex of the rabbit normally contains approximately equal amounts of potassium and sodium, about 70 meq of each per kilogram of wet tissue. When slices are prepared in chilled 0.150 M NaCl, potassium is lost from the tissue and is replaced by approximately equal amounts of sodium. The loss of tissue potassium is initially quite rapid, but the slice composition soon stabilizes at a concentration of 20–30 meq/kg wet weight. The reaccumulation of potassium from a low external concentration (5–10 meq/liter) may then be examined when the slices are incubated under different metabolic conditions. When the incubation is carried out in Warburg vessels, the measured rate of oxygen consumption serves as an index of over-all tissue metabolism. Under optimal conditions, the tissues take up potassium and regain their normal concentration (cf. Table I). The accumulation of potassium is associated with an approximately equivalent loss of sodium, both ions moving against the chemical concentration gradient.

TABLE I

NET EXCHANGE OF SODIUM AND POTASSIUM IN SLICES OF RABBIT
KIDNEY CORTEX

Procedure	Oxygen uptake (%) Control	Tissue composition (meq/kg wet tissue)			
		H_2O (%)	K	Na	Na + K
Fresh tissue	—	77.0	69	69	138
Start of Incubation	—	77.8	28	113	141
After Incubation					
Control—complete system	100	76.6	69	78	147
No added substrate	50	76.7	47	96	143
No oxygen	0	78.7	30	115	145
2°C	0	76.9	29	113	142
Cyanide, $2 \times 10^{-3} M$	25	81.4	21	127	148
Inactive nitrophenols, $2.5 \times 10^{-5} M$	100	77.0	70	77	147
Active nitrophenols, $2.5 \times 10^{-5} M$	120	79.6	34	114	144
Mercuric chloride, $3 \times 10^{-4} M$	100	80.4	40	108	148
Mercuric chloride, $10^{-3} M$	75	83	30	118	148

Detailed experimental procedure is given in ref. 46. The control incubation system was in Warburg vessels at 25°C for 30 min, with 0.010 M acetate as added substrate and an initial potassium concentration in the medium of 10 meq/liter. Upon the addition or omission of the indicated components, the osmotic pressure of the medium was adjusted with NaCl to maintain a constant value calculated to be equivalent to 300 milliosmoles/liter.

These processes of ion transport are dependent on aerobic metabolism and can readily be modified by changes in oxygen tension, temperature, concentration of substrates, etc. All metabolic inhibitors which depress tissue respiration also inhibit potassium accumulation. Other inhibitors, including some heavy metals, depress electrolyte transport without altering the oxygen consumption. The stability of the cellular mechanisms responsible for the transport of electrolytes is of some interest. Slices incubated anaerobically at 25°C for as long as two hours completely recover their ability to accumulate potassium and/or extrude sodium when they are subsequently incubated in oxygen. This is in contrast to the marked sensitivity to anoxia that the same tissue displays in the transport and accumulation of p-aminohippurate.[52] These differences are unexplained in terms of intermediary metabolic reactions, and they warrant further exploration.

Studies with 2,4-dinitrophenol and related compounds have established additional metabolic relationships. In experiments with isolated enzyme systems it has been shown that the phosphorylation reactions associated with aerobic oxidation may be inhibited by certain active nitrophenols, while at the same time the rate of oxygen consumption remains unimpaired.[53] An excellent correlation has been obtained between the action of these agents in uncoupling phosphorylation and their inhibition of the net accumulation of potassium, indicating a dependence of this cellular function on phosphate bond energy.[46]

With the use of radioactive isotopes it has been possible to examine the dynamic aspects of electrolyte transport and their relationship to tissue metabolism. Of considerable interest is the demonstration that the potassium within the cell is nonhomogeneous.[47] Under aerobic conditions, although all the tissue potassium of the kidney cortex is exchangeable with that of the incubation medium, nonuniform intracellular potassium is indicated by the presence of a slow and a rapid component. During anaerobic incubation, a limited amount of intracellular potassium continues to exchange at a rapid rate, whereas almost 50 % of the tissue potassium is found to be virtually nonexchangeable. This fraction amounts to about 8 meq/kg and represents a moiety of potassium whose exchangeability is directly dependent on aerobic metabolic activity. The possibility that this fraction might represent an ion-carrier complex has been discussed in detail elsewhere.[47] From quantitative considerations, the nonhomogeneous nature of intracellular potassium is most striking in the kidney cortex, but qualitatively similar observations have been reported for a variety of other tissues—muscle,[54] nerve,[55–57] liver, and erythrocytes.[58] Regardless of the exact manner in which the different moieties are related to the mechanisms of potassium transport, it is clear that these reactions can not be completely described merely in terms of a cell membrane surrounding a homogeneous internal phase.

In slices of kidney cortex, the behavior of sodium is strikingly different from that of potassium. In the experiments described above, the net changes in tissue sodium reciprocate with those of potassium, but many differences in the handling of these two ions can be made evident by appropriate experimental procedures. When metabolically inactive slices are soaked in chilled isosmotic potassium-free solutions, only about two-thirds of the tissue potassium is lost; in contrast, similar treatment with sodium-free solutions results in the prompt loss of all the tissue sodium. Tissue chloride is similarly very labile and is completely lost when the chloride of the media is replaced by other anions. Although the characteristics of potassium exchange are metabolically conditioned, a similar relationship has not been demonstrated for sodium exchange. The technical difficulties in studying the behavior of sodium in the slice system are considerable and result largely from the fact that a significant concentration of intracellular sodium can not be maintained when the external concentration is lowered. On the basis of the studies reported to date, there is no conclusive evidence that intracellular sodium is heterogeneous.

The problem also arises as to whether the changes in tissue electrolyte composition are the result of an active extrusion of sodium or an active uptake of potassium. Regardless of which ion moves primarily, a compensatory movement of the other would be essential to meet the demands of electro-neutrality. This problem has been extensively considered elsewhere for a variety of other tissues.[1] In the case of the kidney, the absolute rate of the potassium flux is independent of either the internal or external concentration of sodium and the potassium flux is metabolically conditioned in contrast to that of sodium. In terms of these criteria, the uptake of potassium has been considered to be the primary event and not to depend on the extrusion of sodium. This applies to the steady state condition in which there is no net transport between tissue and medium. However, in the case of the intact kidney, it should be noted that there are many reasons to believe that the net reabsorption of most of the filtered sodium is unrelated to and independent of any movement of potassium. Similarly, potassium reabsorption appears unrelated to that of sodium. Only in the case of potassium secretion is there evidence to indicate that the net transport of one ion reciprocates with that of the other. It is not known to what extent this type of cation exchange is being examined in the *in vitro* system.

Considerable interest centers around the action of the organic mercurial diuretics. Some of their effects on the excretion of electrolytes in the intact animal have been reviewed above. An attempt has been made to define their mode of action in the slice system and the results may be briefly summarized. Many metabolic inhibitors, including heavy metals and the organic mercurials, depress electrolyte transport at concentrations of inhibitor considerably less than those required for the suppression of oxygen consumption. This makes it improbable that the action of mercurials is attributable to the inhibition of a specific oxidative reaction. Evidence to the contrary, obtained by different and less direct techniques, has been reported by others.[59, 60] In the intact animal the diuretic effect of mercurials is potentiated by the administration of acidifying agents, and is virtually nullified by the infusion of alkaline salts. Some of the complexities of this problem have been reviewed by Hilton.[61] In the slice system, the effect of mercurials on tissue electrolytes is independent of pH. Although the mercurials inhibit the net accumulation of potassium, they have no discernible effect on the pattern of potassium exchange as determined either aerobically or anaerobically in the steady state. The net loss of tissue potassium results from an increase in the outward rate of potassium movement; in contrast, critical concentrations of dinitrophenol which lead to an equivalent net potassium loss do so in association with a decreased rate of potassium influx. It is to be recalled that in the intact animal the mercurials inhibit the tubular secretion of potassium. Although many factors, including that of inhibitor concentration, make it difficult to compare the results of the *in vivo* and *in vitro* studies, it is apparent that this effect on tubular secretion is consistent with the *in vitro* demonstration that the mercurials prevent the establishment of high intracellular concentrations of this ion.

As previously noted, the administration of powerful inhibitors of carbonic anhydrase to the intact animal is associated with a decreased tubular secretion of hydrogen ions and an increased secretion of potassium. Attempts to study this phenomenon *in vitro* have yielded contradictory results. Mudge[46] was unable to implicate carbonic anhydrase in potassium transport in terms of either net accumulation or of exchange. Davies and Galston, in a preliminary note,[62] have reported a positive effect. Further studies are obviously indicated.

Since the transport of ions is intimately associated with the movement of water, some of the *in vitro* observations that have been made on the regulation of cellular hydration may be summarized. It has generally been held that most mammalian cells are in osmotic equilibrium with their surrounding fluids (cf. ref. 63) and that primary alterations in the osmotic pressure of either the extra- or intracellular phase are compensated for by the appropriate movement of either solute or solvent across the cell membrane. Obvious exceptions to this general concept are to be found in the equilibria established by certain excretory glands (salivary, sweat, kidney, etc.) which elaborate a fluid whose osmotic pressure is not the same as that of plasma. However, these are specialized structures. In the case of the kidney, the evidence has been summarized above that the production of a concentrated urine involves osmotic changes in but a small fraction of the fluid which is transported by the tubular cells. It is doubtful whether this process could be detected by analysis of the whole tissue. Thus, on the basis of the classical concepts, it would be anticipated that the bulk of the intracellular fluid of the kidney would be in osmotic equilibrium with extracellular fluid.

Many studies have been made on the nature of cellular adjustments to changes in external osmotic pressure, but these will not be reviewed here. More recent work has demonstrated that rather great variations in the water content of kidney slices can occur during *in vitro* incubation at constant external osmotic pressure and that these changes can be correlated with cellular metabolism.[46, 64] Similar observations have been made with liver,[65] brain,[66] and other tissues.[49] Minimal tissue hydration is associated with active aerobic metabolism, and a rather striking increase in water content occurs when respiration is inhibited. A correlation between hydration and more specific metabolic functions is indicated by the increased swelling produced by the active nitro-phenols (cf. Table 1). This effect has been attributed to the action of these agents in the uncoupling of aerobic phosphorylation with a re-sultant decrease in the concentration of energy-rich phosphates, such as adenosine triphosphate. With other inhibitors, the magnitude of the increase in hydration varies with the agent employed. For example, mercuric chloride and other heavy metals have a much greater effect than does incubation under anaerobic conditions.

The swelling of inhibited tissues occurs in the presence of an appar-ently constant external osmotic pressure. In the analysis of this phe-nomenon, it is believed that the changes are to be attributed to an increase in the volume of the intracellular compartment rather than to an expansion of the extracellular volume. Such an assumption seems completely reasonable since no physiological forces are known which would increase extracellular volume in the absence of a hydrostatic pressure across the capillaries; confirmatory evidence has been found in the relatively constant values for extracellular volume found by the dilution technique with inulin and sucrose.[64] With a constant external osmotic pressure, the increase in intracellular volume must be attributed to one of the following reactions, either alone or in combination: (1). The cells may take up water with a proportional amount of solute from the extracellular fluid. (2). There may be a net movement of water into the cell in association with the new formation of proportional amount of solute from intracellular stores, i.e., either by the liberation of "bound" ions or by the formation of smaller molecular species by the cleavage of large molecules. (3). The movement of water might occur without any change in the total amount of osmotically active intracellular solute.

If the first two mechanisms applied, it would follow that the osmotic pressure of the inhibited cell remained the same as in the active cell, and that in each instance the cell might be isosmotic with the surrounding fluid. However, if the changes are interpreted as the movement of water without change in intracellular solute, it would then follow that there had been a decrease in the osmotic pressure of the inhibited cell. This latter interpretation has been advanced by Robinson[64] who concluded that the intracellular osmotic pressure of the normal renal cortex was almost twice that of the extracellular fluid and that there was a decrease in this osmotic gradient when normal metabolism was disrupted. Since most mammalian cells are freely permeable to water, as determined with isotopes, it is implicit in such a theory that the increased osmolarity of the normal cell would have to be maintained by the constant outward transport of water, presumably at the expense of metabolically derived energy.

Much evidence of an indirect nature has been accumulated[67] which could be interpreted in terms of cells that are normally either isotonic or hypertonic. However, critical evaluation of the problem can not be made on the basis of balance data derived from whole animal experiments. The more direct observations indicate, at least in the case of the kidney cortex, that the cells are normally isosmotic to their environment and that the swelling of the inhibited cell is associated with a parallel increase in intracellular solute. As was previously pointed out,[46] this conclusion is supported by the following considerations: (1). By virtue of their reabsorptive and/or secretory functions, the cells of the renal tubules are permeable to electrolytes. (2). A similar permeability can be demonstrated in vitro. (3). The concentration in tissue water of the sum of sodium plus potassium (an index of total cation) does not change appreciably in the face of marked changes in tissue hydration. (4). The small decrease in the concentration of measured cations or total base which does occur in inhibited tissues[46, 68] can be explained by the influx of univalent anion from the extracellular fluid. Under these circumstances, when there is a change in the ratio of univalent to multivalent anion in the intracellular fluid, total cation may change in concentration while osmotic pressure remains constant. Evidence has also been presented by Deyrup[69] to indicate that the influx of water is accompanied by the entrance of solutes such as ions and monosaccharides, since no swelling occurs in isosmotic solutions of disaccharides. The more recent estimations of the freezing point depression of kidney cortex indicate that tissue solute increases when experimental conditions are favorable for catabolic reactions. Conway and McCormack[70] found that fresh tissues were isosmotic with plasma, while Brodsky et al.[71] observed only slight deviations from the isosmotic state.

Tissue swelling in isosmotic solutions can therefore be largely attributed to a parallel change in both water and solute without any necessary change in osmotic pressure. The increase in cell solute can be due to one of two causes—breakdown of intracellular compounds or the influx of molecules from the extracellular fluid. The role of metabolic activity for each process can readily be visualized in terms of well-known physiological concepts. In the former case, metabolism continuously synthesizes complex cellular components from relatively simple precursors. In the latter instance, the role of metabolism can be considered in relation to the transport of small molecules. If cellular permeability is effectively increased, either by an increase in influx or a decrease in outflux, a net accumulation of solute and water is to be anticipated by virtue of the osmotic pressure exerted by the large molecules to which the cell membrane still remains impermeable. Such an interpretation does not imply that all intracellular structures (mitochondria, nuclei, etc.) necessarily behave in a similar manner. However, in the case of the kidney cortex, the present evidence clearly indicates that the cell is approximately isosmotic to its environment and that mechanisms of active water transport need not be postulated, at least for the bulk of the cells under consideration.

The demonstration that intracellular potassium is nonhomogeneous and that the exchangeability of one fraction is strongly dependent on aerobic metabolism suggested the desirability of directly examining the electrolyte exchange of specific intracellular components. Mitochondria have been studied because of their high rates of oxidative activity and associated phosphorylations, functions known to be related to potassium transport in an intact cell system. Within the past year, independent studies have been reported by several groups of investigators. The findings are in general agreement despite considerable variations in the experimental procedures.

In mitochondria prepared from rabbit liver, Stanbury and Mudge[72] found a significant amount of potassium which can not be removed by repeated washing in cold saline. This amounts to about 0.8 meq/gm mitochondrial nitrogen. When the mitochondrial suspensions are incubated in Warburg vessels in a medium of relatively low potassium concentration, the potassium level of the mitochondria is maintained during aerobic incubation in the presence of added substrate. Significant losses of potassium are sustained when conditions are unsuitable for aerobic metabolism. When incubated in the presence of isotopic potassium, the mitochondrial potassium exchanges with that of the medium. This exchange is clearly conditioned by metabolic processes, as shown by its decreased rate under anaerobic conditions. Furthermore there is no exchange between mitochondrial and ambient potassium when metabolically inactive mitochondira are washed with cold solutions of potassium chloride.

Under similar circumstances the behavior of sodium is quite different. The mitochondria contain about one-third as much sodium as potassium, and neither the absolute level of sodium nor its rate of turnover are related to metabolic activity. Other types of experiments have revealed striking differences in the behavior of these two ions. The level of mitochondrial potassium is greatly depressed by increasing the concentration of orthophosphate in the incubation medium; orthophosphate has no effect on the level of mitochondrial sodium. In addition, the rate of potassium exchange and, to a lesser degree, its level within the mitochondria are directly influenced by the potassium concentration of the incubation medium, whereas mitochondrial sodium shows no response to variations in its external concentration. Dinitrophenol has a marked effect on potassium without any effect on sodium. The action curve of dinitrophenol is polyphasic in nature and its effect can not be attributed solely to an uncoupling of aerobic phosphorylation. Under the conditions of these experiments, this agent is capable of stimulating one type of phosphorylation, namely the formation of phospho-enol-pyruvate. A limited correlation has been obtained between the mitochondrial levels of potassium and of phospho-enol-pyruvate. However, no specific role in ion transport is at present indicated for this phosphate ester other than the fact that it appears related to potassium and not to sodium exchange.

In somewhat similar experiments, MacFarlane and Spencer[73] have shown that the hydration of the mitochondria is metabolically conditioned. They also claimed to have demonstrated an adenylic requirement for the maintenance of high levels of mitochondrial potassium. However, their experiments were carried out in the presence of inhibitory concentrations of orthophosphate; in the absence of added phosphate an adenylic acid requirement could not be demonstrated.[72] Spector[74] has also reported on the absolute levels of electrolyte maintained by mitochondria from liver during incubation under varying conditions of metabolism. With a number of inhibitors, including dinitrophenol, he noted marked changes in potassium concentration with little or no effect on sodium. The results of Spector and of Stanbury and Mudge are in excellent agreement despite minor experimental variations. In a preliminary note, Bartley and Davies[75] have reported similar studies with kidney mitochondria. They found an extremely rapid turnover of potassium in contrast to the much slower rate obtained for liver. However, insufficient details are available to determine whether this represents a genuine difference between the two organs, or whether it is a consequence of the procedures employed.

Certain features of this type of study warrant emphasis. The employment of an experimental system virtually free of intact cells constitutes an attempt to study some of the biochemical mechanisms of electrolyte transport by isolating them from the rest of the cell. Comparative observations on different organs and on other types of intracellular constituents are clearly indicated. Although the mitochondria of the kidney are so oriented within the cell that they might be visualized as devices for transport, any attempt to correlate mitochondrial function with electrolyte transport in the intact cell must at present be purely hypothetical. The critical dependence of the observed results on the conditions of the experiments can not be overemphasized. The mitochondria appear similar to the intact cell systems in that both demonstrate intracellular potassium to be nonhomogeneous and that its exchange is metabolically dependent. Clear-cut differences between the behavior of potassium and sodium are also apparent in both systems. However, in the mitochondria a loss of potassium is usually not accompanied by a gain of sodium and, in this respect, they differ from most intact cell systems in which a reciprocal relationship between the net changes of the two ions is observed.

In the past, attention has been focused on the role of the cell membrane in electrolyte transport. Present evidence indicates that this structure may not be directly involved in many of the reactions of transport, at least in the case of potassium. The studies on cell-free systems constitute a certain advance in that some of the components on ion transport have been partially isolated. However, it is to be emphasized that the mitochondria are extraordinarily complex. Functionally, they are capable of catalyzing a vast number of biochemical reactions; structurally, they are characterized by many internal ridges which appear to be related to an enveloping membrane.[76] If the biological differences in the behavior of sodium and potassium are to be explained by reference to reactions of cellular metabolism, one of the goals of research must be the isolation of some cellular component which, at least for some of its reactions, is capable of distinguishing between these two ions. In addition, this component itself must have a metabolism which is consistent with the phenomena of ion transport that are observed in the intact cell. To date, no such component has been identified.

REFERENCES

No attempt has been made to compile a complete bibliography; in general, reference has been made to the more recent publications. The excellent monograph of Smith (reference 4) should be consulted for additional references.

1. USSING, H. H. *Physiol. Revs.* **29,** 127 (1949).
2. KROGH, A. *Proc. Roy. Soc. (London)* **B133,** 140 (1946).
3. SHANNON, J. A. *J. Cellular Comp. Physiol.* **11,** 315 (1938).
4. SMITH, H. W., "The Kidney, Structure and Function in Health and Disease." Oxford University Press, New York, 1951.
5. TAGGART, J. V. *Am. J. Med.* **9,** 678 (1950).
6. MAXIMOW, E. A., and BLOOM, W., "A Textbook of Histology." W. B. Saunders, Philadelphia, 1948.
7. SJÖSTRAND, F. S. and RHODIN, J., *Exptl. Cell Research* **4,** 426 (1953).
8. BROWNE, M. J., PITTS, M. W., and PITTS, R. F. *Biol. Bull.* **99,** 152 (1950).
9. DRATZ, A. F., and HANDLER, P., *J. Biol. Chem.* **197,** 419 (1952).
10. WALKER, A. M., BOTT, P. A., OLIVER, J., and MacDOWELL, M. C., *Am. J. Physiol.* **134,** 562 (1941).
11. WESSON, L. G., JR., and ANSLOW, W. P., JR., *Am. J. Physiol.* **153,** 465 (1948).
12. MUDGE, G. H., FOULKS, J. and GILMAN, A., *Am. J. Physiol.* **158,** 218 (1949).
13. PITTS, R. F., *Federation Proc.* **7,** 418 (1948).
14. BERLINER, R. W. *Federation Proc.* **11,** 695 (1952).
15. MONTGOMERY, H. and PIERCE, J. A., *Am. J. Physiol.* **118,** 144 (1937).
16. WALKER, A. M., *Am. J. Physiol.* **131,** 187 (1940).
17. BOTT, P. A., *Trans. 5th Conf. on Renal Function,* Josiah Macy, Jr. Foundation, New York, 1953.
18. FOULKS, J., BRAZEAU, P., and GILMAN, A., *Am. J. Physiol.* **168,** 77 (1952).
19. BERLINER, R. W., KENNEDY, T. J., JR., and HILTON, J. G. *Am. J. Physiol.* **162,** 348 (1950).
20. MUDGE, G. H., AMES, A., FOULKS, J. G., and GILMAN, A. *Am. J. Physiol.,* **161,** 151 (1950).
21. BERLINER, R. W., KENNEDY, T. J., JR., and ORLOFF, J. *Am. J. Med.* **11,** 274 (1951).
22. MUDGE, G. H., FOULKS, J. G., and GILMAN, A. *Am. J. Physiol.* **161,** 159 (1950).
23. VISSCHER, M. B., *Trans. 4th Conf. on Renal Function,* Josiah Macy, Jr. Foundation, New York, 1952.
24. SCHWARTZ, W. B., and WALLACE, W. M., *J. Clin. Invest.* **30,** 1089 (1951).
25. RICE, L., FRIEDEN, J., and SMITH, M. *Am. J. Physiol.* **175,** 47 (1953).
26. FOULKS, J. G., MUDGE, G. H., and GILMAN, A. *Am. J. Physiol.* **168,** 642 (1952).
27. PITTS, R. F., and SARTORIUS, O. W. *J. Pharmacol. and Exptl. Therap.* **98,** 161 (1950).

28. KAPLAN, S. A., FOMON, S. J., and RAPOPORT, S., *Am. J. Physiol.* **166,** 641
    (1951).
29. SURTSHIN, A., MUELLER, C. B., and WHITE, H. L., *Am. J. Physiol.* **169,** 159
    (1952).
30. BERLINER, R. W. *Am. J. Med.* **9,** 541 (1950).
31. LOTSPEICH, W. D. *Am. J. Physiol.* **151,** 311 (1947).
32. SCHIESS, W. A., AYER, J. L., LOTSPEICH, W. D. and PITTS, R. F., *J. Clin.
    Invest.* **27,** 57 (1948).
33. RAPOPORT, S., and WEST, C., *Am. J. Physiol.* **162,** 668 (1950).
34. BRAZEAU, P., and GILMAN, A., *Am. J. Physiol.* **175,** 33 (1953).
35. RELMAN, A. S., ETSTEN, B., and SCHWARTZ, W. B., *J. Clin. Invest.* **32,** 972
    (1953).
36. HUBER, G. C. *Harvey Lectures* **5,** 100 (1910).
37. KENNEDY, T. J., JR., ORLOFF, J. and BERLINER, R. W., *Am. J. Physiol.* **169,**
    596 (1952).
38. BRADLEY, S. E., NICKEL, J. F., and LEIFER, E., *Trans. Assoc. Am. Physicians.*
    65, 147 (1952).
39. WESSON, L. G., JR., and ANSLOW, W. P., JR. *Am. J. Physiol.* **170,** 255 (1952).
40. WEST, C. D., KAPLAN, S. A., FOMON, S. J., and RAPOPORT, S., *Am. J. Physiol.*
    170, 239 (1952).
41. SPERBER, I. Studies on the Mammalian Kidney, *Zool. Bidrag Uppsala* **22,**
    (1944).
42. KOEFOED-JOHNSEN, V., and USSING, H. H. *Acta Physiol. Scand.* **28,** 60 (1953).
43. GARROD, O., personal communication.
44. WIRZ, H., HARGITAY, B. and KUHN, W. *Helv. Physiol. Acta* **9,** 196 (1951).
45. MUDGE, G. H., *Am. J. Physiol.* **165,** 113 (1951).
46. MUDGE, G. H., *Am. J. Physiol.* **167,** 206 (1951).
47. MUDGE, G. H., *Am. J. Physiol.* **173,** 511 (1953).
48. AEBI, H., *Helv. Physiol. Acta* **10,** 184 (1952).
49. AEBI, H., *Helv. Physiol. Acta* **11,** 96 (1953).
50. DAVIES, R. E., and GALSTON, A. W., *Nature* **168,** 700 (1951).
51. WHITTAM, R. and DAVIES, R. E., *Biochem. J.* **55,** 880 (1953).
52. CROSS, R. J., and TAGGART, J. V., *Am. J. Physiol.* **161,** 181 (1950).
53. CROSS, R. J., TAGGART, J. V., COVO, G. A., and GREEN, D. E., *J. Biol. Chem.*
    177, 655 (1949).
54. WESSON, L. G., JR., COHN, W. E., and BRUES, A. M., *J. Gen. Physiol.* **33,**
    691 (1950).
55. ROTHENBERG, M. A., *Biochem. et Biophys. Acta* **4,** 96 (1950).
56. HARRIS, E. J., and McLENNAN, H., *J. Physiol.* **121,** 629 (1953).
57. KATZMAN, R., and LEIDERMAN, P. H., *Am. J. Physiol.* **175,** 263 (1953).
58. TOSTESON, D. C., and ROBERTSON, J. S., *Federation Proc.* **12,** 145 (1953).
59. MUSTAKALLIO, K. K., and TELKKÄ, A., *Science* **118,** 320 (1953).
60. HANDLEY, C. A., and LAVIK, P. S., *J. Pharmacol. Exptl. Therap.* **100,** 115
    (1950).
61. HILTON, J. G., *J. Clin. Invest.* **30,** 1105 (1951).
62. DAVIES, R. E. and GALSTON, A. W., *2nd Intern. Congr. Biochem. Paris*, p. 142
    (1952).

63. PETERS, J. P. "Body Water" Charles C Thomas, Springfield, 1935.
64. ROBINSON, J. R. *Proc. Roy. Soc. (London)* **B137,** 378 (1950).
65. ROBINSON, J. R., *Proc. Roy. Soc. (London)* **B140,** 135 (1952).
66. STERN, J. R., EGGLESTON, L. V., HEMS, R., and KREBS, H. A., *Biochem. J.* **44,** 410 (1949).
67. ROBINSON, J. R., *Biol. Rev.* **28,** 158 (1953).
68. ROBINSON, J. R., *Nature* **169,** 713 (1952).
69. DEYRUP, I. *J. Gen. Physiol.* **36,** 739 (1953).
70. CONWAY, E. J., and McCORMACK, J. I., *J. Physiol.* **120,** 1 (1953).
71. BRODSKY, W. A., REHM, W. S., and McINTOSH, B. J., *J. Clin. Invest.* **32,** 556 (1953).
72. STANBURY, S. W., and MUDGE, G. H., *Proc. Soc. Exptl. Biol. Med.* **82,** 675 (1953).
73. MACFARLANE, M. G., and SPENCER, A. G., *Biochem. J.* **54,** 569 (1953).
74. SPECTOR, W. G., *Proc. Roy. Soc. (London)* **B141,** 268 (1953).
75. BARTLEY, W. and DAVIES, R. E., *Biochem. J.* **52,** xx (1952).
76. PALLADE, G. E., *Anat. Record* **114,** 427 (1952).

Membrane Permeability and Electrical Potential

RANSOM B. PARLIN AND HENRY EYRING

INTRODUCTION

Investigations of the permeability of gas masks to smoke show that the larger particles are strained out because they cannot pass through the pores while the smallest particles diffuse rapidly to the walls and are adsorbed before they have time to traverse the passageways. Only the sluggishly diffusing particles of intermediate size pass through the mask. Thus a penetrating smoke can be made by aging it for a period since the large particles drop out because of gravity whereas the smallest particles aggregate because of their frequent collisions, again leaving only penetrating particles of intermediate size.

In condensed systems of liquids and solids, diffusion proceeds by a relaxation process.[5] Each molecule is surrounded by a sheath of neighbors and only occasionally does an unstable, high-energy constellation occur which allows a molecule to slip through its ring of neighbors into an adjacent site. After a sufficient number of vibrations it will again gain the energy which allows it to slip into a new neighboring site or return to the one it just left.

In Fig. 1 we indicate by a potential energy diagram the situation for simple diffusion. Here c is the concentration of diffusing particles at the first minimum and $\left(c + \lambda \dfrac{dc}{dx}\right)$ that at the second. The number of molecules ready to jump over the middle barrier is λc. Thus, we can write

$$q = \lambda k'c - \left(c + \lambda \frac{dc}{dx}\right)\lambda k' = -\lambda^2 k' \frac{dc}{dx} \equiv -D \frac{dc}{dx} \qquad (1)$$

Here k' is the net number of barrier jumps in either the forward or the backward direction per second per molecule. It is interesting to generalize the diffusion coefficient for long-chain molecules whose center of gravity progresses by the random movement of each of n segments. When a segment moves a distance λ, the center of gravity of the whole molecule moves a distance equal, on the average, to λ/n, and if each segment jumps forward k' times per second, the center of gravity will

103

jump forward nk' times per second. Thus, a large polymer diffusing un-entangled through a solvent consisting of molecules the size of its segments has for its diffusion coefficient the value

$$D' = (\lambda/n)^2 nk' = \lambda^2 k'/n \tag{2}$$

The high polymer of n segments has a diffusion coefficient only one nth as large as the diffusion coefficient for a molecule consisting of but one of these segments.

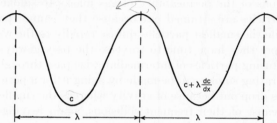

FIG. 1. Simple potential energy diagram for diffusion. Energy is plotted vertically and distance horizontally.

We next consider the diffusion coefficient for the transport of large spherical molecules through small molecules. Einstein[2] has shown that such large molecules diffuse with a coefficient

$$D = kT/6\pi r\eta \tag{3}$$

Here r is the radius of the large molecules and η is the viscosity of the small ones. It has also been shown[3] that the viscosity is related to the self-diffusion coefficient, D_s, by

$$\eta = kT/\lambda D_s \tag{4}$$

Substituting (4) into (3) gives for the diffusion coefficient of the large molecules an expression

$$D = D_s\lambda/6\pi r \tag{5}$$

Thus, if we think of the large spherical molecules moving forward as a result of the cooperative motion of $n = 6\pi r/\lambda$ small molecules, we are provided with a way of thinking of equations (5) and (2) in equivalent terms.

From these general considerations of diffusion, we turn to a consideration of diffusion through membranes.

GENERALIZED RELAXATION THEORY

Figure 2 is a generalized diagram for diffusion over a succession of barriers such as must exist in a membrane.[4, 10, 18] Since an actual molecular lattice is three dimensional, we should think of the λ's as indicating the projection along the direction of the gradient of the appropriate mean jump distance for the molecule. If c_0 is the concentration of molecules per cubic centimeter, at the zeroth position, then $\lambda_0 c_0$ is the number of molecules which are candidates to jump across the barrier in a square centimeter of an area normal to the direction of diffusion. The specific rate constant in the forward direction from the ith position

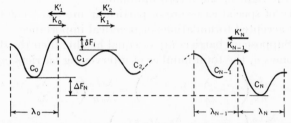

FIG. 2. Potential energy diagram representing diffusion in the liquid or solid state.

is written as k_i, and in the backward direction as k_i'. For the steady state we may indicate by Q the number of molecules passing over each successive square centimeter of barriers, and write for the successive barriers the following set of equations

$$Q = \lambda_0 c_0 k_0 - \lambda_1 c_1 k_1'$$
$$Q = \lambda_1 c_1 k_1 - \lambda_2 c_2 k_2'$$
$$Q = \lambda_2 c_2 k_2 - \lambda_3 c_3 k_3'$$
$$\cdots\cdots\cdots\cdots\cdots\cdots\cdots\cdots\cdots$$
$$Q = \lambda_{n-1} c_{n-1} k_{n-1} - \lambda_n c_n k_n' \tag{6}$$

If we multiply the second equation above by k_1'/k_1, the third by $k_1' k_2'/k_1 k_2$, etc., and the last equation by $(k_1' k_2' \cdots k_{n-1}')/(k_1 k_2 \cdots k_{n-1})$, and add, we obtain

$$Q = \frac{\lambda_0 \, k_0 \left(c_0 - \dfrac{\lambda_n}{\lambda_0} \dfrac{k_1' k_2' \, \cdots \, k_{n-1}' k_n'}{k_0 \, k_1 \, \cdots \, k_{n-1}} \, c_n \right)}{1 + \dfrac{k_1'}{k_1} + \dfrac{k_1' k_2'}{k_1 k_2} + \cdots + \dfrac{k_1' k_2' \, \cdots \, k_{n-1}'}{k_1 k_2 \, \cdots \, k_{n-1}}} \tag{7}$$

Remembering that

$$k_i = \kappa_i (kT/h) e^{-\Delta F_i^{\ddagger}/RT} \tag{8}$$

equation (7) becomes, assuming for κ a value of unity,

$$Q = \frac{\lambda_0 k_0 \left(c_0 - \dfrac{\lambda_n}{\lambda_0} e^{\Delta F_n/RT} c_n \right)}{1 + e^{\delta F_1 \ddagger/RT} + \cdots + e^{\delta F_{n-1}\ddagger/RT}} \tag{9}$$

Here ΔF_n is the free energy of molecules in the nth minimum minus that of those in the zeroth, and $\delta F_i^{\ddagger}$ is the free energy at the top of the barrier to the right of the ith minimum minus that at the top of the barrier to the right of the zeroth minimum.

A variety of special cases are of particular interest since they lead to commonly accepted formulations of practical importance.

Case I. Suppose all barriers are of equal height; then the denominator of (9) becomes n, the total number of intervening barriers, and

$$
\begin{aligned}
Q &= \frac{\lambda_0 k_0}{n} \left(c_0 - \frac{\lambda_n}{\lambda_0} e^{\Delta F_n/RT} c_n \right) = \frac{\lambda_0^2 k_0}{\lambda_0 n} \left(c_0 - \frac{\lambda_n}{\lambda_0} e^{\Delta F_n/RT} c_n \right) \\
&= \frac{\lambda_0^2 k_0}{\gamma_0 \tau} \left(\gamma_0 c_0 - \gamma_0 \frac{\lambda_n}{\lambda_0} e^{\Delta F_n/RT} c_n \right) \\
&= \frac{D_0^0}{\tau} (a_0 - a_n) \\
&= P_0^0 (a_0 - a_n)
\end{aligned} \tag{10}
$$

We have written γ_0 as the activity coefficient at concentration c_0, and $D_0^0 = \lambda_0^2 k_0 / \gamma_0$ may be called the standard diffusion coefficient; $\tau = \lambda_0 n$ is the membrane thickness. The quantities a_0 and a_n are the activities at the zeroth and nth minima, respectively. $D_0^0/\tau = P_0^0$ is the standard permeability.

Case II. We consider now a membrane which consists of n barriers of equal height. If charges of unlike sign lie on the two sides of the barrier with negligible net charge between, this will give rise to a potential difference of ϵ volts between the zeroth and the nth minimum. Thus, in equation (4), we have $\Delta F_n = z \mathcal{F} \epsilon$ (where z the charge on the ion, with sign, and $\mathcal{F} = 23,053$, the faraday in units of volts per calory) and $\delta F_i^{\ddagger} = (i/n) z \mathcal{F} \epsilon$. Also, $k_0 = k_0^0 \exp(-z \mathcal{F} \epsilon/RT)$, where k_0^0 is the specific rate constant over the first barrier in the absence of the applied potential. We write also

$$x = e^{z \mathcal{F} \epsilon / nRT} \tag{11}$$

With these substitutions, equation (9) becomes

$$Q = \frac{\lambda_0 k_0^0 x^{-\frac{1}{2}} \left(c_0 - \frac{\lambda_n}{\lambda_0} x^n c_n \right)}{1 + x + x^2 + \cdots + x^{n-1}} = \frac{\lambda_0 k_0^0 x^{-\frac{1}{2}}(1 - x)}{1 - x^n} \left(c_0 - \frac{\lambda_n}{\lambda_0} x^n c_n \right)$$

$$= \lambda_0 k_0^0 \frac{x^{-\frac{1}{2}} - x^{\frac{1}{2}}}{1 - x^n} \left(c_0 - \frac{\lambda_n}{\lambda_0} x^n c_n \right) \frac{x^{-\frac{n}{2}}}{x^{-\frac{n}{2}}} \tag{12}$$

$$= \lambda_0 k_0^0 \frac{x^{-\frac{1}{2}} - x^{\frac{1}{2}}}{x^{-\frac{n}{2}} - x^{\frac{n}{2}}} \left(x^{-\frac{n}{2}} c_0 - \frac{\lambda_n}{\lambda_0} x^{\frac{n}{2}} c_n \right)$$

making use of (11). Expanding the exponentials, we find that

$$g/n \equiv \frac{x^{-\frac{1}{2}} - x^{\frac{1}{2}}}{x^{-\frac{n}{2}} - x^{\frac{n}{2}}} \approx \frac{1}{n} \tag{13}$$

provided that the total electrical work, $z\mathfrak{F}\epsilon$ is somewhat smaller than RT. In this case

$$\lambda_0 k_0^0 g/n \approx \lambda_0 k_0^0/n \equiv P \tag{14}$$

and

$$Q = P \left(c_0 e^{-z\mathfrak{F}\epsilon/2RT} - \frac{\lambda_n}{\lambda_0} c_n e^{z\mathfrak{F}\epsilon/2RT} \right) \tag{15}$$

Thus the transport of matter, Q, is proportional to a permeability, $P = \lambda_0 k_0^0 n$. If the exponentials in (15) be expanded and only the first terms retained, as is, of course, only consistent with the approximation (13), we have the form (16), which is more like the expression ordinarily used, where one thinks of the total transport as the sum of a diffusion term and an electrical transport term

$$Q = P \left\{ \left(c_0 - \frac{\lambda_n}{\lambda_0} c_n \right) - \frac{1}{2} \left(c_0 + \frac{\lambda_n}{\lambda_0} c_n \right) \frac{z\mathfrak{F}\epsilon}{RT} \right\} \tag{16}$$

In nerve membranes where ϵ is around 80 millivolts, the expansion (13) is not always justified, and the assumption ordinarily made, of an effective permeability which is independent of voltage, should be corrected accordingly. In view of the popularity of expressions of the forms (15), (16), and others involving equivalent assumptions, it may be worthy of note to point out just how much in error such approximations may be. Figure 3 gives the relation between g, (defined by equation (13)) and the transmembrane potential, ϵ, for various values of n, the effective number of barriers in the membrane. We consider it unlikely that the

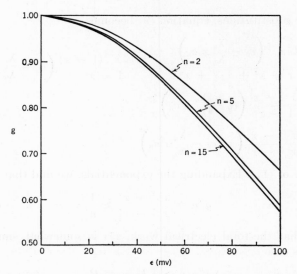

Fig. 3. Permeability coefficient correction for effect of applied voltage.

number of barriers much exceeds the largest figure on the graph, i.e., 15. At large n, g becomes independent of n and approaches the value $\left(\dfrac{z\mathfrak{F}\epsilon}{2RT}\right)\Big/\sinh\left(\dfrac{z\mathfrak{F}\epsilon}{2RT}\right)$. It is also of interest that the assumption of the value of unity for g is in many cases tantamount to the substitution of a hypothetical *thicker* membrane (in terms of the number of barriers) in place of the one actually present. It is, of course, unfortunate that the form of g precludes its inclusion in most of the practical calculations involved in membrane permeability, numerical work aside.

A question may arise as to the propriety of the assumption that negligible net charge accumulates within the membrane. Certainly, if any of the equilibrium positions between the n barriers has at any time an appreciable surplus of charge of one sign over that of the other, the basic premise of a uniform sequence of $\delta F_i^{\ddagger}$'s will be violated and the model will be hopelessly idealized. That this will probably not be the case may be inferred from an argument which proceeds thus: if there were to exist, at any instant, such an excess charge distribution in a particular "pocket," this charge in itself would cause the potential gradient to decrease automatically the driving force for transport in one direction and increase it in the reverse direction until the potential gradient as a whole is again essentially constant. This "Le Chatelier" principle we may perhaps term the "incompressibility of ions" in a membrane. In a similar way, one may argue that if the membrane is such that there exists *a priori* a barrier which is much higher than those on either side, the piling up of charge at this barrier will reduce its effective height and bring about the situation in which the sequence of barriers is very nearly a uniform one. Thus, in either case, there will be an effective rate constant appropriate to the uniform distribution which, in conjunction with the equations for flux through such a uniform set of barriers, will lead to the same result as the correct rate constant with the more complex flux expression and the nonuniform distribution of barrier heights. It would appear exceedingly difficult to distinguish between the two formulations experimentally.

It may also be pointed out that through the use of equation (12) one may also derive expressions for, e.g., the liquid junction potential in accordance with those obtained by Planck,[17] Henderson,[7] and others[13, 14] by classical treatments.

Membrane Resting Potential

As a simplified model of a nerve cell in its environment, consider the membrane to separate two solutions containing the ions Na^+, K^+, and Cl^-. If the membrane is permeable to all of the above ions, there will, of course, be no potential across it at equilibrium and there will be a complete symmetry in the concentrations of the various species. There are two alternatives which will cause an asymmetry to appear: in one case, there may be a nondiffusable molecule which will associate with one of the ions to form a charged particle which also cannot pass through the membrane. This is the case of the Donnan equilibrium, leading to an asymmetric distribution of ions in the two solutions. Alternatively, there may be a molecule, charged or not, which associates with an ion in a similar way but which *can* diffuse in this condition through the membrane. If, under these conditions, there should exist as well a steady net flux of this metabolite from one side of the membrane to the other, and if the complex has a different permeability coefficient than that of the unassociated ion, it is possible for both an asymmetry in ion concentrations and a finite transmembrane potential to exist. Such a condition may arise if, for example, a metabolic product is constantly being formed in the interior of the cell and destroyed, or otherwise removed from the scene of action at its outer surface.[1, 12]

To investigate the consequences of such a postulated state of affairs, we consider a particularly simple model and write the various conditions of conservation, expressing the fluxes in the form of equation (12). Since interest has centered on the anomalous behavior of sodium ion, we shall assume that there is some substance P which complexes preferentially with the sodium and, in this approximation, does not enter into combination with potassium. A number of such species are known,[11, 15] most of them being phosphates or sulphates of molecules possessing carboxylic groups, such, for example, as acetic acid and its derivatives. Denoting the species Na^+, NaP^+, K^+, Cl^-, and P by the subscripts 1 through 5, respectively, where P is an unspecified metabolite and NaP^+ a charged association complex, we must have, in the steady state

$$Q_1 + Q_2 = 0 \qquad (17)$$

i.e., the net flux of all of the sodium, bound and free, must vanish. Similarly, according to the postulated mechanism, the net flux (stoichiometric) of the metabolite is a fixed quantity, q

$$Q_2 + Q_5 = q \qquad (18)$$

The flux of the other ions is taken to vanish

$$Q_3 = Q_4 = 0 \qquad (19)$$

In addition, it is assumed that there is no piling up of P in either solution, whence

$$c_{02} + c_{05} = p_0$$
$$c_{n2} + c_{n5} = p_n \qquad (20)$$

where c_{0i} and c_{ni} are the concentrations of the ith species within and without the membrane, respectively, and p_0 and p_n denote the corresponding steady-state concentrations of metabolite.

Conservation of charge requires that

$$c_{01} + c_{02} + c_{03} = c_{04}$$
$$c_{n1} + c_{n2} + c_{n3} = c_{n4} \qquad (21)$$

and the equilibrium between sodium ion and metabolite is expressed in the equations

$$K = c_{02}/c_{01}c_{05} = c_{n2}/c_{n1}c_{n5} \qquad (22)$$

The ten relations (17) through (22) suffice to determine the concentrations of the five species in each of the two solutions in terms of the transmembrane potential, ϵ, and the various constants above. It should be noted that in (22) it has been assumed that the concentrations are a reasonable approximation to the activities in the solution.

The algebraic treatment of these equations is fairly lengthy, but may be simplified by expressing all concentrations in terms of c_{01} and c_{n1}, i.e., the concentration of Na in each solution. Thus we obtain

$$c_{02} = \frac{Kp_0 c_{01}}{1 + Kc_{01}} \qquad c_{n2} = \frac{Kp_n c_{n1}}{1 + Kc_{n1}} \tag{23}$$

$$c_{03} = \frac{x^n}{x^{2n} - 1} \left\{ \frac{(1 + Kp_n) + Kc_{n1}}{1 + Kc_{n1}} c_{n1} - x^n \frac{(1 + Kp_0) + Kc_{01}}{1 + Kc_{01}} c_{01} \right\}$$
$$= x^n c_{n3} \tag{24}$$

$$c_{04} = \frac{x^n}{x^{2n} - 1} \left\{ \frac{(1 + Kp_n) + Kc_{n1}}{1 + Kc_{n1}} c_{n1} - \frac{1}{x^n} \frac{(1 + Kp_0) + Kc_{01}}{1 + Kc_{01}} c_{01} \right\}$$
$$= \frac{1}{x^n} c_{n4} \tag{25}$$

$$c_{05} = \frac{p_0}{1 + Kc_{01}} \qquad c_{n5} = \frac{p_n}{1 + Kc_{n1}} \tag{26}$$

from equations (19) through (22); from (17) and (18), with the above, we have in addition two equations which fix c_{01} and c_{n1}, namely

$$\frac{(1 + kKp_0) + Kc_{01}}{1 + Kc_{01}} c_{01} = x^n \frac{(1 + kKp_n) + Kc_{n1}}{1 + Kc_{n1}} c_{n1} \tag{27}$$

and

$$\frac{\dfrac{nk'x^{\frac{3}{2}}}{g} + Kc_{01}}{1 + Kc_{01}} = \frac{p_n}{p_0} x^n \frac{\dfrac{nk'}{gx^{\frac{3}{2}}} + Kc_{n1}}{1 + Kc_{n1}} + q' \tag{28}$$

where we have written $k = k_2^0/k_1^0$, $k' = k_5^0/k_2^0$, and

$$q' = \{x^{\frac{3}{2}} n/(\lambda_{02} k_2^0 p_0 g)\} q.$$

The former two quantities express the ratios of the specific rates for diffusion of bound to free sodium, and free to bound metabolite, respectively, and may in general be expected to exceed unity in each case. In the equations above, the variables x_i have been taken as

$$x_1 = x_2 = x_3 = 1/x_4 = x; \qquad x_5 = 1 \tag{29}$$

In view of the charges on the respective species. In addition, it has been assumed that the barrier lengths, λ, approximately cancel when they appear as ratios.

To illustrate the properties of such a model, we take rather arbitrarily the following set of values for the parameters:

$$\epsilon = 36.08 \text{ mv} \qquad\qquad n = 15 \text{ barriers}$$
$$Kp_0 = 5.00 \qquad\qquad Kp_n = 0.25$$
$$k = 48.832 \qquad\qquad k' = 2.000$$
$$Kq = 5.808\lambda_{02}k_2^0$$

and derive the values shown in Table I for the quantities of interest, using, in place of concentrations, the dimensionless values $Kc_{0i} = y_i$, $Kc_{ni} = z_i$, and, similarly for the fluxes, $Q_i' = KQ_i/\lambda_{01}k_1^0$. A number of facts are immediately apparent: the sodium ion exists at a high concentration in the region of high positive potential, whereas the positive potassium ion follows the Nernst equation in being predominantly in the negative interior of the cell. The chloride ion is necessarily in excess in the external medium, since we have required that the ion concentrations must effectively conserve charge, although experience indicates that this is not generally the role of Cl^- in practice.

It is well known that a number of ions as well as neutral molecules in addition to those of the model above are present in any actively metabolizing cell, and their influence must complicate the algebra of any such model discussion. We take this fact as primary explanation for the chloride deficiency within the cell in this model. We note, however, that although the sodium ion, *as an ion*, follows the equivalent of a Nernst equation for its flux, the stoichiometric flux of *all* of the sodium is zero in spite of both the concentration and the electrical gradients. It appears to be a well known, but often ill-interpreted, phenomenon that certain ions are "pumped";[12] the model above offers an example of probably the simplest way in which an ion may be pumped, i.e., not follow the Nernst equation for transport.

TABLE I

| | Concentrations | | |
	Inside	Outside	Fluxes
Na^+	0.719	14.308	−1.742
NaP^+	2.092	0.234	1.742
K^+	0.879	0.220	0.
Cl^-	3.690	14.762	0.
P	2.908	0.016	282.414

Finally, in the model case for which one can calculate numerical values for all of the parameters, we point out the interesting fact that even if the potential gradient through the membrane is constant—the incompressibility of ions—the relation (12) together with the additional restrictions required by a comparable treatment will not give a uniform concentration gradient through the membrane. Thus if, following equation (12), we compute the flux through the mth minimum, we obtain

$$Q = \frac{\lambda_0 k_0^0}{m} \, g_m \left\{ x^{-m/2} c_0 - x^{m/2} \frac{\lambda_m}{\lambda_0} \, c_m \right\}; \qquad m \leqq n \qquad (30)$$

Assuming that the process is in a steady state and all fluxes are equal for a given species, one may derive the result

$$\frac{c_m}{c_0} = \left\{ \frac{c_0 - c_n}{c_0} \frac{x^n}{x^n - 1} \right\} \frac{1}{x^m} - \frac{c_0 - x^n c_n}{c_0(x^n - 1)} \qquad (31)$$

where again the λ's have been assumed to cancel approximately when they appear as ratios. We have taken as a definition the relation

$$g_m = \left(\frac{x^{\frac{1}{2}} - x^{-\frac{1}{2}}}{x^{m/2} - x^{-m/2}} \right) m \qquad (32)$$

For the numerical model above, the relation (31) is shown in Fig. 4. One notes that the distribution in population in each minimum neces-

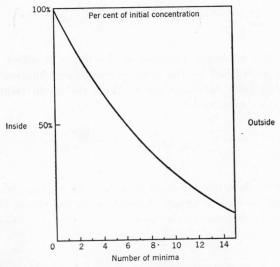

FIG. 4. Distribution of concentration through a barrier for constant potential gradient.

sarily has an exponential relation with the potential, since it is linear with the quantity x^{-m}.

The Non-Steady State

The fluxes of the various species through the membrane present a rather complicated algebraic picture when all of the possible variations are considered. The idea of ionic incompressibility permits one to retain the simplifying formalism of equation (12), although the exact treatment of the factor g presents some problem in itself. However, one may assume that in a transient state the distribution within the membrane is dilute, from the point of view of charge distribution, and that the initial and final concentrations must bear the burden of any change in conditions. There is another assumption which permits considerable progress: that is, although a relatively large measurable current may flow, very few ions are required to provide it, i.e., under the experimental conditions which exist, even the initial and final concentrations change only negligibly on a macroscopic scale. Now although it is certain that adjustments in the measurable concentrations of the various ions probably do occur, one may treat the problem at least approximately in the following way: the change in the charge distribution per square centimeter normal to the direction of the field will be given by the form

$$\sum_{i=1}^{4} \frac{z_i \lambda_{0i} k_i^0}{n} \left(c_{0i} e^{-z_i \mathcal{F} \epsilon / 2RT} - \frac{\lambda_{ni}}{\lambda_{0i}} c_{ni} e^{z_i \mathcal{F} \epsilon / 2RT} \right) \tag{33}$$

Equation (33) is simply the sum of the fluxes of all of the various species, each multiplied by the appropriate charge number (with sign) z_i. Here g has been taken as unity. With the usual requirements of electrostatics, we may write

$$\frac{d\sigma}{dt} = \frac{4\pi\lambda_0}{D} \sum_{i=1}^{4} z_i \lambda_{0i} k_i^0 \{ c_{0i} e^{-z_i \mathcal{F} \epsilon / 2RT} - c_{ni} e^{z_i \mathcal{F} \epsilon / 2RT} \} \tag{34}$$

where D is the dielectric constant and λ_0 is an average length for the barriers. If all species be singly charged, as in the model above, equation (34) may be reduced to the form

$$\frac{d\sigma}{dt} = a\{ m e^{-\sigma} - n e^{\sigma} \} \tag{35}$$

where

$$\sigma = \frac{\mathfrak{F}\epsilon}{2RT}$$

$$m = \sum_{i=1}^{3} k_i^0 c_{0i} + k_4^0 c_{04} \tag{36}$$

$$n = \sum_{i=1}^{3} k_i^0 c_{ni} + k_4^0 c_{n4}$$

and we assume the conservation conditions, equations (20), (21), and (22), although these do not enter directly into the problem. Equation (35), from its derivation, certainly expresses the fact that at a potential σ_∞ the system is in equilibrium. Thus, if at a time t_n the potential is σ_n, we may integrate and obtain

$$\sigma = 2\sigma_\infty - \sigma_n + \ln\left\{\frac{\tanh \alpha e^{\sigma_\infty}(t - t_n) + e^{\sigma_n - \sigma_\infty}}{\tanh \alpha e^{\sigma_\infty}(t - t_n) + e^{\sigma_\infty - \sigma_n}}\right\} \tag{37}$$

and in particular, if $t_n = 0$, $\sigma(0) \equiv \sigma_0 = \sigma_n$

$$\sigma = 2\sigma_\infty - \sigma_0 + \ln\left\{\frac{\tanh \alpha e^{\sigma_\infty}(t) + e^{\sigma_0 - \sigma_\infty}}{\tanh \alpha e^{\sigma_\infty}(t) + e^{\sigma_\infty - \sigma_0}}\right\} \tag{38}$$

where the quantity α is defined as

$$\alpha = \frac{4\pi\mathfrak{F}\lambda_0^2}{2RT}\left\{\sum_{i=1}^{3} k_i^0 c_{ni} + k_4^0 c_{04}\right\} \tag{39}$$

If then at some instant the parameters of α, for example, the specific rate constant for one or more of the species, should assume new values, the course of the potential in seeking its new equilibrium value σ_∞ will be given by (37), where σ_n is the previous resting potential and t_n the time at which the parameters changed. In this picture, it is necessary to assume a cooperative, catastrophic process in the membrane which leads to a nearly instantaneous shift in the rate constants for transport. Otherwise, a rather more complicated integration of the equations for flux will be required. The superposition of two such curves, with the σ_∞ of the first higher and that of the second lower than the value initially assumed, will lead to curves of the form of Fig. 5. The sharpness of the break at the maximum is a measure of the degree of cooperation in the membrane breakdown process. It is evident that this picture reproduces at least the qualitative aspects of measured action potentials for nerves.[8, 9] Again, a quantitative representation must await a more so-

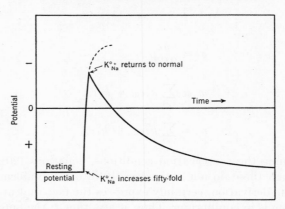

FIG. 5. Potential changes arising from membrane breakdown (schematic).

phisticated model, but there seems to be little doubt that the experimental results can be fitted into this general picture.

As has been shown, an ionic concentration gradient, by promoting diffusion, generates an electrical potential. Other ions diffuse in a direction to nullify the potential except as they are restrained by membrane impermeability. The enzymes of a living cell, by chemically transforming molecules, set up a variety of gradients. The particular metabolites formed preferentially inside the cell and destroyed outside provide an important class of such gradients. If such a metabolite is itself ionized, or if it combines with some ion to make a charged complex, the concentration gradient will cause diffusion, which in turn sets up a potential, and the ion entering into the complex is said to be pumped. Any ion which in the steady state does not obey the Nernst potential equation is obviously being pumped. In a reacting system, full of concentration gradients of many types, it would be surprising if a fair share of the ions failed to enter into complexes and get pumped to a greater or lesser degree. For pumping of an ion, it is sufficient if the complexing causing the diffusion occurs only inside the membrane and not in the aqueous solutions outside.

The molecule responsible for Na^+ transport upon traversing the nerve membrane may be supposed to liberate acetyl choline from an acceptor molecule, perhaps, if the metabolite is an acid, by lending its proton to replace the quaternary nitrogen of the acetyl choline.[6, 16] The liberated acetyl choline then complexes with the membrane, tending to bring about the permeable state characteristic of the action potential phase of nerve action. The choline esterase acts to offset this situation by hydrolyzing the acetyl choline.

The reaction in which impermeable membrane changes to permeable membrane can be characterized in the usual way by a Gibbs free energy change ΔF_0 , where

$$\Delta F_0 = \Delta H_0 - T\Delta S_0 + \sum f_i(c_i) + \mu\epsilon \qquad (40)$$

The quantities ΔH_0 , T, ΔS_0 , $f_i(c_i)$, μ and ϵ are the standard heat of reaction, absolute temperature, standard entropy of reaction, free energy change arising from component i, effective chemical potential of the reacting unit, and the electric field across the membrane, respectively. Now, if the membrane molecules behave highly cooperatively, then, when ΔF is positive, the membrane will be highly impermeable, and when negative, highly permeable. If the molecules are less cooperative, then the transition will simply be correspondingly less sharp. Too little calcium, for example, will make F negative and, therefore, permeable, as will a sufficient decrease in the potential ϵ or a sufficient increase of acetyl choline. The acetyl choline is of especial importance at synapses.

It has been our purpose to sharpen the basic physical chemical theory, realizing that the detailed behavior is more complicated than the illustrative models presented. It appears that the general theory as outlined will be competent to treat the known facts; in particular, the discussions of the conference on nerve impulse[16] and many of the questions there raised seem to be understandable in terms of this treatment.

REFERENCES

1. COLE, K. C., "Four Lectures in Biophysics." Institutio de Biofisia, Universidada do Brasil, 1947.
2. EINSTEIN, A., *Ann. Phys.* **17**, 549 (1905); **19**, 371 (1906).
3. EYRING, H., *J. Chem. Phys.* **4**, 283 (1936).
4. EYRING, H., LUMRY, R., and WOODBURY, J. W., *Record Chem. Progr. Kresge-Hooker Sci. Lib.* **10**, 100 (1949).
5. GLASSTONE, S., LAIDLER, K. J., and EYRING, H., "The Theory of Rate Processes," Chapter IX. McGraw-Hill Book Co., New York, 1941.
6. GRUNDFEST, H., NACHMANSOHN, D., KAO, C. Y., and CHAMBERS, R., *Nature* **169**, 190 (1952).
7. HENDERSON, P., *Z. physik. Chem.* **59**, 118 (1907); **63**, 325 (1908).
8. HODGKIN, A. L., HUXLEY, A. F., AND KATZ, B., *J. Physiol.* **116**, 424 (1952).
9. HODGKIN, A. L., and HUXLEY, A. F., *Cold Spring Harbor Symposia Quant. Biol.*, **17**, 43 (1952); *J. Physiol.* **116**, 449, 473 (1952).
10. JOHNSON, F. H., EYRING, H., and POLISSAR, M., "The Kinetic Basis of Molecular Biology," John Wiley & Sons, New York (in press).

11. DE JONG, H. G. B., *in* "Colloid Science" (H. R. Kruyt, ed.), Vol II, Chapter
    IX. Elsevier Publishing Co., New York, 1949.
12. KROGH, A., *Proc. Roy. Soc. (London)* **B133,** 140 (1946).
13. LEWIS, G. N., and SARGENT, L. W., *J. Am. Chem. Soc.* **31,** 363 (1909).
14. MACINNES, D. A., "Principles of Electrochemistry," p. 231 *et seq.* Reinhold
    Publishing Corp., New York, 1939.
15. MARTELL, A. E., and CALVIN, M., "Chemistry of the Metal Chelate Com-
    pounds." Prentice-Hall, New York, 1952.
16. *Trans. 2nd Conf. on Nerve Impulse,* Josiah Macy, Jr. Foundation, New York
    (1951).
17. PLANCK, M., *Ann. Physik* **39,** 161 (1890); **40,** 561 (1890).
18. ZWOLINSKI, B. J., EYRING, H., and REESE, C., *J. Phys. & Colloid Chem.,* **53,**
    1426 (1949); other important references may be found in this article.

Transport of Ions Through Biological Membranes From the Standpoint of Irreversible Thermodynamics[a]

JOHN G. KIRKWOOD

Irreversible thermodynamics provides a systematic phenomenological description of the transport of heat and matter in systems departing from thermodynamic equilibrium, which still permit the definition of local thermodynamic states at each point in their interior, determined by a local temperature, density, and composition.[1-6] Such systems are frequently encountered in living organisms, the metabolic processes of which are intimately related to the transport of substances through the cell membrane and other biological membranes. An exact description of such transport processes on the phenomenological level by means of the formalism of irreversible thermodynamics possesses value in clearly defining the problems confronting the investigator of these processes, even if the description contains physical quantities, which might be practically inaccessible to measurement in the living organism. Such a description does not constitute an explanation of the observed phenomena, since it provides no information concerning underlying mechanisms on the molecular level. Nevertheless, any acceptable specific mechanism must be consistent with its general requirements.

We shall undertake here an investigation of the transport of ions through membranes, the properties of which simulate those of biological membranes. The results are also applicable to macroscopic ion-exchange-resin membranes. The model to be discussed is the following: an external fluid phase 1 separated by a membrane phase (M) from an internal phase 2. We shall suppose that the membrane phase possesses components insoluble in either exterior phase, which we shall cumulatively designate as component o, as well as some or all of the r components present in the exterior phases. The membrane phase will be bounded by two planes normal to the x-axis, at $x = 0$ and $x = a$. Referring all diffusion currents j_α to the membrane component as the reference component, we have at any point in the interior of the membrane phase[5]

[a] Contribution No. 1211 from the Sterling Chemistry Laboratory, Yale University.

119

$$j_\alpha = -\sum_{\beta=1}^{r} \Omega_{\alpha\beta} \frac{\partial \bar{\mu}_\beta}{\partial x} - \Omega_{\alpha T} \frac{\partial \log T}{\partial x} ; \qquad \alpha = 1 \cdots r$$

$$q = -\sum_{\beta=1}^{r} \Omega_{T\beta} \frac{\partial \bar{\mu}_\beta}{\partial x} - \Omega_{TT} \frac{\partial \log T}{\partial x}$$

(1)

where q is the heat current density, $\bar{\mu}_\alpha$ is the total chemical potential of component α, and T is the temperature. The mass current densities j_α may be expressed in any desired mass units, grams or moles, flowing through unit area in unit time in the x-direction. The coefficient $\Omega_{\alpha\alpha}$ determines that part of the current of component α arising from its own chemical potential gradient. In a binary system it is related to the diffusion coefficient, $D_{\alpha\alpha}$, in the following manner

$$D_{\alpha\alpha} = \frac{RT}{C_\alpha} \Omega_{\alpha\alpha} \left[1 + \left(\frac{\partial \log \gamma_\alpha}{\partial \log C_\alpha} \right)_{T,P} \right]$$

(2)

where C_α is the concentration of component α and γ_α is its activity coefficient. The codiffusion coefficient $\Omega_{\alpha\beta}$ determines that part of the current of α produced by the chemical potential gradient of component β, and $\Omega_{\alpha T}$ determines the thermal diffusion of component α, whereas $\Omega_{T\alpha}$ determines the heat transferred by the mass diffusion of component α. The origin of the codiffusion coefficients $\Omega_{\alpha\beta}$ is to be found in the forces acting between the molecules of the several components. If the average intermolecular force is one of attraction, $\Omega_{\alpha\beta}$ is positive and the diffusion of component β induces a current of component α in the same direction. If, on the other hand, the force is one of repulsion, the diffusion of component β induces a current of α in the opposite direction. The coefficients $\Omega_{\alpha\beta}$ and $\Omega_{\alpha T}$ satisfy the reciprocal relations of Onsager

$$\Omega_{\alpha\beta} = \Omega_{\beta\alpha}$$

$$\Omega_{\alpha T} = \Omega_{T\alpha}$$

(3)

Therefore, the description of transport processes in a system of r components requires the measurement not of all r^2 elements of the matrix of the coefficients of equation (1), but only of $r(r + 1)/2$ of them. Thus the thermal diffusion coefficient determining the current of component α produced by a temperature gradient also determines the heat current produced by diffusive transfer of component α. Similarly, a single codiffusion coefficient $\Omega_{\alpha\beta}$ determines the flux of component α produced by a chemical potential gradient of β and the flux of β produced by a chemical potential gradient of α.

For ionic components it is convenient to separate the total chemical potential $\bar{\mu}_\alpha$, designated as the electrochemical potential, into two parts

$$\bar{\mu}_\alpha = \mu_\alpha + Z_\alpha \mathfrak{F}\varphi \tag{4}$$

where μ_α is a part designated as the purely chemical potential, dependent only on temperature, pressure, and composition; $Z_\alpha\mathfrak{F}$ is the charge carried by unit mass of the ionic component; and φ is the electrostatic potential. The current densities j_α of the several components satisfy the equations of continuity, expressing conservation of mass,

$$\frac{\partial j_\alpha}{\partial x} = -\frac{\partial C_\alpha}{\partial t}; \qquad \alpha = 1 \cdots r \tag{5}$$

where C_α is the concentration of component α. For a stationary regime, in which all $\partial C_\alpha/\partial t$ vanish, we note that the currents j_α are constants, independent of x and the time t.

We shall henceforth assume the system to be isothermal, so that terms involving the temperature gradient in equation (1) vanish. The inclusion of transport terms involving the temperature gradient, when they are important, presents no special difficulty, and they will be omitted here only in the interest of simplicity. Solution of equation (1) for the chemical potential gradients then leads to the expression

$$\frac{\partial \bar{\mu}_\alpha}{\partial x} = -\sum_{\beta=1}^{r} R_{\alpha\beta} j_\beta$$

$$R_{\alpha\beta} = \frac{|\,\Omega\,|_{\alpha\beta}}{|\,\Omega\,|} = (-1)^{\alpha+1}\frac{|\Omega|_{\beta\alpha}}{|\Omega|} \tag{6}$$

where $|\,\Omega\,|$ is the determinant of the matrix $\Omega_{\alpha\beta}$ and $|\,\Omega\,|_{\alpha\beta}$ is its appropriate minor. The chemical potential gradients are thus determined as linear functions of the currents by the resistance matrix $R_{\alpha\beta}$, which is the inverse of the diffusion matrix. We now integrate equation (6) with respect to x across the membrane for a stationary regime in which the currents j_α are constant

$$\bar{\mu}_\alpha(a) - \bar{\mu}_\alpha(0) = -\sum_{\beta=1}^{r} \gamma_{\alpha\beta} j_\beta$$

$$\gamma_{\alpha\beta} = \int_0^a R_{\alpha\beta}(x)\,dx \tag{7}$$

if we further assume local heterogeneous equilibrium at the boundaries of the membrane with the exterior phases 1 and 2, we have

$$\bar{\mu}_\alpha{}^{(1)} = \bar{\mu}_\alpha(0); \qquad \bar{\mu}_\alpha{}^{(2)} = \bar{\mu}_\alpha(a) \tag{8}$$

and equations (7) become

$$\Delta \bar{\mu}_\alpha = - \sum_{\beta=1}^{r} \gamma_{\alpha\beta} j_\beta$$

$$\Delta \bar{\mu}_\alpha = \bar{\mu}_\alpha{}^{(2)} - \bar{\mu}_\alpha{}^{(1)}$$

(9)

where $\Delta \bar{\mu}_\alpha$ is the difference in chemical potential of component α in the exterior phases, and $\gamma_{\alpha\beta}$ is the resistance matrix for the membrane as a whole. We may now solve equation (9) for the currents to obtain

$$j_\alpha = - \sum_{\beta=1}^{r} \omega_{\alpha\beta} \Delta \bar{\mu}_\beta$$

$$\omega_{\alpha\beta} = \frac{|\gamma|_{\alpha\beta}}{|\gamma|}$$

(10)

where we may call $\omega_{\alpha\beta}$ the permeability matrix of the membrane as a whole, which like the $\Omega_{\alpha\beta}$, satisfy the Onsager reciprocal relations. Equations (9) and (10) provide a general basis for the description of the transport of ionic and neutral components through membranes. They apply to membranes of macroscopic thickness, such as ion exchange membranes. They apply not only to biological membranes of macroscopic thickness, but also to cell membranes of microscopic thickness, let us say of the order of magnitude of 100 Å. In the latter case, equations (9) and (10) may be regarded as fundamental laws, equivalent to, but not operationally derivable from, equations (1), since the interiors of membranes of thickness of the order of molecular dimensions cannot properly be treated as a macroscopic phase in the thermodynamic sense. They can be more appropriately envisaged as insoluble films possessing in some instances a monolayer and in others a multilayer structure.

We shall now employ equations (9) and (10) for the determination of the electrical potential difference maintained across a membrane by the flow of ionic components. The electric current density I is related to the mass current densities of the several components in the following manner

$$I = \sum_{\beta=1}^{r} Z_\beta \mathfrak{F} j_\beta$$

(11)

where $Z_\alpha \mathfrak{F}$ is the charge carried by unit mass of component α. Substitution of equations (10) into equation (11), with use of equation (4), yields

$$I = - \sum_{\alpha,\beta=1}^{r} Z_\beta \mathfrak{F} \omega_{\alpha\beta} \Delta \mu_\alpha - \left[\sum_{\alpha,\beta=1}^{r} Z_\alpha Z_\beta \mathfrak{F}^2 \omega_{\alpha\beta} \right] \Delta \varphi$$

(12)

where $\Delta\mu_\alpha$ is difference in chemical potential of component α in the exterior fluid phases. Solving equation (12) for the membrane potential $\Delta\varphi$, we obtain

$$\Delta\varphi = E - ZI$$

$$\frac{1}{Z} = \sum_{\alpha,\beta=1}^{r} Z_\alpha Z_\beta \mathfrak{F}^2 \omega_{\alpha\beta} \qquad (13)$$

where Z is the specific impedance of the membrane, and E is the electro-motive force, arising from the purely chemical potential increments $\Delta\mu_\alpha$ across the membrane

$$-\mathfrak{F}E = \sum_{\alpha=1}^{r} \frac{\tau_\alpha}{Z_\alpha} \Delta\mu_\alpha$$

$$\tau_\alpha = \frac{\sum\limits_{\beta=1}^{r} Z_\alpha Z_\beta \omega_{\alpha\beta}}{\sum\limits_{\beta,\gamma=1}^{r} Z_\beta Z_\gamma \omega_{\beta\gamma}} \qquad (14)$$

where τ_α is electric transport number of component α for the membrane as a whole, and τ_α/Z_α is the mass transport number, equal to the mass current of component α associated with the passage of unit electric current through the membrane. It is to be remarked that neutral components as well as ionic components contribute to the sum of equation (14), since the nondiagonal terms $\omega_{\alpha\beta}$ in the permeability matrix lead to the production of currents of neutral species by the transport of the ionic species carrying the electric current. For the zero electric current, the membrane potential becomes equal to the electromotive force. It will be remarked that equation (14) bears a close resemblance to the usual expression for the diffusion potential associated with a liquid junction, with the difference that the τ_α are the transport numbers of the membrane as a whole rather than local transport numbers at a plane in the diffusion boundary. It is, of course, also possible to express the membrane potential as an integral across the membrane of

$$-\sum_{\alpha=1}^{r} \frac{t_\alpha}{Z_\alpha \mathfrak{F}} d\mu_\alpha$$

where t_α are the local transport numbers. However, the resulting expression lacks operational utility, since it is seldom possible to determine the local transport numbers t_α at all points in the interior of the membrane phase, whereas it is possible to determine the over-all transport numbers τ_α without dissecting the membrane. It is of course true that the τ_α depend implicitly on the distribution of the diffusible components in the membrane, which is in turn determined by the compositions of the exterior phases. Therefore, the τ_α must be regarded not only as properties of the membrane alone, but of the membrane and the exterior phases with which it is in contact. When thermodynamic equilibrium is established across the membrane, the chemical potential increments are related to the Donnan value E_D by the relations

$$\Delta\mu_\alpha = -Z_\alpha \mathfrak{F} E_D ; \qquad \alpha = 1 \cdots r \tag{15}$$

which, when substituted into equation (15), lead to the consistent result that $E = E_D$ with E_D itself determined by any one of equations (15).[b]

The foregoing analysis has been limited to the stationary regime, in which the membrane composition is independent of time, and the mass currents of all components are independent of time and position in the membrane. We shall now consider a generalization to a quasi-stationary regime, in which we assume equations (1) still to be valid, but in which the mass currents j_α are dependent upon position and time. For very rapid changes of state, it might be necessary to supplement equations (1) with inertial terms $\theta_\alpha \, \partial j_\alpha / \partial t$ on the right-hand sides. However, it is unlikely that sufficiently high frequencies would be encountered in biological systems for such terms to be important. Integration of equations (6) across the membrane, with the use of equations (5) leads to the following expressions for the currents $j_\alpha(a)$ and $j_\alpha(0)$ at the right and left boundaries of the membrane

$$j_\alpha(a) = -\sum_{\beta=1}^{r} \omega_{\alpha\beta} \Delta\bar{\mu}_\beta - \sum_{\beta=1}^{r} \int_0^a \sigma_{\alpha\beta}(x) \, \frac{\partial C_\beta}{\partial t} \, dx$$

$$j_\alpha(0) = j_\alpha(a) + \int_0^a \frac{\partial C_\alpha}{\partial t} \, dx \tag{16}$$

$$\sigma_{\alpha\beta}(x) = \sum_{\gamma=2}^{r} \omega_{\alpha\gamma} \int_0^x R_{\gamma\beta} \, dx$$

From equations (16) it is apparent that the detailed structure of the membrane must be known in order to determine the currents in the non-

---

[b] It must be remembered that the use of equation (14) is attended by the customary operational difficulties in the measurement of the chemical potentials of individual ionic components across a membrane or phase boundaries and can be compared with experiment only to the approximation that liquid potentials between the exterior phases and measuring electrodes can be eliminated by the use of such devices as salt bridges.

stationary case. The time derivatives $\partial C_\alpha/\partial t$ are determined by the following system of generalized diffusion equations, obtained by substituting equations (1) into equations (5),

$$\frac{\partial C_\alpha}{\partial t} = \sum_{\beta=1}^{r} \frac{\partial}{\partial x}\left(D_{\alpha\beta} \frac{\partial C_\beta}{\partial x}\right) + \frac{\partial}{\partial x}\left(u_\alpha C_\alpha \frac{\partial \varphi}{\partial x}\right)$$

$$D_{\alpha\beta} = \sum_{\gamma=1}^{r} \Omega_{\alpha\gamma}\left(\frac{\partial \mu_\gamma}{\partial C_\beta}\right)_{T,p,C_\sigma} \tag{17}$$

$$u_\alpha = \sum_{\gamma=1}^{r} Z_\beta \mathfrak{F}\Omega_{\alpha\beta}/C_\alpha$$

where it is to be noted that the elements of the diffusion tensor $D_{\alpha\beta}$ and the electrical mobilities u_α depend on the concentrations, so that equations (17) are in general nonlinear. Consequently, although they are apparently linear, equations (16) will actually lead, in conjunction with equations (17), to nonlinear relations between the currents and the electrochemical potential gradients of the components. Equations (17) are to be solved subject to the conditions of continuity of mass current at the membrane boundaries. If the component mobilities in the interior of the membrane are small relative to those in the exterior phases, this condition will be closely approximated by the conditions of local thermodynamic equilibrium at the boundaries.

Let us now suppose that an alternating electric potential difference of frequency ν is applied across the membrane in excess of the electromotive force, given by equation (14), by an amount $-Ve^{2\pi i\nu t}$, so that

$$\Delta\varphi - E = -Ve^{2\pi i\nu t} \tag{18}$$

The time derivatives, $\partial C_\alpha/\partial t$, will be determined through equations (17) by the applied excess potential difference, and the perturbations in the membrane concentrations C_α will in general differ in phase from the applied electric field, since a diffusion boundary possesses a finite relaxation time. Let us suppose that the solution of equations (17) leads to the following result for the membrane integrals of equations (16)

$$\int_0^a \sigma_{\alpha\beta} \frac{\partial C_\beta}{\partial t}\,dx = 2\pi\nu[\lambda_{\alpha\beta} - i\kappa_{\alpha\beta}]Ve^{2\pi i\nu t} \tag{19}$$

where $\lambda_{\alpha\beta}$ and $\kappa_{\alpha\beta}$ may in general depend upon V, but will be independent of V for small applied fields. The electric current density arising from the flow of ionic components through the membrane is then given by

$$I_1 = \sum_{\alpha,\beta=1}^{r} \{Z_\alpha Z_\beta \mathfrak{F}^2\omega_{\alpha\beta} + 2\pi\nu Z_\alpha \mathfrak{F}\lambda_{\alpha\beta} - 2\pi i\nu Z_\alpha \mathfrak{F}\kappa_{\alpha\beta}\}Ve^{2\pi i\nu t} \tag{20}$$

To obtain the total current, we must add the displacement current

$$\frac{1}{4\pi} \frac{\partial D}{\partial t} = \frac{\nu}{2a} \left[\epsilon'' - i\epsilon'\right] V e^{2\pi i\nu t} \tag{21}$$

to the ionic current, where ϵ' and ϵ'' are the real and imaginary parts of the membrane dielectric constant, the values of which are determined by the displacement of electric charges carried by the membrane component, which are absent from the exterior phases. The specific impedance Z of the membrane is then given by

$$\frac{1}{Z} = \sum_{\alpha,\beta=1}^{r} \{Z_\alpha Z_\beta \mathfrak{F}^2 \omega_{\alpha\beta} + 2\pi\nu Z_\alpha \mathfrak{F}\lambda_{\alpha\beta}\} + \frac{\nu\epsilon''}{a}$$
$$- 2\pi i\nu \left\{ \sum_{\alpha,\beta=1}^{r} Z_\alpha \mathfrak{F}\kappa_{\alpha\beta} - \frac{\epsilon'}{4\pi a} \right\} \tag{22}$$

Both from the Maxwell-Wagner effect on the ratio of the field in the membrane to the exterior field and from diffusion boundary relaxation, we may expect the coefficients $\kappa_{\alpha\beta}$ to be positive, and thus to give rise to membrane inductance. From the foregoing analysis, we see that our description of membrane permeability is sufficiently general to account for a complex membrane impedance, which may depend on the field strength, and which possesses resistive, inductive, and capacitative components.

We note that the membrane permeabilities, $\omega_{\alpha\beta}$, depend on temperature, pressure, and composition, and, in particular, on the thermodynamic state of the membrane component. If the membrane component is in a metastable thermodynamic state, in which, let us say, a phase transformation or a chemical reaction may be induced, the initiation of this transformation will produce a change in the membrane transference numbers and, according to equation (14), a change in the membrane electromotive force, except in the special case of electrochemical equilibrium between the exterior phases. Such a change would give rise to an electric current, which would flow until the electric potential difference had adjusted itself to the new value of the electromotive force. If certain conditions are fulfilled, a phase transformation may propagate itself in a metastable phase like a detonation wave, with a stationary velocity determined by the Hugoniot and Chapman-Jouguet conditions,[7] which, for small amplitudes, approaches the velocity of sound. If we imagine that such a phase change or chemical transformation can be initiated at any point on the membrane by an electric impulse itself, we possess a general model for the propagation of the nerve impulse. Properly, the membrane of a nerve cell should be envisaged as a surface phase rather than a macroscopic membrane phase. The responsible phase transformation must therefore be a surface phase change, possibly a rotational phase change of the kind observed by Harkins and others in insoluble films. The theory of the propagation of detonation waves is still applicable, but we should be concerned with the propagation of a film pressure wave, producing alterations in ionic permeabilities, the velocity of which would be determined by film compressibility. Such a membrane would have a refractory period after the passage of each pulse, during which the metastable phase is being reformed by metabolic processes. It is attractive to speculate that any specific model of the nerve membrane should possess the features of the general model which we have proposed.

REFERENCES

1. ECKART, C., *Phys. Rev.* **58,** 267, 269, 919 (1940).
2. TOLMAN, R. C., and FINE, P. C., *Revs. Mod. Phys.* **20,** 51 (1948).
3. ONSAGER, L., *Phys. Rev.* **37,** 405 (1931); **38,** 2265 (1931).
4. PRIGOGINE, I., "Étude thermodynamique des processes irreversibles." Desoer, Liége, 1947.
5. DE GROOT, S. R., "Thermodynamics of Irreversible Processes." Interscience Publishers, New York, 1951.
6. KIRKWOOD, J. G., and CRAWFORD, B. L., *J. Phys. Chem.* **56,** 1048 (1952).
7. COLE, R. H., "Underwater Explosions " Chapter 3. Princeton University Press, Princeton, 1948.

Transport of Ions Across Charged Membranes[a]

GEORGE SCATCHARD

My own interest in charged membranes has been the search for some which are impermeable to proteins and as highly selective as possible to small cations or anions. An ion exchanger membrane which meets these requirements well can be made sufficiently thick to be treated as a bulk phase. Many properties may be measured. It may make a satisfactory model for protein-containing membranes, which also have ionic charges fixed in a rigid lattice.

MEMBRANES

These membranes should not be pictured as diaphragms, that is, as very thin plates with holes, which are small, but not nearly as small as the thickness of the plates, for the holes are very small relative to the thickness of the membrane. They should not be pictured with right-cylindrical circular pores, like a honey comb with rounded cells. They are much more like a sand pile, a brush pile, a sponge, or a dish of spaghetti. The membrane is a continuous resin network and a continuous aqueous network which are interpenetrating. In ion exchangers the volumes of the two are about equal. The interstices in the lattice are continuously branching and coming together. One common type of ion exchanger is based on polystyrene (polyvinylbenzene) cross-linked with divinylbenzene. The unit is (RC_6H_4) —(HC)—(CH_2) and the cross link is (CH_2)—(CH)—(RC_6H_3)—(CH)—(CH_2). Another common lattice is based on phenol-formaldehyde. The unit is —(RC_6H_2OH)—$(CH_2$— and the cross link is $\rangle(C_6H_2OH)$—. The most useful exchangers for most purposes are the strong electrolytes in which R is SO_3^- for the cation

[a] This paper is based on talks given in New York City at a Symposium of the American Electrochemical Society, "Application of Electrochemistry to Biology and Medicine," April 13–16, 1953, and at this symposium.

128

exchanger and a quaternary ammonium ion for the anion exchanger. The corresponding weak acid or base, in which R is COO⁻ or a tertiary ammonium ion, might serve as an even better model of a protein membrane.

Ionics, Inc., has published a rather complete description of one membrane,[1] Neptonic CR-51, of the phenol-formaldehyde sulfonate type. It contains 1.26 milliequivalents of sulfonate per cubic centimeter of resin, or 1.72 milliequivalents per gram of water. The distribution of sodium chloride between membrane and water indicates that the activity coefficient of sodium chloride in the membrane changes rapidly with its concentration. The conductance of the sodium resin is 0.0080 $ohm^{-1} cm^{-1}$, which is about a fifth of the conductance of sodium ion in 1.26 aqueous solution. The increased conductance due to 0.35 milliequivalents of sodium chloride per cubic centimeter is 0.010, which is about a third of its conductance in water. They have also measured the quantities which can be measured for thinner films, the transfer of water and of salt and the electromotive force. Through the sodium form of the resin without sodium chloride, 300 cm^3 of water are transferred per equivalent of electricity.

ELECTRICAL TRANSFERENCE

A cell for the measurement of either transference or electromotive force consists of a pair of reversible electrodes with one or more solutions between. If two solutions meet at a liquid junction we will indicate the junction by | ; if they are separated by an uncharged membrane we will use | O | ; if the membrane has a fixed negative charge, and is therefore a cation exchanger, we will use | C | ; and we will designate an anion exchanger membrane by | A | .

For the measurement of a transference number in solution, there is but a single solution, and we represent the cell as

electrode α,   solution,   electrode ω

or for a specific case

Ag—AgCl, NaCl (0.1 M), AgCl—Ag

We will consider that there are three components in the system: sodium ion, chloride ion, and water; and one restriction: the solution must be everywhere neutral. If positive current goes through the cell from left to right, for each equivalent of electricity one chloride ion is used up at α by the reaction Ag + Cl^- = AgCl + ϵ^-, and one is formed at ω by the reverse reaction. About 0.4 Na^+ goes to the right and about 0.6 Cl^- to the left. There is also a transference of a certain amount of water. We are interested only in the motion of the components relative to each other, so we may consider any one of them as standing still. Since the days of Hittorff, it has been customary to consider motion relative to the water. So the net effect of the current is to transfer 0.4 equivalent of sodium chloride from α to ω. The transference number of water is zero, that of sodium ion is 0.4, and that of chloride ion is -0.6.[b]

As soon as this transfer starts there is a deficiency of sodium chloride at electrode α, and an excess at electrode ω; sodium chloride begins to diffuse from right to left near the electrodes. In a successful transference experiment, the portions for analysis are taken large enough to include all parts which have changed in concentration due to diffusion.

It is considerably more difficult to measure transference in a cell containing a membrane in which the transference numbers are not the same as in the solution. Consider the cell

$$Ag\text{—}AgCl, \ NaCl(0.1 \ M) \ | \ C \ | \ NaCl(0.1 \ M), \ AgCl\text{—}Ag$$

If we consider the water to be fixed, the membrane must be considered to move. It is more convenient to consider that the membrane is stationary. If the membrane is Neptonic CR-51, the transference number of the sodium ion is more than 0.9 and that of chloride ion less than -0.1. As a result, sodium chloride will accumulate at the right of the membrane as well as at electrode ω, and there will be a deficiency at the left of the membrane as well as at electrode α. As soon as the transference begins, sodium chloride will diffuse away from the right-hand side of the membrane and toward the left-hand side, both through the solutions and through the membrane. If the transference numbers in the membrane vary with the concentration, the transference will correspond to a higher concentration than 0.1 M because of the easier availability of chloride ion on the right-hand side. The experimental difficul-

---

[b] There is a great advantage in defining the transference number of component i, t_i, as the number of moles of i carried in the direction of the positive current per equivalent of electricity, so that the transference number of an anion, like its valence, z_i, is negative, for it is much more important to know which way a component travels than how fast it goes. This is particularly true of a neutral component, which may have either a positive or negative transference number The transport number or fraction of the current carried, T_i, is then equal to $t_i z_i$, which is positive for any ion and zero for any neutral component.[2] It is also convenient to consider the mobility, u_i, as having the same sign as the transference number.

ties are also greater because now the portion for analysis must contain everything to the very edge of the membrane.

The concentration changes at the edges of the membrane are compensated to a small extent by the transfer of water, which has a transference number of 300/18 in this membrane. The transference number of water is

$$t_w = \frac{u_w \, m_w}{\sum_j z_j \, u_j \, m_j}$$

in which m is the number of equivalents per kilogram of water. The mobility of the water when the membrane is stationary is -1 times the mobility of the membrane when the water is stationary. The mobility of the membrane so calculated is almost the same as that of sodium ion relative to the water. I would expect the same order of magnitude but that it would not be so large.

Electrical Potentials

The simplest cell for the measurement of electrical potential differences consists of two different electrodes and a single solution. It is not interesting for our present discussion. The next simplest cell is two identical electrodes with two solutions of different concentrations, but the same electrolyte and with no membrane. An example would be

$$\text{Ag—AgCl, NaCl(0.1 } M) \mid \text{NaCl(0.01 } M), \text{AgCl—Ag}$$

The electrical potential difference for the general case with any number of liquid junctions or membranes is given by

$$E\mathfrak{F}/RT = -\Delta G/RT = E_{0\alpha}\mathfrak{F}/RT - \sum_i \nu_{i\alpha} \ln a_{i\alpha} - \int_\alpha^\omega \sum_i t_i \, d \ln a_i$$
$$- \sum_i \nu_{i\omega} \ln a_{i\omega} - E_{0\omega}\mathfrak{F}/RT$$

in which $-\Delta G$ is the decrease in Gibbs free energy per equivalent of electricity passed through the cell, $E_{0\alpha}$ and $E_{0\omega}$ are the standard electrode potentials, written as anode potentials, $\nu_{i\alpha}$ and $\nu_{i\omega}$ are the number of moles of component i formed at electrodes α and ω per equivalent of electricity, and the sums include all components, charged or uncharged. In this special case the electrode potentials cancel, the water may be considered stationary, and the equation reduces to

$$E\mathfrak{F}/RT = - \int_\alpha^\omega t_{\text{Na}} \, d \ln a_{\text{Na}} a_{\text{Cl}}$$

Relating the electrical potential difference to the change in free energy, or even stating that there is a change in free energy, requires more than classical thermodynamics, for the system is not in equilibrium. As soon as the two solutions are placed in contact, sodium chloride will diffuse from left to right. A successful measurement requires that the concentrations at the electrodes are not changed measurably either by diffusion or by the electrical current. In the usual potentiometric method a very small current flow is imposed on the diffusion, first in one direction and then in the other, and the electrical potential difference is taken as the electromotive force when no current flows.

To justify our expression, we use the most fundamental principle of nonequilibrium thermodynamics, which is so basic that it is often not stated—that in a system not too far from equilibrium the potentials, such as temperature, pressure, and chemical potentials, exist at each point, and that the chemical potential of any component is a function only of the temperature, pressure, and composition at that point and does not depend upon their rates of change with distance or with time. Professor Debye has offered the criterion that the change in composition must be small over distances comparable to the thickness of the ionic atmosphere, which, in Ångstroms, is about three over the square root of the ionic strength in aqueous solutions. There is a second criterion which depends somewhat upon the geometry of the apparatus. The equations in general assume constant temperature, but the diffusion across a boundary may absorb or evolve heat and thus tend to change the temperature. Unless the conduction of heat away from the junction is sufficiently rapid to make the temperature difference very small, there may be an effect on the electrical potential.[3]

Provided that these two criteria are satisfied, it is not necessary to know the details of the boundary between two solutions of different concentrations of the same salt, for the transference numbers are single-valued functions of the mean activity since all are single-valued functions of the concentration. If the solute composition is different on the two sides, however, we do need to know the details of the composition of the boundary layer. We need to consider only the integral

$$\int_\alpha^\omega \sum_i t_i \, d \ln a_i \, ,$$

and in many cases the integrand will be sufficient. In the ideal case with $a_i = m_i$, the integrand becomes $(\sum_i u_i\,dm_i)/\sum_j z_j\,u_j\,m_j)$. Obviously the integral depends upon the relation of each m_j to m_i.

The simplest boundary is the Henderson,[4] or mixture, boundary, in which each $m_j = (1 - x)m_{j\alpha} + xm_{j\omega}$, and x varies from zero to unity across the boundary, so that each portion is equivalent to $(1 - x)$ parts of solution α and x parts of solution ω.

The initial boundary in the Clark cell for pH measurement[5] is a mixture boundary about 1 cm thick. Diffusion is so slow that the change from the initial state is usually unimportant during a measurement. A flowing junction[6-8] is an extremely thin mixture boundary which is maintained in a quasi-stationary state by continued renewal. Any boundary formed by shearing, such as the boundary at the stopcock in the MacInnes glass electrode,[9] is initially a mixture boundary, usually quite thin.

The change with time of a boundary at which two solutions meet initially in a plane is closely reproduced when the flow of a flowing junction is stopped.[8] The theory has been studied by Taylor[10] and by Guggenheim.[11]

The first theoretical study of a liquid junction was that of Max Planck,[12] who treated the case of an ideal mixture of any number of ions, each with valence $+z$ or $-z$, in a region between two boundaries; each concentration is kept constant at $m_{j\alpha}$ or $m_{j\omega}$ outside the respective boundary, and between the boundaries a stationary state is maintained by diffusion without current flow. This type of junction requires a diaphragm or membrane, at the opposite sides of which are the solutions α or ω. Their compositions may be kept constant by continuous flow. This is the simplest model of a membrane and should be the (idealized) limit which a charged membrane approaches as the fixed charge on the lattice approaches zero. Although Planck makes very clever use of the fact that the sum of the molal concentrations of cations is the same as that of the anions, his answer is an implicit exponential equation in

$$\int_\alpha^\omega \sum_i t_i\,d\ln a_i\,.$$

Cumming and Gilchrist[13] have compared the values calculated by the Henderson and Planck equations for boundaries between hydrochloric acid and the alkali chlorides. Their discussion of the thickness of the junction is irrelevant, for both expressions are independent of the thickness. For a single salt they both reduce to the classical Nernst expression. For equal total concentrations they also agree. If the concentration ratio is greater than 10, they differ by 10 to 20%. This difference depends entirely on the different assumptions as to the structure of the boundary layer.

In a cell such as

$$\text{Ag—AgCl, NaCl}(\alpha) \mid C \mid \text{NaCl}(\omega), \text{AgCl—Ag}$$

the membrane should be regarded as stationary, so

$$\sum_i t_i \, d \ln a_i = t_{\text{Na}} \, d \ln a_{\text{Na}} + t_{\text{Cl}} \, d \ln a_{\text{Cl}} + t_w \, d \ln a_w$$

$$= d \ln a_{\text{Na}} + t_{\text{Cl}} \, d \ln a_{\text{Na}} a_{\text{Cl}} + t_w \, d \ln a_w$$

The first term may be integrated directly to give $\ln (a_{\text{Na}\omega}/a_{\text{Na}\alpha})$ which is the same as would result from a pair of sodium electrodes, one in each solution. The other terms, which measure the inefficiency of the membrane electrode, are expressed in terms of activities of neutral components. Since t_{Cl} is negative and $d \ln a_w$ has the opposite sign to $d \ln a_{\text{Na}} a_{\text{Cl}}$, both diminish the measured electrical potential difference.

The sodium chloride will diffuse through the membrane from the more concentrated solution to the more dilute. The desired potential is for the steady state with uniform composition outside the two limits, just as in a Planck boundary. Although the thickness of the membrane makes no difference, it is important that these limits should come just at the surface of the membrane, for t_{Cl} varies from almost zero within the membrane to about 0.6 outside. Presumably the change does not come at a mathematical surface but in a transition layer in which there is enough structure to prevent efficient stirring. If so, the measured transference number of chloride ion will be larger than that within the membrane. Once more the effect of water transfer is compensatory, for the water transfer will be reduced in the transition layers.

MEMBRANE POTENTIALS

Our measurements have been made on cells of the type

$$\text{Hg—Hg}_2\text{Cl}_2, \text{KCl(sat.), NaCl}(\alpha) \mid C \mid \text{NaCl}(\beta) \mid A \mid \text{NaCl}(\alpha), \text{KCl(sat.),}$$
$$\text{Hg}_2\text{Cl}_2\text{—Hg.}$$

The cell is symmetrical except for the section

$$\text{NaCl}(\alpha) \mid C \mid \text{NaCl}(\beta) \mid A \mid \text{NaCl}(\alpha)$$

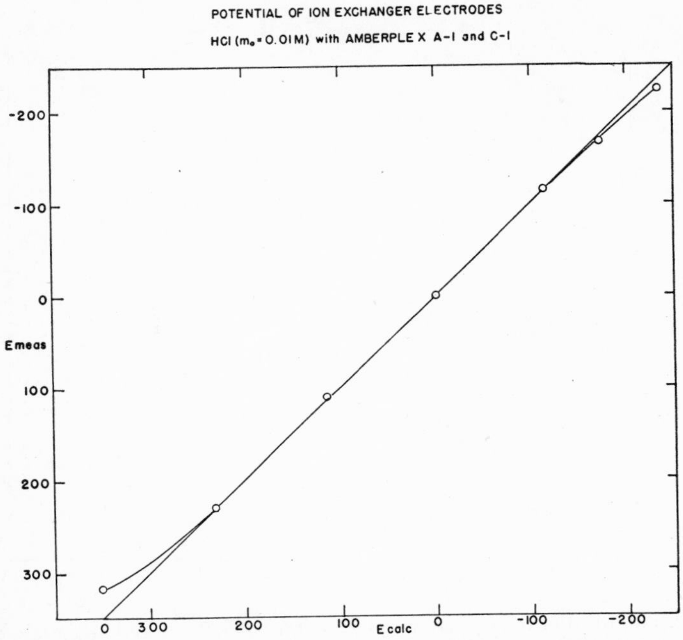

POTENTIAL OF ION EXCHANGER ELECTRODES

HCl (m_o = 0.01M) with AMBERPLEX A-1 and C-1

FIG. 1. Potential of ion exchanger electrodes HCl($m_0 = 0.01\ M$) with Amberplex A-1 and C-1.

The electrical potential difference is given by

$$E\mathfrak{F}/RT = \ln\frac{(a_{\text{Na}}\,a_{\text{Cl}})_\beta}{(a_{\text{Na}}\,a_{\text{Cl}})_\alpha} + \int_\alpha^\beta (t_{\text{Cl}C} - t_{\text{Na}A})d\ln a_{\text{Na}}\,a_{\text{Cl}}$$

$$+ \int_\alpha^\beta (t_{wC} - t_{wA})d\ln a_w$$

The solution α was always 0.01 M, and the solution β was varied over a wide range. The figures show the measured electrical potential difference plotted against the value calculated from the first term alone.[c] Figure 1

[c] J. S. Coleman, Ph.D. Thesis, Department of Chemistry, Massachusetts Institute of Technology (1953); some of the measurements were made by Amy L. Shen.

The Neptonic membranes were prepared by Ionics, Inc., and the Amberplex membranes by Rohm and Haas. We are indebted to both of these companies for supplying us with membranes before they were commercially available. In both cases the membranes had sufficient conductivity and diffusion so that they were used as ribbons (edgewise) rather than as membranes.

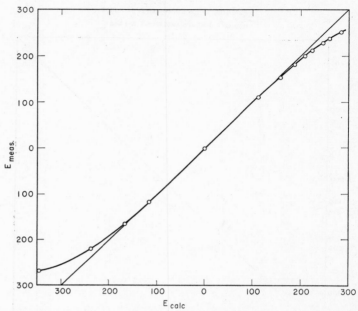

FIG. 2. Potential of ion exchanger electrodes NaCl($m_0 = 0.01$ M) with Nepton CR-51 and ARX-102.

shows hydrochloric acid, from 10^{-5} M to 1 M; Fig. 2 shows sodium chloride, from 10^{-5} M to 3 M. In the middle of the range both show excellent agreement. Both begin to deviate at about 0.1 M. The curves in concentrated solutions are almost superposable. This must be a coincidence for membranes and solutes are both very different. In dilute solutions the deviations of the hydrochloric acid solutions begin only at one-tenth the concentration at which deviations for sodium chloride appear.

Figure 3 shows the measurements for CaCl$_2$ from 10^{-4} M to 1 M. For this cell

$$E\mathfrak{F}/RT = \ln \frac{(a_{Ca}^{1/2} a_{Cl})_\beta}{(a_{Ca}^{1/2} a_{Cl})_\alpha} + \int_\alpha^\beta (t_{ClC} - 2t_{CaA})d \ln a_{Ca}^{1/2} a_{Cl}$$

$$+ \int_\alpha^\beta (t_{wC} - t_{wA})d \ln a_w$$

The deviations at high concentrations are about the same as those for sodium chloride or hydrochloric acid at twice the chloride ion concen-

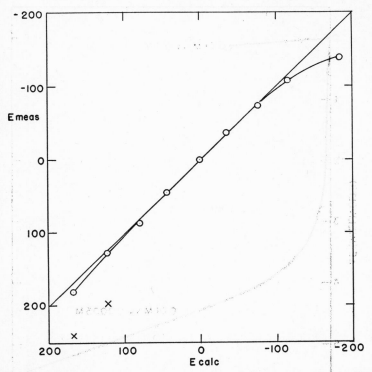

Fig. 3. Potential of ion exchanger electrodes $CaCl_2(m_0 = 0.01\ M)$ with Nepton CR-51 and ARX-102.

tration, or four times the salt concentration. In dilute solutions the deviations give too large a slope.

Figure 4 shows the effect of stopping the flow along one side of the membrane. For both curves, solution α was 0.01 M sodium chloride continuously flowing. The upper curve shows the small effect of stopping flow in a solution β twenty-fold more concentrated than α. The lower curve shows the effect with a solution β one-twentieth as concentrated as α. There is a very rapid drop immediately and a rapid drop for at least half an hour.

BI-IONIC POTENTIALS

The solutions in the cells we use, as in many other arrangements, may contain any number of ion components. The separation of $d\ln a_s$ is still convenient if all the cations at a cation exchanger have the same

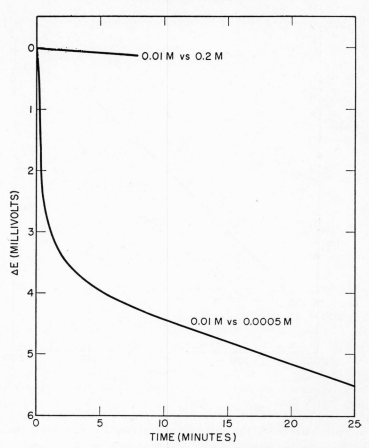

Fig. 4. Change of potential on stopping flow NaCl with Nepton CR-51 and ARX-102.

valence. The correcting terms become more complicated and a new one is added depending upon the variation of $u_i\gamma_S/u_S\gamma_i$ across the membrane; the main term integrates to

$$\ln \sum_i^+ (a_i u_i \gamma_S/u_S \gamma_i)_\beta / \sum_i^+ (a_i u_i \gamma_S/u_S \gamma_i)_\alpha$$

in which $\sum_i^+$ indicates summation over the cations, and S is a standard component. If S is Na^+ and the only other cation is H^+, this becomes

$$\ln[a_{Na} + (u_H\gamma_{Na}/u_{Na}\gamma_H)a_H]_\beta/[a_{Na} + (u_H\gamma_{Na}/u_{Na}\gamma_H)a_H]_\alpha$$

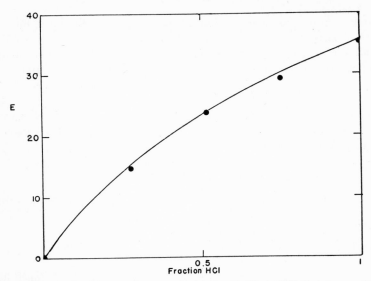

F$_{\text{IG}}$. 5. Potential of ion exchanger electrodes NaCl + HCl (total m = 0.01M) with Nepton CR-51 and ARX-102.

$(RT/\mathcal{F})$ ln $(u_H\gamma_{Na}/u_{Na}\gamma_H)$ is called the bi-ionic potential. It is the potential corresponding to hydrogen ion in β and sodium ion at the same activity in α. Figure 5 shows the potential difference when α is 0.01 M NaCl, and β is a 0.01 M mixture of sodium chloride and hydrochloric acid. The curve corresponds to $u_H\gamma_{Na}/u_{Na}\gamma_H$ = 4. We have also found that $u_{OH}\gamma_{Cl}/u_{Cl}\gamma_{OH}$ = ¼.

INTERPRETATION

A pioneer theoretical study of membranes was made by Michaelis,[14] who considered that the charge on the membrane was due to the adsorption of one kind of ions. Then, almost simultaneously, Teorell[15] and Meyer and Sievers[16] developed the theory of membranes with charges fixed in the lattice. Later workers have attempted to remove the restrictions of ideal solutions from this theory. Goldman[17] and Teorell[18] have replaced the Henderson equation by the generally more appropriate Planck equation within the membrane.

There are two problems. The first is to determine the transference numbers of the various species as functions of the salt concentration, and the second is to learn about the membranes themselves from these relations.

To determine transference numbers from electrical potential measurements, it is convenient to consider separately the deviations from efficiency. We may use the Gibbs-Duhem relation in the aqueous solution of concentration m', in equilibrium with the membrane, to give

$$d \ln a_w = - 0.018 \, m'd \ln a_{Na}a_{Cl}$$

For generality we will now include the transference of the ions of water. Then, with an aqueous solution of sodium chloride and a cation exchanger, we have

$$\sum_i t_i d \ln a_i = d \ln a_{Na} + (t_{Cl} - 0.018 \, m' t_w)d \ln a_{Na}a_{Cl}$$
$$+ (t_H - t_{OH})d \ln a_H$$

and with an anion exchanger

$$\sum_i t_i d \ln a_i = -d \ln a_C + (t_{Na} - 0.018 \, m' t_w)d \ln a_{Na}a_{Cl}$$
$$+ (t_H - t_{OH})d \ln a_H$$

It is obvious that, in the range in which the efficiency is nearly unity, we will find out nothing further about the membrane for we measure only the first term. The deviations in concentrated solutions arise from the second terms. Those in solutions so dilute that the concentration of the ions of water is only one order of magnitude smaller than the concentration of salt may come from the last term. Then only hydrogen ion in the cation exchanger and hydroxyl ion in the anion exchanger need to be considered.

In the cation exchanger, in solutions so dilute that m_{Cl} may be neglected

$$t_H = \frac{u_H m_H}{u_{Na} m_{Na} + u_H m_A} = \frac{u_H \gamma_{Na}}{u_{Na} \gamma_H} \frac{a_H}{a_{Na}} \Big/ \left(1 + \frac{u_H \gamma_{Na}}{u_{Na} \gamma_H} \frac{a_H}{a_{Na}}\right) \cong \frac{u_H \gamma_{Na}}{u_{Na} \gamma_H} \frac{m'_H}{m'_{Na}}$$

The coefficient is the 4 which we determined from the bi-ionic potential. Since the low-concentration deviations are much larger for sodium chloride than for hydrochloric acid, which cannot hydrolyze, it is tempting to attribute this effect to hydrolysis. However, quantitative calculations show that hydrolysis accounts for less than a tenth of the measured effect. We are, in fact, unable to explain the deviations in dilute solutions.

In concentrated solutions the deviations are the sums of two effects: transfer of chloride ion and of water. The water transfer is the more important in the first deviations. In our membranes it is the more important even to high concentrations. Let us suppose however that the two transference numbers can be separately determined. Then

$$t_w = \frac{u_w\, m_w}{u_{Na}\, m_{Na} - u_{Cl} m_{Cl}} = \frac{u_w/0.018}{u_{Na}\, m_{Na} - u_{Cl}\, m_{Cl}}$$

The denominator is proportional to the electrical conductance of the membrane. If u_w is a constant, the electrical conductance is inversely proportional to the transference number of water. The proportionality factor is undetermined. This relation has been verified for Neptonic CR-51 for various concentrations of sodium chloride and for the replacement of sodium by other ions.

For the chloride ion

$$t_{Cl} = \frac{u_{Cl} m_{Cl}}{u_{Na}\, m_{Na} - u_{Cl}\, m_{Cl}}$$

For Michaelis' assumptions, $m_{Cl} = m_{Na}$, so $t_{Cl} = u_{Cl}/(u_{Na} - u_{Cl})$, and any variation in the transference number must arise from variation in the relative mobilities.

With a fixed charge of concentration m_R, $m_{Na} = m_R + m_{Cl}$ and

$$t_{Cl} = \frac{(u_{Cl}/u_{Na}) m_{Cl}/m_R}{1 + (1 - u_{Cl}/u_{Na}) m_{Cl}/m_R}$$

moreover

$$m_{Cl}(m_R + m_{Cl}) = a_{Na}\, a_{Cl}/\gamma_{Na}\, \gamma_{Cl} = a_{\pm}^2/\gamma_{\pm}^2$$

$$\frac{m_{Cl}}{m_R} \left(1 + \frac{m_{Cl}}{m_R} \right) = a_{\pm}^2/\gamma_{\pm}^2\, m_R^2$$

The ratio m_{Cl}/m_R may be eliminated, and the relation between t_{Cl} and $a_{\pm}$ depends upon the two parameters (u_{Cl}/u_{Na}) and $\gamma_{\pm} m_R$. If each of the quantities is constant, the two may be determined from the relation of t_{Cl} to $a_{\pm}$. Then m_{Cl}/m_R may be determined from either equation. This is essentially the method of Teorell and of Meyer and Sievers. They assumed that $\gamma_{\pm}$ is unity and that all the deviations in the electrical potential arise from t_{Cl}, and none from t_w. Measurements of the distribution of sodium chloride between CR51 and water indicate a large variation in $\gamma_{\pm} m_R$, and the conductance measurements indicate a large variation in u_{Cl}/u_{Na} in this membrane.

Let us return to a consideration of the dilute solutions of calcium chlo-

142 GEORGE SCATCHARD

ride shown in Fig. 3. In these experiments the first measurements after conversion of the membranes from sodium form were with 0.01 M solution throughout and then by progressive dilution to 10^{-4} M in β, giving the crosses in the two most dilute solutions. Then the concentration was progressively increased from 0.03 M to 1 M. Since the crosses did not fall on a smooth curve, the measurements at these concentrations were repeated giving the circles.[d] The first measurements seem to have been made with some sodium ion remaining in the exchanger. It was found that very irregular behavior resulted from using cation exchanger membranes containing much sodium ion with calcium chloride solutions. An asymmetry potential of 0.3 volts resulted in one case. We are not sure that we did not cause considerable chemical changes in the membranes in converting from one form to the other, and this effect needs further investigation. It is possible, however, that this phenomenon, which we cannot now explain, may be more important in physiological systems than those others which we understand at least partially.

Conclusion

Our results indicate that the ion exchanger membranes may be very useful as electrodes at which there is no oxidation or reduction and no restriction to special classes of ions, except as to size. They show almost no specificity. Our results also indicate that these membranes may serve as useful models for physiological membranes, since they can be studied in more detail because the measurements of electromotive force and transference may be supplemented by measurements of electrical conductance, Donnan distributions, etc. At present the knowledge of ion exchanger membranes is very limited, and the variety of membranes available is not very great. They can be made in much greater variety, however, and the study of their properties is not very difficult.

REFERENCES

1. Juda, W., Marinsky, J. A., and Rosenberg, N. W., *Ann. Rev. Phys. Chem.* **4**, 373 (1953).
2. Scatchard, G., *J. Am. Chem. Soc.* **75**, 2883 (1953); this paper contains the mathematical treatment of transport through charged membranes.
3. Scatchard, G., and Buehrer, T. F., *J. Am. Chem. Soc.* **53**, 574 (1931).
4. Henderson, P., *Z. physik. Chem.* **59**, 118 (1907); **63**, 325 (1908).
5. Clark, W. M., The Determination of Hydrogen Ions, 3rd ed. Williams & Wilkins Co., Baltimore, 1928.

[d] Similar results with calcium chloride have been noted earlier by M. R. J. Wyllie in a private communication.

6. LAMB, A. B., and LARSON, A. T., *J. Am. Chem. Soc.* **42,** 229 (1920).

7. MacINNES, D. A., and YEH, Y. L., *J. Am. Chem. Soc.* **43,** 2563 (1921).

8. SCATCHARD, G., *J. Am. Chem. Soc.* **47,** 696 (1925).

9. MacINNES, D. A., The Principles of Electrochemistry. Reinhold Publishing Co., New York, 1939.

10. TAYLOR, P. B., *J. Phys. Chem.* **31,** 1478 (1927).

11. GUGGENHEIM, E. A., *J. Am. Chem. Soc.* **52,** 1315 (1930).

12. PLANCK, M., *Ann. Physik u. Chem.* **40,** 561 (1890); see also ref. 9.

13. CUMMING, A. C., and GILCHRIST, E., *Trans. Faraday Soc.* **9,** 174 (1913).

14. MICHAELIS, L., and FUJITA, A., *Biochem. Z.* **158,** 28 (1925) (first paper); MICHAELIS, L., *Kolloid Z.* **10,** 575 (1933) (review).

15. TEORELL, T., *Proc. Soc. Exptl. Biol. Med.* **33,** 282 (1935).

16 MEYER, K. H., and SIEVERS, J. F., *Helv. Chim. Acta* **19,** 649 (1936).

17. GOLDMAN, D. E., *J. Gen. Physiol.* **27,** 37 (1943).

18. TEORELL, T., *Z. Elektrochem.* **55,** 460 (1951).

Electrochemical Studies with Model Membranes[a]

KARL SOLLNER, with SHELDON DRAY, EUGENE GRIM,
and REX NEIHOF

The Fundamental Electrochemistry of Membranes of Porous Character[b]

The purpose of this paper is to review briefly certain phases of the basic electrochemistry of membranes of porous character with particular reference to work which was carried out during the last fifteen years by the senior author and his collaborators, and to present some studies on systems involving such membranes that seem to be of specific interest in connection with the main topic of this symposium.

Membranes of porous character can be arbitrarily classified into two groups: membranes of high porosity, as exemplified by ordinary dialyzing membranes; and "molecular sieve" or "ion sieve" membranes with pores so narrow that different low-molecular-weight species of molecules and ions are retarded to a differential degree or prevented altogether from passing across them.[1, 2] Membranes of both types of porosity are found in living organisms and are therefore of primary biological importance.

Of particular interest is the interplay between such membranes and solutions of electrolytes; that is, the electrolyte or, more correctly, the ion permeability of the membranes; and the concomitant electrical phenomenon: the functional electrochemistry of membranes.

The basic observations in the electrochemistry of membranes refer to their electromotive action, which becomes conspicuous when a membrane separates two solutions which are not identical with respect to their electrolyte content, the simplest case of this nature being the membrane concentration chain.

If a membrane prepared from collodion, silicates, proteins, or almost any other material is interposed between two solutions, e.g. of different concentration of the same electrolyte, an electromotive force arises that is different in most instances from the liquid junction potential which would arise between the same two solutions on free diffusion, that is, in

[a] Received: February 4, 1954.
[b] By Karl Sollner.

the absence of a membrane. The electromotive forces arising in such membrane concentration chains customarily are referred to as "concentration potentials."

The sign and the magnitude of the concentration potential depend on the absolute concentrations, the concentration ratio and the nature of the electrolyte in the two adjacent solutions, and last, but not least, on the nature of the membrane.

With membranes of highest porosity (porous diaphragm), the concentration potentials are in sign and magnitude identical with, or not much different from, the corresponding liquid junction potentials. The concentration potentials deviate more and more from the liquid junction potential if successively denser membranes are used.

The direction of the deviation of the concentration potential from the liquid junction potential is functionally correlated with the electrokinetic charge of the membrane. With electropositive membranes, the dilute solution is more negative, and with electronegative membranes it is more positive than is the case with free diffusion. From this it may be concluded that electronegative membranes are preferentially cation permeable, and electropositive membranes preferentially anion permeable, as is readily confirmed by direct observation. This is the most fundamental fact in the whole electrochemistry of membranes of porous character.

With certain membranes of very low porosity, the concentration potential may reach the magnitude of the potential difference which would arise between the two solutions if they were connected to each other through a pair of reversible electrodes, specific either for the cations or the anions in solution, as the case may be. This "thermodynamically possible maximum value" of the concentration potential represents the upper limit of the possible membrane concentration potentials, the liquid junction potential being the other limit.

The correlation of ionic membrane selectivity and concentration potential in formal electrochemical terms is the basic concept in the electrochemistry of these membranes. It can readily be visualized along the following lines of thought. The virtual transportation of electricity across the membranes is divided between anions and cations in a proportion which is different from the ratio of the *transference numbers* of these ions in free solution.[3] In electronegative membranes, a greater fraction of the current is transported by cations across the membrane than in free solution, and the transference number of the cations in the pores of the membrane (τ_+) is larger than the transference numbers of the cations in free solution t_+ ($\tau_+ > t_+$; and $\tau_- < t_-$). With positive membranes the inverse holds true.

The correlation of membrane concentration potential, ϵ, and the transference numbers, τ_+ and τ_- , may be expressed quantitatively by the use of a modified Nernst equation. For the case of a uni-univalent electrolyte and a negative membrane, it reads

$$\epsilon = \frac{\tau_+ - \tau_-}{\tau_+ + \tau_-} \frac{RT}{F} \ln \frac{a_\pm{}^{(1)}}{a_\pm{}^{(2)}} \tag{1}$$

where $a_\pm{}^{(1)}$ and $a_\pm{}^{(2)}$ are the activities of the electrolyte in the two solutions, the sum of τ_+ and τ_- being unity by definition.

If a membrane is exclusively permeable to cations, the transference number of the cation in the membrane, τ_+ , is unity. It is an electronegative *"membrane of ideal ionic selectivity."* Correspondingly, an electropositive membrane of ideal ionic selectivity is permeable exclusively to anions, τ_- being unity.

The essence of the physical situation which explains the correlation of the electrokinetic charge of membranes and their electromotive action has been clearly understood for a long time. The charges (ions) which form the immovable part of the electric double layer at the pore wall-solution interface are attached firmly to the pore walls; they are unable to move and thus do not participate in ionic processes across the membrane, such as diffusion or the transportation of electricity. The counter ions of the fixed wall charges are dissociated off into the liquid in the pores; they are freely movable and therefore able to participate in ionic processes across the membrane, for instance, in the transportation of electricity, the current being transported by the counter ions of the fixed wall charges and whatever other electrolyte, both anions and cations, may be present in the pores. Thus, the movable counter ions of the fixed wall charges are the vehicle for a larger and larger fraction of all ionic processes across the membranes as membranes of decreasing porosity are considered.

Ions of the same sign of charge as the membrane are prevented by electric repulsion from approaching the spots at the pore walls where the fixed charges of the same sign are located. From sufficiently narrow pores, such ions are virtually excluded. In this case, the membrane acts as a membrane of ideal ionic selectivity; all the possible pathways across it are blocked completely for the ions in solution which carry the same charge as the membrane itself.

With increasing concentration of the outside electrolyte solutions, an increasing quantity of electrolyte, equivalent quantities of anions and cations, enter the pores. The specific influence of the membrane is thereby decreased. This explains why the ionic selectivity of a given membrane decreases if the concentration of the adjacent electrolyte solutions is increased.

Multivalent ions with a charge of the same sign as the membrane are much more restricted in their permeation across the membrane than univalent ions because of their large size and because their high charge prevents them, by electric repulsion, from entering narrow pores which are accessible to univalent ions of the same sign.

At this point, it is necessary to introduce the often neglected but highly important concept of membrane heteroporosity.[4] Any membrane which is available at present for experimental investigation must be assumed to be heteroporous, a mosaic of wider and narrower channels.[5, 6] The pores are the interstices between micelles which are arranged in a more or less random manner. The observable membrane effects are the gross result of the processes which occur across the different pores and arise because of their interaction. Certain of the consequences of heteroporosity were stressed by Collander,[7] Michaelis,[3] and Sollner.[4, 8-10]

For the foregoing considerations it has not been necessary to make any special assumptions as to the specific mechanism by which the charge of the membranes arises. From the formal point of view, it could be considered to be immaterial up to a point, although it is of primary importance for the further conceptual development of the theory, and any attempt at a quantitative theoretical treatment.

Twenty years ago, the nearly universal opinion among colloid and surface chemists was that the charge of the common, inert materials from which membranes were customarily prepared, such as collodion, is due to the adsorption of ions from solution. Although this concept holds true in certain instances, it has been found to be incorrect as far as the interplay between solutions of strong inorganic electrolytes and any common membranes is concerned. The basic electrochemical behavior, even of the presumably inert materials, such as, for instance, collodion, is due to dissociable groups such as carboxyl groups (probably stray and end groups) which form an inherent, integral part of the molecules, or at least a fraction of the molecules, of these substances, and are not shown in the conventional structural formulas. Thus the supposedly inert materials, for instance the commonly used collodion, are, strictly speaking, ionizable substances and therefore, in their electrochemically important properties, essentially identical with materials like clays, zeolites, or protein gels, which are customarily classified as *ion exchangers*. If acidic in character they are cation exchangers; if basic, anion exchangers. The difference between these substances and the more inert materials is only of a quantitative nature. Potentially dissociable groups are distributed much more sparsely on the surfaces of the "inert" materials than on the substances which are commonly referred to as ion exchangers, the latter having a much higher exchange capacity per unit of accessible surface area.[1, 11]

In many instances, membrane materials nearly devoid of electrochemically active, dissociable groups have been "activated" by the adsorption of dissociable substances of high molecular weight, such as proteins. The latter, like other polyelectrolytes, when adsorbed on an inert membrane skeleton, impress on its microstructure the essential property of ion exchangers, a definite and usually fairly high charge density or number of fixed dissociable groups per unit area.

The concept of membranes as ion exchange bodies leads to the presentation of the fixed charge theory of electrical membrane behavior. This theory, on the basis of a clear physical picture, namely the ion exchange character of the membranes, correlates in a quantitative manner the previously outlined facts and ideas concerning membrane selectivity and the concomitant electrical effects.

The physical essence of the fixed charge theory can be stated qualitatively in a simple manner. The rather elaborate mathematical terms in which this theory was originally presented by Teorell[12] and later in much greater detail by Meyer and Sievers[13, 14] are far too complex to be outlined here.

According to the fixed charge theory, the walls of the pores of the membranes carry inherently a definite number of potentially dissociable groups, anionic (acidic) groups, such as carboxyl groups, in the case of electronegative membranes, and cationic (basic) groups, such as amino groups, in the case of electropositive membranes. These dissociable groups are an integral, invariable part of the membrane structure. Their number is independent of the nature or concentration of the adjacent electrolyte solutions. Any current which flows across the membrane is transported by the counter ions of the fixed charged wall groups and whatever other "nonexchange" electrolyte may be present in the pores. The concentration of the latter is determined by a distribution equilibrium, which is somewhat similar to a Donnan equilibrium, that exists between the electrolytic pore structure of the membrane and the adjacent outside electrolyte solution, the fixed wall groups being the "nondiffusible" ions. In a concentration chain, two such distribution equilibria are set up between the two solutions and the two adjacent surface layers of the membrane, with a corresponding concentration drop across the membrane. The concentration potential is considered as the algebraic sum of the two distribution potentials and the liquid junction potential within the pores.

Although based on assumptions which are oversimplified as far as membranes of porous character are concerned, the core of the fixed charge theory is destined to play a dominant role in the further development of the theory. Whether it will be ultimately advisable to split up the observed membrane potential into three parts, two nonoperational distribution potentials (of doubtful meaning) and one diffusion potential, or whether it may not be preferable to consider statistically the probability that individual ions will pass critical spots in a heteroporous structure, cannot yet be decided. The former method of approach has the advantage of being based on rather fully developed concepts, but it will be applicable only after considerable modifications to the actual physical situation which involves microheterogeneous interphases, where the conventional electrochemical concepts of phase boundary potentials, for instance, become blurred. The latter method of approach, namely a consideration of molecular processes occurring at individual spots, might be much closer to the physical facts and conceptually less involved. However, it could not be connected quite as conveniently to prior work in theoretical electrochemistry.[1, 4, 11]

The fixed charge theory implicitly gives directions towards the *preparation of membranes of highest electrochemical activity*. It postulates that, *ceteris paribus*, the electrochemical properties of membranes of porous character will be the more pronounced the greater the number of potentially dissociable groups per unit area on the walls of the pores. This is of great importance because the experimental study of the fundamental electrochemistry of membranes and their use in model studies has been retarded in the past, to a great extent, by the lack of suitable objects for such investigations. Now, however, one can plan systematically for the preparation of membranes which are suitable—tailor made, so to speak—for particular purposes.

The obvious objective was to prepare membranes which would yield the electrical and permeability phenomena under investigation to a very pronounced degree.

The methods of preparation of membranes of highest electrochemical activity have been reviewed recently[2] and need not be repeated in detail here. It is sufficient to note that: membranes of high electrochemical activity, that is, membranes with relatively high charge density (or number of potentially dissociable groups) per unit area, can be prepared from material which carries an adequate number of dissociable groups; an activating material of polyelectrolyte nature may be dissolved in the solution of an electrochemically fairly inert material, such as collodion, from which membranes can be prepared; an inherently inert membrane may be activated by the adsorption of some polyelectrolyte which attaches itself in a virtually irreversible manner to preformed membrane structure; and a membrane prepared from inactive material may be activated by a chemical reaction, for instance, by oxidation, which results in the formation of dissociable groups, for instance, carboxyl groups, on the accessible pore wall of the preformed membrane structure.[15-21]

The electrical properties and the electrochemical behavior of membranes are characterized by a variety of methods which differ according to the degree of porosity. Only some selected aspects of this matter can be touched upon here. The discussion is confined to basic data of particular significance in connection with studies of more specific biological interest which will be presented later.

A rather sensitive and very convenient way to define empirically the electrochemical activity of *membranes of high porosity* is the study of the rate of anomalous osmosis across them. This phenomenon, well known and much investigated by biologists, has been shown by Girard,[22] Bartell,[23] Loeb,[24] and others to be essentially a spontaneous electro-osmosis which occurs when an electrolyte diffuses across a charged membrane. Its theory had been developed several years ago by the author, who based his considerations on the heteroporosity of the membranes.[8-10] The driving force of anomalous osmosis is due to the electrolyte diffusion itself, being functionally related to the dynamic membrane potential. Thus the rate of anomalous osmosis is dependent both on the magnitude of the electrokinetic potential of the membrane and, in a rather complicated manner, on the dynamic membrane potential. It is, therefore, a particularly sensitive indicator of the electrochemical activity of membranes of the dialyzing type. Anomalous osmosis has been used extensively in recent years for the characterization of such membranes,[1, 4, 16, 19, 20, 21, etc.] particularly in view of the great interest which biologists have shown in this phenomenon for many decades.

Space does not permit a review of the details of Loeb's well-known experimental method of studying the transitory, dynamic phenomenon of anomalous osmosis.[1, 20, 21, 24, etc.] Suffice it to say that membrane bags fitted with capillary glass tubes are filled with solutions of various concentrations of different electrolytes and suspended in a beaker filled with distilled water. The pressure rises observed after a standard time, usually 20 min., are noted. The difference between the rise with electrolytes and a nonelectrolyte reference substance is commonly considered as a measure of anomalous osmosis.

Electronegative membranes of high porosity and a degree of electrochemical activity which previously had never been obtained have been prepared by the use of collodion which had been oxidized in bulk;[16] by the dissolution of polyelectrolytes such as polyacrylic acid or sulfonated polystyrene in the collodion solution from which the membranes are prepared;[17, 18] by the adsorption method;[17-19] and by the oxidation of formed collodion membranes.[16, 20, 21]

In Fig. 1 are compared the activities of (A) a membrane prepared from an impure collodion preparation containing a significant quantity of dissociable groups;[1, 16, 20] (B) of a membrane of about the same porosity prepared from pure commercial collodion and nearly devoid of dissociable groups; and (C) of the same membrane after the oxidative production of dissociable acidic groups at the walls of its pores. The abscissas give the concentration of the solution inside the test-tube-shaped membrane immersed in distilled water. The ordinates represent

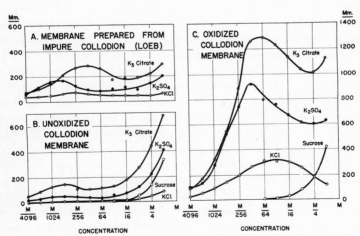

FIG. 1. A comparison of the extent of anomalous osmosis through collodion membranes of about equal porosity but different electrochemical activity. *B* and *C* represent the same membrane specimen before and after activation by oxidation.

the pressure rise (in millimeters of water) observed after 20 min. As can be seen from Figs. 1B and 1C, the behavior of the membranes towards sucrose, a typical nonelectrolyte, is hardly changed by the oxidation.

Highly active electropositive (basic) *membranes of high porosity* have been obtained by the adsorption, on collodion membranes, of protamines, basic proteins with an isoelectric point of about pH 12 and a molecular weight of around 3000.[25] These membranes are extremely stable and maintain their essential characteristics over a wide pH range, about 2.8 to 8.5. Highly porous protamine collodion membranes are the exact analogues to the corresponding electronegative membranes described in the preceding paragraphs.[1, 25]

With *membranes of ion-sieve character*, it was obvious to strive for membranes which would be of virtually ideal ionic selectivity. At the same time, these membranes should allow a fast rate of diffusion of the critical ions across their thickness. In other words, they should be membranes of low resistance. Such membranes would be much more useful for physicochemical experimentation and also for model studies of biological interest. For this type of ion-sieve membranes of highest ionic selectivity and high permeability, the designation "megaperm-selective" or *"permselective" membranes* was suggested, the latter term being now commonly used.[15]

"Permselective" electronegative membranes of highest activity and low resistance have been prepared by a variety of methods. The preparation of the original weak-acid type of these membranes, oxidized collodion membranes, and of the strong-acid type of sulfonated polystyrene collodion-base membranes has been described in detail.[15, 17, 19, 26] These nearly glass-clear membranes have a thickness of the order of 20 to 40 μ, their water content by weight is about 14 to 23 %. The resistance of these membranes, in particular, can be adjusted over a wide range by the proper choice of the experimental conditions; membranes of lower resistance, that is, of greater absolute permeability, have at higher concentrations a somewhat smaller ionic selectivity.

"Permselective" electropositive membranes were first prepared by the adsorption of protamine on one-, two-, or three-layer collodion membranes of high porosity which are later dried under carefully controlled conditions,[27, 28] the method of their preparation being strictly analogous to that of the permselective oxidized collodion membranes.

Ion exchangers of the commercial type, because of their high charge density per unit area and their low inherent porosity, are obviously a suitable material for the preparation of permselective membranes.[2]

Having an exchange capacity of several equivalents per liter, membranes prepared from such material can be expected to have a very low resistance, that is, a very high permeability for the critical ions.

Several groups of investigators have recently taken up this line of work.[29, 30] With one possible exception which gave high selectivity at high concentrations,[29] none of these membranes seems to offer as yet any advantages over the permselective collodion-base membranes described here either for physicochemical investigations or for model studies of biological interest.

The most important property of permselective membranes is their electromotive behavior in concentration chains.

The measurement of the membrane concentration potentials consists of the determination of the electromotive force which arises in the chain, electrolyte c_1 | membrane | electrolyte c_2 , the sign referring to the solution with the concentration c_2 , the more dilute solution. Following an established procedure, the concentration ratio 2:1 was used.[17, 19, 31, 32]

The significance and the physical meaning of membrane concentration potentials, ϵ, can be visualized by reference to its theoretical upper limit, the calculated potential, $E_{\max}$, which would arise if the membrane behaved under a given set of conditions as an ideal machine for the reversible transfer of the critical ion.

The calculations of the theoretically possible maximum values of the concentration potential, $E_{\max}$, are based on well known conventional assumptions concerning the meaning of single ion activities, a topic which cannot be discussed here.[33, 34] The computation of $E_{\max}$ is based on the general equations

$$E_{\max} = \frac{RT}{nF} \ln \frac{a_+^{(1)}}{a_+^{(2)}} \tag{2a}$$

and

$$E_{\max} = -\frac{RT}{nF} \ln \frac{a_-^{(1)}}{a_-^{(2)}} \tag{2b}$$

for negative and positive membranes respectively. $a_+^{(1)}$ and $a_+^{(2)}$ are the activities $c_+^{(1)}\gamma_+^{(1)}$ and $c_+^{(2)}\gamma_+^{(2)}$ of the cations in solutions 1 and 2; $a_-^{(1)}$ and $a_-^{(2)}$, correspondingly, are $c_-^{(1)}\gamma_-^{(1)}$ and $c_-^{(2)}\gamma_-^{(2)}$. In the case of uni-univalent electrolytes, the mean activity coefficients were used ($\gamma_+ = \gamma_\pm$; $\gamma_- = \gamma_\pm$). With the uni-bivalent and bi-univalent electrolytes, potassium sulfate and magnesium chloride, the activity coefficient for the univalent critical ions is calculated on the assumption that their activities are the same as those of the potassium and chloride ions, respectively, in potassium chloride solution of the same ionic strength.

The accuracy of the calculated E_{max} values in the more dilute solutions, depending on the electrolyte used, might be estimated to be of the order of $\pm$ 0.05 to 0.10 mv. With the highest concentrations the error might be appreciably greater.

Table I presents the data for potassium chloride and hydrochloric acid chains obtained with an oxidized collodion membrane and a sulfonated polystyrene collodion-base membrane. The reproducibility of the individual measurements is here better than $\pm$ 0.05 mv, except at the highest concentrations of hydrochloric acid. Analogous data for lithium chloride and potassium sulfate measured ($\pm$ 0.1 mv) across a typical oxidized permselective collodion membrane are presented for easier visualization in Fig. 2. The broken line represents calculated E_{max} values, the circles are experimental points, the concentrations noted in the figure being the lower concentration in each chain.[31, 19]

Table II and Fig. 3 give corresponding data ($\pm$ 0.1 mv) for four electrolytes and a typical permselective protamine collodion membrane.[32]

The deviation of the experimental concentration potential, ϵ, from E_{max} at any given concentration level is a direct measure of the deviation of the membrane from ideality under the conditions of the experiment.

The data of Fig. 2 and of Table I show that the electronegative, acidic membranes attain, in fairly dilute solutions, a very high degree of ionic selectivity—here they act electromotively like virtually reversible electrodes for the critical, potential-determining ion. At higher concentrations they deviate considerably from this ideal. The permselective protamine collodion membranes (Fig. 3 and Table II) have obviously not yet reached the same high degree of perfection as the electronegative permselective membranes.

The differences between different electrolytes and different membranes are in the best agreement with expectation. The details of this problem have been discussed repeatedly elsewhere and may be passed over here.[2, 31, 32]

The resistance of the permselective membranes can be adjusted at will over a wide range upwards from 25 Ω for 1 cm^2 in 0.1 N potassium chloride solution. With the present preparative methods, membranes of smaller resistances are not of the highest degree of ionic selectivity. Some of our best membranes fall in the resistance range (in 0.1 N potassium chloride) of 50–200 Ω-cm^2.[19] The resistance of the membranes, according to the mode of their preparation, varies more or less pronouncedly with the concentration of the solution with which they are equilibrated.[35]

Closely related to the resistance of the membranes is the rate of ion exchange across them. This rate, under standard conditions, is a convenient measure of ionic membrane permeability. It is also important in the use of the membranes in various physicochemical studies.

If an ideally ion-selective membrane separates two solutions of strong electrolytes, only the "critical" ions exchange across the membrane. If a membrane is not ideally ion selective, a "leak" of noncritical ions occurs.

For the determination of the rates of ion exchange and the leak of noncritical ions, the test-tube-shaped permselective membranes (active area about 50 cm^2) were filled with 25 ml of solution of one electrolyte and immersed in a larger test tube containing 25 ml of solution, at the same concentration, of some other electrolyte with a different cation and a different anion. Both solutions were stirred, and samples were withdrawn for analyses after measured periods. Representative results obtained with a sulfonated polystyrene collodion-base membrane of a resistance of about 80 Ω-cm^2 in 0.1 N potassium chloride are given in Table III; the last column of this table gives the ratio of the initial rate of movement of critical ions to that of the noncritical ions.[19] This ratio is a direct measure of the degree of ionic selectivity of the membrane under the conditions of the experiment; its reciprocal may be defined as the "leak" of noncritical ions.

The selectivity of the membranes in the presence of divalent noncritical ions is several orders of magnitude higher, and thus their leak is several orders of magnitude lower than with the univalent noncritical ions.[19]

The water permeability of the permselective membranes is low. From the practical point of view it is negligible in many instances.[15, 19] For example, a solution of 0.2 M sucrose was placed inside a membrane with a resistance of about 150 Ω-cm^2 in 0.1 N potassium chloride solution; the rate of water movement under these conditions amounted only to 0.0001 ml/cm^2 of membrane area per hour.[15]

The permselective collodion-base membranes have a degree of ionic selectivity which is higher by several orders of magnitude than any previously available membranes of high ionic selectivity.[1, 15] Equally important, their resistance per unit area is several orders of magnitude

TABLE I

CONCENTRATION POTENTIALS ($c_1:c_2 = 2:1$) OF TWO ELECTROLYTES ACROSS A
TYPICAL PERMSELECTIVE OXIDIZED COLLODION MEMBRANE AND A REPRESEN-
TATIVE PERMSELECTIVE SULFONATED POLYSTYRENE COLLODION-BASE MEM-
BRANE ($T = 25.00 \pm 0.05°$ C)

1	2	3	4	5	6	7
	Potassium chloride			Hydrochloric acid		
Concentration of electrolyte solutions $c_1:c_2$	Theoretical maximum E_{max}	Concentration potential, ϵ		Theoretical maximum E_{max}	Concentration potential, ϵ	
		Oxidized collodion membrane	Sulfonated polystyrene collodion membrane		Oxidized collodion membrane	Sulfonated polystyrene collodion membrane
(equiv./liter)	(mv)	(mv)	(mv)	(mv)	(mv)	(mv)
0.002/0.001	17.45	17.20	17.25	17.45	17.45	17.45
0.004/0.002	17.31	17.04	17.19	17.34	17.26	17.26
0.01/0.005	17.10	16.95	16.97	17.15	17.02	17.08
0.02/0.01	16.86	16.74	16.74	16.97	16.66	16.88
0.04/0.02	16.63	16.47	16.52	16.84	16.04	—
0.1/0.05	16.30	15.80	16.10	16.76	15.31	16.59
0.2/0.1	16.11	15.09	15.74	16.87	15.33	—
0.4/0.2	15.95	13.90	15.40	17.49	15.66	17.37
1.0/0.5	16.32	10.93	14.58	19.89	17.7	19.1
2.0/1.0	17.34	8.01	13.86	24.39	22.0	23.2

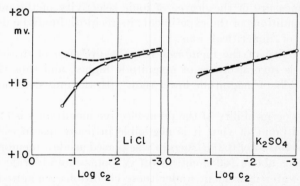

FIG. 2. Concentration potentials $c_1:c_2 = 2:1$ across a typical permselective
oxidized collodion membrane.

lower. Ionic processes across permselective membranes occur therefore
at rates which are several orders of magnitude greater than those ob-
tainable with the older types of membranes. The permselective membranes thus provide a new and unique tool for a great variety of studies

TABLE II

CONCENTRATION POTENTIALS ($c_1:c_2 = 2:1$) OF TWO ELECTROLYTES ACROSS A
TYPICAL PERMSELECTIVE PROTAMINE COLLODION MEMBRANE
($T = 25.00 \pm 0.05°$ C)

Concentration of electrolyte solutions $c_1:c_2$	Potassium chloride		Potassium iodate	
	Theoretical maximum E_{max}	Concentration potential ϵ	Theoretical maximum E_{max}	Concentration potential ϵ
(equiv./liter)	(mv)	(mv)	(mv)	(mv)
0.002/0.001	−17.5	−16.7	−17.5	−16.2
0.004/0.002	−17.3	−16.8	−17.3	−16.2
0.01/0.005	−17.1	−16.5	−16.9	−16.1
0.02/0.01	−16.9	−16.5	−16.7	−16.0
0.04/0.02	−16.6	−16.2	−16.1	−14.9
0.1/0.05	−16.3	−15.5	−15.1	−12.4
0.2/0.1	−16.1	−14.8	−14.1	−10.2
0.4/0.2	−16.0	−13.5	—	—

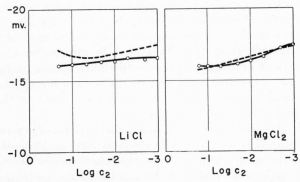

FIG. 3. Concentration potentials $c_1:c_2 = 2:1$ across a typical permselective protamine collodion membrane.

on the fundamental and applied electrochemistry of membranes and membrane systems.

MEMBRANES OF HIGH ELECTROCHEMICAL ACTIVITY IN PHYSICOCHEMICAL AND MODEL STUDIES OF BIOLOGICAL INTEREST[c]

The membranes described in the preceding pages, both the highly porous and the permselective ones, which show all characteristic electrochemical properties in an exaggerated manner, lend themselves readily

[c] By Sheldon Dray, Eugene Grim, Rex Neihof, and Karl Sollner.

TABLE III

The Rates of Exchange of Critical and Noncritical Ions Across a Typical
Permselective Sulfonated Polystyrene Collodion-Base Membrane at
Various Concentration Levels in the System, $NH_4Cl(c_1) || KNO_3(c_1)$;
$(T = 25.0°\,C)$ [From R. Neihof[19]]

1	2	3	4
Concentration (c_1) (equiv./liter)	Initial rate of movement of NH_4^+ (μequiv./hr-cm²)	Initial rate of movement of Cl^- (μequiv./hr-cm²)	Ratio of initial rates of movement of NH_4^+ to Cl^-
0.01	9.8	0.000147	67,000
0.02	9.8	0.00054	18,100
0.05	10.2	0.00223	4,600
0.10	11.5	0.0090	1,280
0.20	12.3	0.0277	440
0.50	14.5	0.143	101
1.00	17.0	0.44	39
2.00	19.0	1.34	14.2

to a great variety of studies of biological interest. Some of our investigations in this direction are reviewed in the following pages.

Anomalous osmosis across membranes of significant electrolyte permeability—of the dialyzing type—has been of interest to physiologists
since the days of Dutrochet[36] because this phenomenon seems to offer
some basis for an explanation of the translocation of liquids across living
membranes which seem to defy any explanation based on the concept
of the normal Pfeffer-van't Hoff osmosis.[37-41]

Although the basic physicochemical mechanism of anomalous osmosis, as outlined before, is now reasonably well understood,[8-10,29] the
possible physiological significance of this phenomenon is still contro-
versial. The main shortcoming of the available data, certainly as far as
mammalian physiology is concerned, is that they do not demonstrate
clearly that anomalous osmosis can occur to a significant extent under
conditions which are at least superficially similar to those existing
in vivo. The published data refer almost exclusively to the rates of pressure rise in systems in which a membrane separates the solution of an
electrolyte from distilled water (or an extremely dilute solution of the
same electrolyte), a situation which is not likely to be akin to anything
found in mammalian physiology. Furthermore, the magnitude which
is of primary physiological interest in the majority of instances is probably not the conventionally measured pressure rise in such systems but
the rate at which liquid is transported by anomalous osmosis across a
membrane against relatively small pressures. Virtually no data are

available which demonstrate that anomalous osmosis occurs at a significant rate under conditions of prime interest in mammalian physiology, namely, that a membrane separates two solutions of different composition which are of physiologically significant concentration.

Because anomalous osmosis, as discussed previously, is an electrokinetic phenomenon, several prominent investigators (Loeb,[42] Freundlich,[43] Höber,[39] and, quite recently, Teorell[44]) have doubted that anomalous osmosis can occur at concentrations above approximately 0.05 M; they are inclined to believe that osmotic effects observed at higher concentrations are due solely to normal osmosis.

Grim and Sollner[45, 46] have studied certain aspects of these questions in some detail. The first problem was to find a method which permits a clear distinction between the contribution of normal osmosis and the contribution of anomalous osmosis towards the over-all, observed effect. Although the data of Loeb,[24, 42] of Bartell,[23] and of others indicate that the contribution of normal osmosis is relatively small in the region of low concentrations in which these investigators were primarily interested, this is not the case at the higher concentrations which are of physiological significance. Customarily it is assumed that the extent of normal osmosis across a given membrane at a given concentration can be determined with solutions of the same concentration of some arbitrarily chosen nonelectrolyte. This, however, is not the case; nonelectrolytes of different molecular weight differ greatly in their osmotic efficacy because of the difference in permeability of a membrane for various solutes. Thus, it is inadvisable to estimate the magnitude of normal osmotic effects by the use of an arbitrarily chosen nonelectrolytic reference solute.[45, 46]

The solution of this problem lies in the use of membranes which can be brought in a reversible manner and without changes in geometrical structure into a charged state, positive or negative as the case may be, and into the uncharged, isoelectric state.[45, 46] With the membranes in the charged state, anomalous osmosis can occur; the observed, gross osmotic effect is composed of a normal and an abnormal component. With the membrane in the isoelectric state, anomalous osmosis does not occur; here the total observed osmotic effect is due to normal osmosis. Thus, the difference, Δ, in the effects with the membrane in the charged state and with the membrane in the isoelectric state is a measure of the true anomalous osmosis. Amphoteric, essentially nonswelling membranes are the tool of choice for an investigation along these lines.

We have used preferentially oxyhemoglobin-collodion membranes which are prepared, according to the method of Loeb, by the adsorption of hemoglobin on collodion membranes of suitably high porosity. These membranes have an isoelectric point near pH 6.75 at which they do not show any net charge; they can be readily charged positively or negatively by adjusting the pH of the solutions with which they are in contact. pH 4 and pH 10 were chosen in our work.[45, 46]

The experiments on osmotic transport rates were carried out with bag-shaped membranes tied to glass rings which were fitted with a rubber stopper carrying a cut-off part of a burette. The membrane was filled with one solution and immersed in a beaker containing the other solution. The liquid level of the inside solution was a few centimeters higher than the outside solution, back filtration at this pressure being negligible. Both solutions were stirred. After the membrane had reached a satisfactory quasi-stationary state in preliminary runs, the initial rates of liquid movement were determined in experiments of 5 min. duration with fresh portions of the two solutions. These initial transport rates are expressed as milliliters per 100 cm² of membrane area per hour.

Figure 4 demonstrates how the outlined method permits the separation of the anomalous osmotic effect from the over-all observed liquid movement, both in the case of anomalous positive and anomalous negative osmosis, a minus sign indicating a movement of liquid into the more dilute solution. The osmolar concentration given in the graph refers to the inside solution which has twice the concentration of the outside solution. The heavy solid line curves give the difference, Δ, of the effects observed in the charged and in the isoelectric state and thus represents the true anomalous osmotic component of the observed effect.

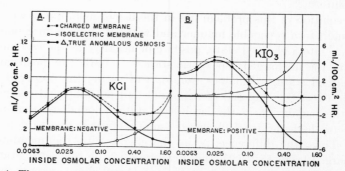

FIG. 4. The rates of transportation of liquid through an oxyhemoglobin collodion membrane in the charged and in the isoelectric state, and the rates of true anomalous osmosis. $c_{in}:c_{out} = 2:1$.

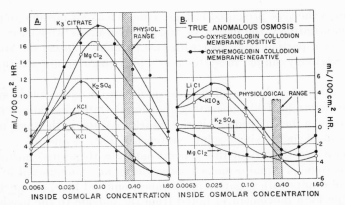

FIG. 5. The rates of transportation of liquid by true anomalous osmosis across an oxyhemoglobin collodion membrane in the charged state. c_{in}:c_{out} = 2:1. A: Systems in which the theory predicts anomalous positive osmosis only. B: Systems in which the theory predicts anomalous positive osmosis for low concentrations, and anomalous negative osmosis for higher concentrations.

Figure 5 presents the rates of liquid transport by true anomalous osmosis through an oxyhemoglobin membrane arrived at in this manner for several systems giving anomalous positive as well as anomalous negative osmosis. The data in this figure are also plotted on an osmolar, not on a molar basis, the concentration range of particular interest in mammalian physiology being indicated by cross-hatching.

Figures 4 and 5 prove that, for single-solute, low-concentration-ratio systems, anomalous osmosis can occur at a rather conspicuous rate at physiological concentration levels. Thus the main question as to the possible feasibility of the occurrence of this phenomenon in mammalian organisms is answered in the affirmative.

Of greater specific interest for mammalian physiology, however, than the just discussed single-solute systems with 2:1 concentration ratios are systems containing more than one solute, particularly systems of this nature in which two solutions of identical over-all concentration (in the physiological range) are separated by the membrane.

Anomalous osmosis in systems with more than one solute has not been considered in the literature from a theoretical viewpoint.[45, 46] Space does not permit a discussion of this rather involved matter in any detail. Suffice it to say that such systems can be considered theoretically on the same basis as single-solute systems according to the general treatment of Sollner.[8-10, 39]

Data of the type presented in Figs. 4 and 5 make it possible to predict semiquantitatively the extent of anomalous osmosis which can be expected in a particular system with two or more solutes, the situation being relatively simple in systems in which single-solute solutions are used.

The rates of true anomalous osmosis in two-or-more-solute systems can be determined by measuring the liquid transport rates with the membrane in the charged and in the isoelectric state, in the same manner as was done in the single-solute systems of Figs. 4 and 5.

Several experiments of this general nature with positive membranes and solutions of equal osmolar concentration are summarized in Table IV. The results with negative membranes, omitted here, are analogous. In Table IV a movement of liquid from the outside to the inside solution is indicated by a plus sign; a movement in the opposite direction by a minus sign.

Table IV shows that true anomalous osmosis occurs at a very considerable rate in systems with more than one solute. With iso-osmotic,

TABLE IV

REPRESENTATIVE RATES OF TRANSPORTATION OF LIQUID AND OF TRUE ANOMALOUS OSMOSIS ACROSS AN OXYHEMOGLOBIN COLLODION MEMBRANE IN THE ELECTROPOSITIVE AND IN THE ISOELECTRIC STATE

Inside solution		Outside solution		Rates of transport of liquid		
				Membrane		Δ True anomalous osmosis ($ml/100$ cm^2-hr)
Solute	Concentration (osmolarity)	Solute	Concentration (osmolarity)	Charged ($ml/100$ cm^2-hr)	Isoelectric ($ml/100$ cm^2-hr)	
KCl	0.40	Glucose	0.40	+13.2	−7.0	+20.2
$MgCl_2$	0.20	Glucose	0.20	+70.0	+2.2	+67.8
$MgCl_2$	0.40	Glucose	0.40	+53.1	+1.7	+51.4
K_2SO_4	0.40	Glucose	0.40	−16.2	+0.8	−17.0
$MgCl_2$	0.40	KCl	0.40	+17.3	+3.4	+13.9
$MgCl_2$	0.40	KIO_3	0.40	+31.2	+1.4	+29.8
$MgCl_2$	0.40	K_2SO_4	0.40	+15.4	−1.8	+17.2
$MgCl_2$ + glucose	0.20 0.20	Glucose	0.40	+58.5	+0.2	+58.3
$MgCl_2$ + KCl	0.20 0.20	KCl	0.40	+8.7	0.0	+8.7
$MgCl_2$ + KCl	0.20 0.20	K_2SO_4 + KIO_3	0.20 0.20	+12.1	−3.7	+15.8

0.40-osmolar solutions of electrolytes, the true anomalous osmotic liquid transport rates found are in the range of 8 to 30 ml/100 cm²-hr. If one of the solutes is a nonelectrolyte these rates are about twice as high.

The potential physiological significance of the data on transport rates given in Table IV can be seen from the fact that they are, for instance, several times as high as the highest reported rates of intestinal absorption. They are of the same order of magnitude and in some cases considerably higher than the unidirectional rates of fluid movement which have been postulated as the physical basis of intestinal absorption.[47] However, it must be emphasized that the foregoing data do not prove in any way that anomalous osmosis actually is an important mechanism in the translocation of liquid in the mammalian organism; it only furnishes the proof that such a process is a possibility from the strictly physicochemical point of view. Further work, particularly on the energetic efficiency of anomalous osmosis, seems highly desirable. At this point the matter rests for the time being.

The use of *permselective membranes in preparative chemistry* (and in industrial operations) for the purpose of the exchange, between solutions, of ions (including the exchange of the ions of water) is beginning to be explored.[2] For example, the salts of pH-sensitive organic acids may be converted into the free acid either by membrane hydrolysis or by dialytic ion exchange against an acid without ever coming into contact with the latter, as occurs in precipitation reactions. It might prove to be of practical significance that ion exchange operations can be effected between phases of different water activity without a disturbing extent of osmotic movement of solvent.

Nonelectrolytes of medium and even of low molecular weight might be separated from electrolytes by the simultaneous use of both electropositive and electronegative membranes in diffusion-dialysis; or ion exchange dialysis against outside solutions of an acid and a base, respectively, might be employed for the same purpose in a three-cell outfit; or, most promising, electrodialysis might be used to accelerate the speed of electrolyte removal from the middle cell.[2] This latter possibility has recently attracted considerable industrial and popular interest. The use of permselective membranes of necessity eliminates various complications in electrodialysis, which are too involved to be taken up here, such as the well-known changes in H^+ and OH^- ion concentrations at the membranes.[48, 49] The movement to the middle cell of anions from the cathode compartment and of cations from the anode compartment can be eliminated by the use of permselective membranes; outside solutions of considerable conductance thus become feasible. Their use would greatly increase the efficiency of the process. Thus, the use of permselective membranes can, it is hoped, make electrodialysis a more attractive preparative method.

The separation of bivalent and univalent ions of the same sign of charge by means of permselective membranes of carefully adjusted porosity seems to be a problem of some interest.

The theoretical investigation of the *Gibbs-Donnan membrane equilibrium* has in the past outrun its experimental study. Extensive theoretical discussions of Gibbs-Donnan membrane equilibria can be found in the literature; their experimental study, however, was long confined to systems containing colloidal or semicolloidal ions as nondiffusible ions, and to a few systems in which the ferrocyanide ion acted as the nondiffusible ion in conjunction with a copper-ferrocyanide membrane.[50-52] Except for this latter case, Donnan equilibria involving only strong inorganic electrolytes in which relatively small ions act as "nondiffusible" ions could not be studied; suitable membranes for such investigations were nonexistent. Now, however, the permselective membranes lend themselves admirably to this purpose, as is shown in a preliminary series of experiments.[53]

In order to demonstrate the existence of a membrane equilibrium across a certain membrane it is only necessary to test experimentally the classical Donnan equations. For the case of two uni-univalent electrolytes A^+X^- and B^+X^- and a membrane permeable for the cations A^+ and B^+, and impermeable for the anion X^- (such as the permselective collodion membranes), the Donnan equation, written in a convenient manner, reads

$$\frac{a_{A^+}^{(1)}}{a_{B^+}^{(1)}} = \frac{a_{A^+}^{(2)}}{a_{B^+}^{(2)}} \tag{3}$$

where a is the activity of the respective ions in solutions 1 and 2. If the experimental system is selected so that the ions A^+ and B^+ have the same activities in solutions of the same ionic strength, then the ratios of the activity coefficients will be unity, and one may use concentrations, c, instead of activities; equation (3) becomes the expression

$$\frac{c_{A^+}^{(1)}}{c_{B^+}^{(1)}} = \frac{c_{A^+}^{(2)}}{c_{B^+}^{(2)}} \tag{4}$$

The theoretically predicted equilibrium conditions hold true if the ratio of the analytical concentrations of the two ions on both sides of the membrane, as determined by analytical procedures, is identical (and if the same final condition is reached independent of the original distribution of the diffusible ions between the two solutions).

Equation (4) was tested with the same experimental arrangement as described previously for the studies on the rate of exchange of ions across membranes. Osmotic equilibration can be established by the addition of the proper amount of a nondiffusible nonelectrolyte (sucrose) to the more dilute solution, although this is not always necessary from the experimental point of view on account of the low water permeability of the permselective membranes which has been referred to.

The Donnan membrane equilibrium was established in the various systems in 3 to 24 hours according to the nature (resistance) of the membrane used. The systems did not significantly change further for periods of several days; thereafter a slight "leak" of noncritical ions became noticeable in many instances.

The results of three typical experiments on membrane equilibria across permselective collodion membranes are given in Table V. The

TABLE V

GIBBS-DONNAN EQUILIBRIA ACROSS PERMSELECTIVE COLLODION MEMBRANES WHICH INVOLVE ONLY STRONG INORGANIC ELECTROLYTES (THE ANIONS ARE THE NONDIFFUSIBLE IONS)

Ratio of volumes of solution in to solution out	Solute	Original state (milli-moles/liter)		Equilibrium state				Concentration ratio $\frac{In}{Out}$	
				Experimental (milli-moles/liter)		Calculated (milli-moles/liter)			
		In	Out	In	Out	In	Out	Experimental	Calculated
1:1	NH_4^+	20.0	10.0	22.4	7.5	22.5	7.5	2.99 ± 0.05	3.00
	K^+	10.0	—	7.4	2.4	7.5	2.5	3.08 ± 0.10	3.00
	Cl^-	30.0	10.0	30.0	10.2	30.0	10.0	2.94 ± 0.05	3.00
	Sucrose	—	33	—	(33)	—	(33)	—	—
1:1	NH_4^+	30.0	—	22.4	7.5	22.5	7.5	2.99 ± 0.05	3.00
	K^+	—	10.0	7.5	2.5	7.5	2.5	3.00 ± 0.10	3.00
	Cl^-	30.0	10.0	29.8	10.1	30.0	10.0	2.95 ± 0.05	3.00
	Sucrose	—	33	—	(33)	—	(33)	—	—
1:10	NH_4^+	50.2	2.51	37.4	3.79	37.5	3.78	9.9 ± 0.3	9.9
	K^+	—	2.56	12.0	1.27	12.7	1.29	9.4 ± 0.4	9.9
	$C_2O_4^-$	25.1	2.54	24.7	2.53	25.1	2.54	9.8 ± 0.2	9.9
	Sucrose	—	39	—	(39)	—	(39)	—	—

ratio of the activity coefficients of the K^+ and NH_4^+ salts used in the pairs of solutions given in this table are nearly identical.

Preliminary tests have shown that protamine-collodion membranes are also usable for Donnan experiments.

The significance for the pure physical chemistry of electrolyte solutions, as well as for the study of colloidal systems, of the possibility of the experimental study of membrane equilibria which may involve almost any desired combination of uni-univalent and many combinations of uni-multivalent strong electrolytes hardly requires any emphasis. Work along these lines, currently under way, will become increasingly fruitful as it will be extended in the direction of more and more concentrated electrolyte solutions as membranes with a greater range of virtually ideal ionic selectivity become available.[54]

Of considerable scientific and practical interest is the use of *permselective membranes as "membrane electrodes,"* which was demonstrated ten years ago.[55, 56]

The potential usefulness of membrane electrodes was first recognized by Haber[57] after Nernst and Riesenfeld[58] had shown that any interphase (membrane), which in a concentration chain selectively allows the reversible transfer of only a single ion species from the one solution to the other, gives rise to a potential and acts electromotively in a manner strictly analogous to a conventional reversible electrode for this ion.

The general theory of membrane electrodes has been discussed in some detail by Haber and collaborators,[57] Horowitz,[59] Tendeloo,[60] and Marshall,[61] and most recently by Scatchard,[62] and therefore need not be reiterated here.

For many years the only membrane electrode of practical usefulness was the glass electrode until Marshall and collaborators succeeded in the preparation of clay membranes which are useful in the determination of the activities of univalent, and in some instances also of bivalent, cations.[61]

A detailed discussion of Marshall's pioneering work in this field is outside the scope of this review, since he now seems to consider his membranes rather as solid electrolyte phases than as membranes of porous character as the term is used in this article.

Permselective membranes, by virtue of their ability to act electromotively in the presence of a single species of critical ions like specific reversible electrodes, may be used for the electrometric determination of ion activities in such solutions. By their use it becomes possible to determine (with the restriction indicated) the activities of many ions for which specific reversible electrodes do not exist, as is the case with many anions, F^-, NO_3^-, acetate, ClO_3^-, ClO_4^-, IO_3^- etc., or where specific reversible electrodes of the conventional type involve considerable experimental difficulties, as is the case with the alkali and alkaline earth cations, Li^+, Na^+, K^+, Rb^+, Cs^+, Mg^{++}, Ca^{++}, etc., and with NH_4^+.[55, 56] For cation determinations, the strong-acid type sulfonated polystyrene collodion membranes[18, 19] will be preferable in the future to the oxidized collodion membranes originally used.

The determination of ion activities by means of the permselective "membrane electrodes" may be made in various ways. The potential difference which arises between a known solution on the one side of the membrane and the solution of unknown concentration on the other side of the membrane may be evaluated on the basis of some calculated standard curve. Or better, it may be compared to an empirical curve determined in advance for a specific membrane. A third method consists of an electrometric titration: the membrane separates the solution of unknown concentration from water, to which electrolyte solution of known higher concentration is added stepwise; thereby the potential difference is diminished stepwise, and finally it is reversed. Zero potential difference indicates that the activity of the critical ion is the same on both sides of the membrane. The zero point is obtained conveniently and with considerable accuracy by plotting potential-versus-concentration data. The titration method makes it possible to minimize the uncertainties of the asymmetry of the liquid junction potentials arising from the use of nonspecific (e.g., calomel) electrodes. It also is less sensitive towards slight "leaks" of the membrane than are the two other methods. With membranes which are already saturated with the critical ions under investigation, activity determinations can be made within a few minutes. Results with an error of less than $\pm 1\%$ may now be obtained routinely in wide concentration ranges. This method is readily applicable on the semimicrochemical and microchemical level.[55, 56]

The variety of ions, the activity of which can be determined by means of the permselective collodion-base and similar membranes, has not been explored; the examples mentioned before by no means circumscribe the range of their usefulness. Generally speaking, the determination of the activities of all critical ions which form highly dissociated surface compounds with the fixed wall groups can be expected to fall within the range of the method.

The concentration range within which the membranes described in this paper can be used as membrane electrodes has likewise not been explored fully; it depends considerably upon the accuracy which is desired. At higher concentrations where the membranes are significantly leaky, the nature of the noncritical ion in the two solutions becomes gradually more significant. However, it can be stated that the methods of empirical calibration curves and titration through zero, judiciously applied, permit the performance of fairly accurate determinations, at least up to concentrations of several tenths normal, where other factors such as the asymmetry of the liquid junction potentials begin to play a significant role.

It is obvious that any exchange-resin type of membranes with an adequate electromotive response may in principle be used as membrane electrodes. Their relative merits have to be decided on the basis of practical experimental considerations.

The obvious usefulness of membrane electrodes in protein chemistry, for instance, in connection with the problems of ion binding is borne out by the pioneering work of Carr in this direction.[63, 64]

The experimental study of Donnan equilibria involving only the ions of strong inorganic electrolytes by means of the permselective membranes and the use of the latter as membrane electrodes has furnished a lead to a theoretically fairly satisfactory solution of an old and vexing electrochemical problem.[65]

Heretofore, the *determination of the activities of several coexisting species of ions of the same sign* in solution could be carried out unequivocally only if specific electrodes, which are lacking for many common ions, could be used. The numerous attempts to overcome this difficulty indirectly, e.g., by "compensation dialysis," were only indifferently successful until Marshall[61] devised an ingenious method, to be discussed below, which in certain instances makes possible the solution of this problem in a roundabout manner. The Gibbs-Donnan membrane equilibrium principle, however, permits a direct and general solution of this problem, restricted neither by the lack of specific electrodes nor by the necessity of having available membranes of specific selectivity for different critical ions. It is based on a consideration of the ion distribution under equilibrium condition *and* of the concomitant membrane potential.

A solution 1 contains the anions R^- and NO_3^-, and the cations K^+, Na^+, and NH_4^+, the activities of which, $a_{K^+}^{(1)}$, $a_{Na^+}^{(1)}$, and $a_{NH_4^+}^{(1)}$. have to be determined. A permselective membrane permeable to all cations and impermeable to all anions separates solution 1 from a KCl solution of known concentration. Solution 2, in principle, should be iso-osmotic with 1; if required by the experimental conditions, it may be made iso-osmotic by the addition of nondiffusible nonelectrolyte. The volume of solution 1 is made much larger than that of 2 so that the composition of 1 is not changed significantly after equilibration with solution 2.

After the system is equilibrated, the membrane potential ϵ is measured using calomel electrodes, and solution 2 is analyzed. The final state of the system is

$$[K^+]_1[Na^+]_1[NH_4^+]_1[R^-]_1[NO_3^-]_1 \parallel [K^+]_2[Na^+]_2[NH_4^+]_2[Cl^-]_2$$

The activities in solution 2 of the cations, $a_{K^+}{}^{(2)}$, $a_{Na^+}{}^{(2)}$, and $a_{NH_4^+}{}^{(2)}$, are calculated from the known analytical concentrations according to the Debye-Hückel theory.

The Gibbs-Donnan theorem postulates for the ion distribution

$$\frac{a_{K^+}{}^{(1)}}{a_{K^+}{}^{(2)}} = \frac{a_{Na^+}{}^{(1)}}{a_{Na^+}{}^{(2)}} = \frac{a_{NH_4^+}{}^{(1)}}{a_{NH_4^+}{}^{(2)}} \tag{5}$$

and for the membrane potential

$$\epsilon = \frac{RT}{F} \ln \frac{a_{K^+}{}^{(1)}}{a_{K^+}{}^{(2)}} = \frac{RT}{F} \ln \frac{a_{Na^+}{}^{(1)}}{a_{Na^+}{}^{(2)}} = \frac{RT}{F} \ln \frac{a_{NH_4^+}{}^{(1)}}{a_{NH_4^+}{}^{(2)}} \tag{6}$$

The unknown activities in solution 1 of the cations, $a_{K^+}{}^{(1)}$, $a_{Na^+}{}^{(1)}$, and $a_{NH_4^+}{}^{(1)}$, can be evaluated from equation (6). The accuracy of this method is limited, like most other practical electrometric measurements, by the uncertainties inherent in the use of salt bridges.

This method is, of course, not restricted to the simple conditions illustrated here, but it may be extended to more involved ionic systems. It will furnish considerable help in the solution of numerous problems in colloid chemistry, physiology, and biochemistry.

The heterogeneities which can be found in real membranes are by no means confined to differences in pore size, or charge density and distribution, or a combination of these factors. Layered membranes and *"mosaic" membranes* composed of parts varying in other respects must likewise be considered. A convenient starting point in this field is the study of the simplest possible mosaic membranes, namely membranes composed of parts which are strictly anion selective and other parts which are strictly cation selective. A quantitative theory of the electrolyte permeability of this latter type of membrane outlined more than twenty years ago by one of us[66] could more recently be tested, owing

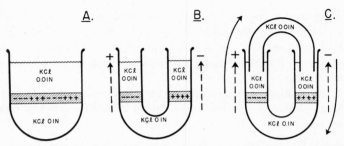

FIG. 6. Pictorial development of the theory of electrolyte permeability of mosaic membranes which are composed of ideally anion selective and ideally cation selective parts. *A*: Mosaic membrane with adjacent cation selective and anion selective parts. *B*: Spatial and electrical separation of the cation selective and anion selective parts of the membranes. *C*: The spatially separated cation selective and anion selective parts joined electrically by a bridge of solution in an all-electrolytic circuit.

to the availability of the permselective collodion and protamine collodion membranes.

The theory of the electrolyte permeability of mosaic membranes which are composed of ideally anion-permeable and cation-permeable parts is most easily developed by reference to a sequence of line drawings.[66]

Figure 6A illustrates schematically a system in which a mosaic membrane of this type separates a lower compartment (of invariable volume) from an upper compartment, the striated structure in the figure indicating the membrane. The electronegative, cation-permeable (anion-impermeable) parts of the membrane are indicated by minus signs, and the electropositive, anion-permeable (cation-impermeable) parts by plus signs. The lower compartment is assumed to be filled with 0.1 N potassium chloride solution and the upper compartment with 0.01 N solution of the same electrolyte.

Contrary to certain ideas which are reviewed in Höber's book,[39] it was postulated that such membranes must permit the penetration of electrolytes from the lower compartment to the upper one. Cations move through the electronegative parts of the membrane and anions through the electropositive parts, neutralizing each other electrically. Thus a continuous movement of the electrolyte occurs across the membrane and does not cease until equilibrium between the two compartments is established.

In formulating this qualitative concept in a manner which is susceptible to a quantitative test it is necessary to consider a system in which the cation-permeable and anion-permeable parts are separated from each other. Figure 6B shows a U-tube containing in its left arm an electronegative (cation-permeable) and in its right arm an electropositive (anion-permeable) membrane, both membranes being assumed to be of an ideal degree of ionic selectivity. The lower part of the system (having an invariable volume) is filled with 0.1 N potassium chloride solution, while the two separate compartments above the membranes contain 0.01 N solution of the same electrolyte. The only processes, according to the premises, which can occur in this system consist of the establishment of static membrane potentials (concentration potentials) across the two membranes and the establishment of a hydrostatic pressure in the lower compartment, because of the difference in water activity between the concentrated and the dilute solution.

The magnitude of each of the two membrane potentials in the system of Fig. 6B is numerically defined by the Nernst equation, as applicable to membranes of ideal ionic selectivity

$$\epsilon = RT \ln \frac{a_1}{a_2} \tag{7}$$

where ϵ is the electromotive force and a_1 and a_2 are the molar activities of the electromotively active ion. The direction of the two electromotive forces is shown in Fig. 6B by broken-line arrows pointing at a plus and a minus sign, respectively, their numerical values being $+55.1$ mv and -55.1 mv for the pair of solutions indicated.

In order to reëstablish in Fig. 6B the essential features of the situation represented in Fig. 6A, it would be necessary to connect the two compartments containing dilute solution by a liquid conduit filled with 0.01 N potassium chloride solution, as shown in Fig. 6C.

The system of Fig. 6C may be considered as a "Flüssigkeitsring," an "all-liquid electrical circuit" or, better, an "all-electrolytic electrical circuit" in the sense of Dolezalek and Krüger,[67] a (positive) electric current flowing in a clockwise direction through the system, as is indicated by the solid arrows in Fig. 6C. The total emf in the system, E, is $2 \times 55.1 = 110.2$ mv. The strength of the current, I, is defined by Ohm's law

$$I = \frac{E}{R} \tag{8}$$

where R is the total resistance of the system.

The current which flows in a clockwise direction in the system of Fig. 6C is transported through the negative membrane in the left arm of the system exclusively by cations which move clockwise, in the direction of the broken-line arrow; through the positive membrane in the right arm the electricity is transported exclusively by an equivalent quantity of anions which move in a counterclockwise direction, as indicated by a broken-line arrow.

Accordingly, the quantity of electrolyte (in equivalents) which moves in a given time in the mosaic system of Fig. 6C from the concentrated to the dilute solution must be numerically identical with the number of electrochemical equivalents of current (faradays) which flow in the system during the same period. The experimental proof of the theory of the electrolyte permeability of mosaic membranes thus consists in testing this prediction in model systems identical in all essential features with the all-electrolytic ring system of Fig. 6C.

The obvious approach to this problem lies in some alteration in the simple theoretical model of Fig. 6C which will permit the accurate determination of the current which flows in the system. One practical way of doing this is to cut the system at some suitable point and attach to the two open ends of the interrupted circuit two symmetrical electrodes which can reversibly take the current from and return it to the system. The two electrodes in turn are connected to each other by some conventional current-measuring instrument, a coulometer or a microammeter, and a closed circuit is thus reestablished. The electrodes must be chosen

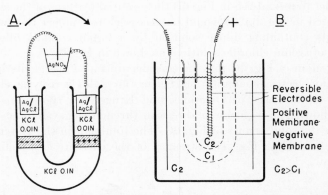

Fig. 7. Mosaic membrane models with auxiliary electrodes through which the current flows. A: A schematic model. B: The experimental model.

so that they do not bring about any significant change in the original system which would not occur on closed circuit in their absence. They may be either specific electrodes for one of the ions in the solutions or nonspecific electrodes of the Cu | CuSO₄ | agar bridge type.[18, 68]

The system shown in Fig. 7A illustrates schematically one possible arrangement which makes use of silver-silver chloride electrodes in chloride solutions. It may be represented as a galvanic cell in the conventional way, double vertical lines representing the negative and the positive membranes

$$\text{Ag} \mid \text{AgCl} \mid \underset{\epsilon_2}{\text{KCl } c_1} \overset{-}{\underset{\epsilon_3}{\|}} \underset{}{\text{KCl } c_2} \overset{+}{\underset{\epsilon_4}{\|}} \underset{\epsilon_2{}'}{\text{KCl } c_1} \mid \text{AgCl} \mid \underset{\epsilon_1{}'}{\text{Ag}}$$

In this chain the electromotive forces ϵ_1 and ϵ_1', and ϵ_2 and ϵ_2' are equal but opposite in direction; they cancel out and do not contribute to the total, effective emf of the cell. The introduction of reversible and symmetrical electrodes in a mosaic-model system makes it, therefore, possible to determine directly and accurately the number of faradays which flow in it during the period for which the circuit is closed.

Another possible approach which avoids the use of auxiliary electrodes through which the current flows consists of determining the current by measuring the potential difference by means of feeler electrodes across an element of the circuit whose resistance is known and does not change during the course of the experiment.[18, 69] Figure 8A sketches such an

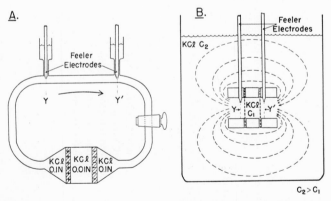

FIG. 8. All-electrolytic mosaic membrane models. *A*: A schematic model. *B*: The experimental model.

TABLE VI

A COMPARISON OF THE QUANTITIES OF ELECTROLYTE AND OF ELECTRICITY MOVED IN MODEL SYSTEMS OF MOSAIC MEMBRANES WHICH ARE COMPOSED OF NEARLY IDEALLY ANION AND CATION SELECTIVE PARTS

Electrolyte used	Concentration on closing of circuit (equiv./liter)	Electrodes	Volume of dilute solution (ml.)	Increase in concentration of dilute solution (equiv./liter)	Correction for leak (equiv./liter)	Equivalents of electrolyte moved (equiv. $\times 10^{-6}$)	Electricity moved ($F \times 10^{-6}$)
KCl	0.050/0.00521	Ag|AgCl	70.0	0.00116	None	81.2	82.2
KCl	0.100/0.01050	Ag|AgCl	65.0	0.00105	0.00008	63.1	61.8
KCl	0.050/0.001500	Cu|CuSO₄|agar	80.0	0.000420	None	33.6	33.5
K₂SO₄	0.050/0.001681	Cu|CuSO₄|agar	74.0	0.000417	0.000064	26.1	25.7
KCl	0.050/0.001554	None	19.00	0.001308	0.000046	24.0	24.6
LiCl	0.050/0.004898	None	19.00	0.000657	0.000009	12.3	12.2
KIO₃	0.050/0.004938	None	19.00	0.000435	0.000019	7.90	8.08

arrangement in a highly schematic manner; the planes of the direction of the feeler electrodes are indicated by Y and Y'.

Space does not permit a discussion of the difficulties in building systems which are suitable from the experimental point of view. The essentials of the geometry of the working models are shown in the schematic Figs. 7B and 8B. The fundamental electrical identity of the systems in Figs. 7A and 7B and of Figs. 8A and 8B is evident.

The self-explanatory Table VI summarizes some of the results obtained with model systems both with and without auxiliary electrodes through which the current flows. The necessary correction for "leak" of electrolyte across the membranes, due to their imperfection, is noted in the sixth column of this table. The theory postulates numerical agreement of the data in the last two columns of this table.[18, 66, 68, 69]

The agreement between the data of the last two columns of Table VI seems fully satisfactory in view of the experimental difficulties involved in these experiments.

The more general importance of this study lies in the fact that it demonstrates that fairly complex membrane systems can be considered from a theoretical viewpoint and that quantitative predictions based on these considerations can be verified experimentally. This indicates that the time is ripe for a similar attack on more complex membrane problems which may be of much more immediate and wider biological interest, such as the problem of specific uptake of ions by living cells and the question of accumulation by living matter of electrolytes, both anions and cations, against concentration gradients.

Whereas the membrane potentials which arise in equilibrium systems and quasi-equilibrium systems are clearly and quantitatively understood on the basis of the theory of the Donnan membrane potential, no general statement can be made concerning the *dynamic membrane potentials* that arise in systems which drift toward equilibrium.

Relatively simple cases of dynamic membrane systems with more than one species of potential determining ions are the chains with membranes of ideal or nearly ideal ionic selectivity, the simplest possible systems of this type being those in which the so-called *bi-ionic potentials* arise.

The bi-ionic potential was defined as the dynamic membrane potential which arises across a membrane separating the solutions of two electrolytes at the same concentration having different "critical" ions, which are able to exchange across the membrane, and the same "noncritical" ion species for which the membrane is (ideally) impermeable.[70-72]

The general scheme of a chain in which a B.I.P. arises across an electronegative membrane can be represented in the following manner

Solution 1	Electronegative membrane	Solution 2
Electrolyte A^+X^-		Electrolyte B^+X^-
c_1		c_1

Here A^+ and B^+ represent univalent cations which are able to pass freely across the membrane, and X^- an anion which is unable to penetrate through it.

Systems of this type have been investigated experimentally only in a limited number of instances.[26, 28, 70, 71, 73, 74] Bi-ionic potentials, according to the nature of the membrane and the combination of critical ions, may be up to 150 mv or more. This magnitude is nearly independent of the nature and valency of the noncritical ions, provided complete dissociation prevails. In a medium concentration range the B.I.P. is likewise

TABLE VII

SEVERAL REPRESENTATIVE BI-IONIC POTENTIALS ACROSS A TYPICAL PERMSELECTIVE OXIDIZED COLLODION AND A TYPICAL PERMSELECTIVE PROTAMINE COLLODION MEMBRANE ($T = 25.0 \pm 0.1°$ C)

1	2	3	4	5	6	7	8
Oxidized collodion membrane ($\rho^* = 1550$ Ω-cm^2)				Protamine collodion membrane ($\rho^* = 1250$ Ω-cm^2)			
Solution 1 (0.0100 N)	Solution 2 (0.0100 N)	Bi-ionic potential (mv)	$\dfrac{\tau_{B^+}^{(2)}}{\tau_{K^+}^{(1)}}$	Solution 1 (0.0250 N)	Solution 2 (0.0250 N)	Bi-ionic potential (mv)	$\dfrac{\tau_{Y^-}^{(2)}}{\tau_{Cl^-}^{(1)}}$
KCl	CsCl	−8.7	1.41	NaCl	NaCNS	+32.0	3.48
KI	NH$_4$I	−6.8	1.30	NaCl	NaNO$_3$	+23.1	2.46
KCl	RbCl	−5.6	1.25	NaCl	NaI	+12.2	1.61
KCl	KCl	±0.0	1.00	NaCl	NaBr	+7.2	1.32
KI	NaI	+35.4	0.252	NaCl	NaCl	±0.0	1.00
KCl	NaCl	+35.5	0.251	NaCl	NaBrO$_3$	−2.2	0.918
KCl	LiCl	+63.7	0.084	NaCl	NaFormate	−7.6	0.744
KI	(CH$_3$)$_4$NI	+81.6	0.042	NaCl	NaSalicyl.	−12.3	0.619
KI	(C$_2$H$_5$)$_4$NI	+110.0	0.014	NaCl	NaBenzoate	−38.6	0.222
				NaCl	NaIO$_3$	−45.1	0.173
				NaCl	NaAcetate	−46.2	0.165
				NaCl	NaPropion.	−59.3	0.099
				NaCl	NaButyrate	−65.9	0.077
				NaCl	NaLactate	−68.6	0.069

fairly independent of the absolute concentration; at high concentrations it is slightly lower in most instances;[75, 76] at very low concentrations the drop may become quite considerable, particularly with membranes of low resistance. This drop in potential can be assumed to be due primarily to the influence of the unstirred diffusion layers at the membrane solution interfaces.[75, 76] For this reason the use of membranes of relatively high resistance is often indicated in the study of the B.I.P. and related phenomena.

The chemical nature of the membrane, its charge density, and its porosity have a rather involved, at present in part unpredictable influence on the absolute magnitude of the bi-ionic potentials. Table VII gives some representative B.I.P. data obtained with some permselective membranes of fairly high standard resistance (in 0.1 N KCl), ρ^*; columns 1–3, and 5–7 are self-explanatory; columns 4 and 8 should be disregarded for the time being.

Table VIII shows the influence of concentration on the B.I.P. across some permselective membranes of different standard resistance, ρ^*,[75, 76] for a medium range of concentrations.

The various critical cations and anions can be arranged into two consistent and characteristic sequences according to the relative magnitude of the bi-ionic potentials which are caused by their presence (as was done in Table VII). These two ionic sequences are the so-called Hofmeister series.[73, 74]

From the formal electrochemical point of view, as was pointed out by Michaelis, the sign and the magnitude of the B.I.P. must depend on the relative ease with which the two species of critical ions can pene-

TABLE VIII

THE VARIATION WITH CONCENTRATION OF THE BI-IONIC POTENTIAL ACROSS FOUR REPRESENTATIVE PERMSELECTIVE MEMBRANES ($T = 25.0 \pm 0.1°$ C)

Chain	KCl|sulfonated polystyrene collodion membrane|LiCl		KCNS|protamine collodion membrane|KCl	
Concentration (equiv./liter)	$\rho^* = 30\ \Omega\text{-}cm^2$ (mv)	$\rho^* = 1325\ \Omega\text{-}cm^2$ (mv)	$\rho^* = 435\ \Omega\text{-}cm^2$ (mv)	$\rho^* = 5500\ \Omega\text{-}cm^2$ (mv)
0.0100	+22.8	+47.0	−32.2	−42.1
0.0200	—	—	−32.0	−42.9
0.0500	+30.0	+47.0	−33.7	−42.8
0.1000	+32.2	+47.4	−34.5	−44.1
0.2000	+33.6	+47.1	−34.9	−43.4
0.500	+32.5	+44.1	−34.5	−41.9

trate across the membrane.[70, 71] The more readily permeable critical ions impress a potential on the other solution which is identical in sign with that of their own charge.

In order to obtain quantitative information concerning the relative ionic "mobilities" of the two critical cations in the membranes, Michaelis[70, 71] employed—not without misgivings—the Planck-Henderson equation for the liquid junction potential as applicable to the simplest possible case, namely, two solutions of uni-univalent electrolytes of equal concentration having two different cations and a common anion

$$E = \pm \frac{RT}{F} \ln \frac{u_{A^+} + u_{X^-}}{u_{B^+} + u_{X^-}} \qquad (9)$$

where E is the experimentally determined potential, u_{A^+} and u_{B^+} the "mobilities" of the two cations, and u_{X^-} the "mobility" of the common anion within the membrane. If the membrane is impermeable to anions, u_{X^-} is zero, and the equation for an ideally cation selective membrane becomes

$$E = \pm \frac{RT}{F} \ln \frac{u_{A^+}}{u_{B^+}} \qquad (10)$$

where E is now the bi-ionic potential.

The concept of ionic "mobilities" in the membrane, if understood in analogy with the concept of ionic mobilities in free solution, embodies of necessity several rather specific assumptions which are not likely to be adequate for the particular situation within a membrane of porous character.

The magnitude of a B.I.P. is quite obviously a function of the relative contributions of the different species of ions in the system toward the (virtual) transportation of current across the membrane. For this reason Gregor and Sollner suggested that the quantitative evaluation of the B.I.P. be based on the more basic and more general concept of the transference numbers which permits the quantitative interpretation of the experimental B.I.P. values in terms of molecular (ionic) processes with a minimum of hypothetical assumptions.[26, 72]

In order to evaluate quantitatively from the magnitude of the B.I.P. the true relative contributions of the different ions to the virtual transportation of current across the membrane, it is necessary only to express the above equation in terms of transference instead of Michaelis' "ionic mobilities," and equation (10) becomes the expression

$$E = \frac{+RT}{F} \ln \frac{\tau_{A^+}{}^{(1)}}{\tau_{B^+}{}^{(2)}} \tag{11a}$$

the sign referring to the charge of solution 2.[72]

For electropositive membranes (of ideal ionic selectivity), equation 10 is changed to the expression

$$E = \frac{-RT}{F} \ln \frac{\tau_{X^-}{}^{(1)}}{\tau_{Y^-}{}^{(2)}} \tag{11b}$$

In order to visualize in a quantitative way the differences in the behavior of various ions in the experimental chains referred to in Table VII, the ratios $\tau_{B^+}{}^{(2)}/\tau_{K^+}{}^{(1)}$ and $\tau_{Y^-}{}^{(2)}/\tau_{Cl^-}{}^{(1)}$ were calculated from equations (11a) and (11b) and are given in columns 4 and 8 of Table VII.

A reasonably satisfactory physical picture which can explain the data of Table VII can be based on the consideration of the membranes as ion exchange bodies according to the fixed charge theory.[72] The two exchangeable (critical) species of ions compete for positions as counterions of the fixed dissociable groups of the membrane. Concerning the general phenomenon of competitive ion exchange, it is well known from extensive studies in ion exchange that the various competing ions are taken up by ion exchangers to a very different extent. The sequences of the relative adsorbabilities of the various ions are roughly the two Hofmeister series of cations and of anions, unless steric hindrance and related factors come into play as complicating factors. The adsorbed critical ions are dissociated off in the pores according to their nature and the nature of the fixed ionic wall groups. The assumption of complete dissociation is undoubtedly justified in many instances, e.g., in the majority of the systems shown in Table VII.

The relative abundance of the two species of critical ions in the pores multiplied by their relative diffusion velocities (and valencies) determine their relative contributions toward the virtual transportation of electricity across the membrane, and thus the sign and the magnitude of the B.I.P.

Figure 9 represents the situation pictorially. The small, continuous circles around the plus or minus signs in this figure represent the size of the ions, including their effective shell of hydration. The large dotted circles indicate the effective range of electrical repulsion between the fixed charges situated on the pore walls and ions of identical signs in the

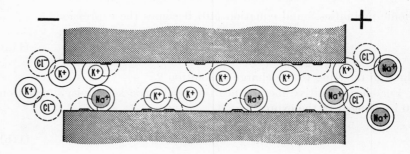

$$D_{K^+} > D_{Na^+}$$

FIG. 9. The origin of the bi-ionic potential KCl∥NaCl in a pore; the Na^+ ion is larger and less adsorbable than the K^+ ion.

solutions and between such ions; the solid-line large circles surrounding the critical ions indicate the spheres of the mutual repulsion of the latter.

Of the nine anionic wall groups of the pore shown in Fig. 9, six are compensated for electrically by the more strongly adsorbable (and smaller) K^+ ions, the other three by the less strongly adsorbable (and larger) Na^+ ions. Complete dissociation is assumed. If the ratio of the diffusion velocities of K^+ to Na^+ in the pore is taken as 76 to 52, the ratio of their ionic mobilities in free solution, then the ratio of their transference numbers $\tau_{K^+}/\tau_{Na^+} = (6 \times 76):(3 \times 52)$. The magnitude of the B.I.P. according to equation (11a) would (at 25.0° C) amount to $E = +59.1 \log \dfrac{456}{156} = +28.6$ mv.

The elucidation of the mechanism of the origin of the bi-ionic potential leads directly to an insight into the mechanisms of the *dynamics of polyionic membrane systems* in general, which involve membranes of ideal or nearly ideal ionic selectivity.

As *polycationic potentials* we denote the membrane potentials which arise across ideally cation selective membranes in systems with two or more species of cations which may be present at the two sides of the membrane in pure or mixed solutions at the same or at different activities. *Polyanionic potentials* involve analogous anion selective membranes and two or more species of anions. Thus one may refer to a two-cationic potential, a three-anionic potential, etc. Making a slight change in definition by switching from concentrations to activities, the bi-ionic potential can be redefined as the special case of a two-ionic potential, cationic or anionic, in which the two critical ions are present at the same activity in single electrolyte solutions.

From the experimental point of view one may consider as polycationic and polyanionic systems all systems which involve membranes of sufficiently high degree of ionic selectivity, under the conditions of the particular experiment, so that the contribution of the noncritical ions towards the virtual transportation of electricity may be neglected.

The essential problem in dealing with polyionic systems is to find the quantitative correlation of the potentials that arise with any ratio of activities of two or more species of critical ions in the two outside solutions and the potential in some standard system.

The theoretical treatment of polyionic systems in general can be based on the Planck and Henderson equations in a manner similar to the treatment of the bi-ionic potential. Marshall has investigated the electromotive behavior of clay membranes in polycationic systems primarily from the point of view of the use of these membranes as membrane electrodes in solutions containing two or more species of cations.[61] Following the example of Michaelis, he bases his considerations on a concept of ionic "mobilities" within the membrane, and this is beset with numerous difficulties, some of which have been outlined above. As in the case of the bi-ionic potential, a more satisfactory physical picture can be arrived at on the basis of the concept of transference, the mode of presentation which is chosen here.[75, 76] To simplify the theoretical discussion we shall, in subsequent paragraphs, explicitly treat electronegative, cation permeable membranes only, since the electropositive membranes represent a strictly parallel case.

The simplest case of a polyionic potential across a membrane of ideal selectivity, next to the bi-ionic potential, is the situation in which the two solutions separated by the membrane each contain only one of two species of critical ions, but at *different* activities. The Planck-Henderson equation may be applied to the system of the type, a_1 KCl | membrane | a_2 LiCl; introducing transference numbers we may write

$$E = \frac{+RT}{F} \ln \frac{\tau_{K^+}}{\tau_{Li^+}} \tag{12}$$

where τ_{K^+} and τ_{Li^+} are the transference numbers of the critical ions in the membrane in the particular two-cationic system under consideration.

Equation (12) assumes its true, full meaning only if the transference numbers of a pair of critical ions for any particular system can be correlated quantitatively to the transference numbers of an appropriate reference system on the basis of clear-cut, simple assumptions.

The simplest possible assumptions are that the bi-ionic potentials and the relative adsorbabilities of the two species of critical ions are independent of concentration, and that the relative adsorbed quantities of the two ions are a linear function of the ratio of their activities in the two solutions. On the basis of these assumptions it must be anticipated that the ratio of the transference numbers of the two critical ions within the membrane, τ_{K^+}/τ_{Li^+}, in the system, a_1 KCl | membrane | a_2 LiCl, is directly proportional to the ratio of the transference numbers of the two critical ions within the same membrane in the corresponding bi-ionic potential system (when the ratio of the two activities is unity) and to the ratio of the activities of the two critical ions in the two external solutions of the particular system under discussion. If the transference numbers pertaining to the bi-ionic reference system are denoted as $\tau_{K^+}{}^0$ and $\tau_{Li^+}{}^0$, the ratio of the transference numbers in the general two-cationic system above can be expressed as

$$\frac{\tau_{K^+}}{\tau_{Li^+}} = \frac{a_{K^+}{}^{(1)}\ \tau_{K^+}{}^0}{a_{Li^+}{}^{(2)}\ \tau_{Li^+}{}^0} \tag{13}$$

and the two-cationic potential as

$$E = \frac{+RT}{F} \ln \frac{a_{K^+}{}^{(1)}\ \tau_{K^+}{}^0}{a_{Li^+}{}^{(2)}\ \tau_{Li^+}{}^0} \tag{14}$$

To test equation (14) and its analogue for positive membranes, a number of systems of various concentration ratios, with cation as well as with anion selective permselective membranes, were studied. Representative calculated and experimental potential data are shown in Table IX. The calculated values are based on standard transference numbers derived from bi-ionic potentials measured at 0.050 N, and on ionic activities which were computed according to the Guggenheim assumption. No attempt has been made to correct for the asymmetry of the two liquid junction potentials which arise when saturated KCl-agar bridges are inserted into the two solutions of different composition and different concentration.

The data of Table IX show that the calculated and experimental potential values agree within a few millivolts in all instances.

A further extension of the use of the Planck-Henderson equation, combined with the concept of transference numbers within the mem-

TABLE IX

A COMPARISON OF SEVERAL CALCULATED AND EXPERIMENTAL TWO-IONIC
POTENTIALS WITH SINGLE ELECTROLYTE SOLUTIONS AT DIFFERENT CONCEN-
TRATIONS ACROSS THREE REPRESENTATIVE PERMSELECTIVE MEMBRANES
($T = 25.0 \pm 0.1°$ C)

Membrane	Solution 1	Solution 2	Two-ionic potential	
			Calculated (mv)	Experimental (mv)
Sulfonated polystyrene	0.0100 N KCl	0.0500 N LiCl	+8.2	+8.0
collodion	0.0100 N KCl	0.200 N LiCl	−25.5	−25.0
$\rho^* = 1325$ Ω-cm²	0.0100 N KCl	0.500 N LiCl	−48.2	−49.3
$\dfrac{\tau_{K^+}^0}{\tau_{Li^+}^0} = 6.27$				
Protamine collodion	0.200 N KCNS	0.0100 N KCl	−113.8	−109.7
$\rho^* = 5450$ Ω-cm²	0.200 N KCNS	0.0500 N KCl	−74.6	−74.2
$\dfrac{\tau_{CNS^-}^0}{\tau_{Cl^-}^0} = 5.30$	0.200 N KCNS	0.500 N KCl	−21.8	−24.4
Protamine collodion	0.500 N KCNS	0.0100 N KCl	−130.0	−124.7
$\rho^* = 1400$ Ω-cm²	0.500 N KCNS	0.0500 N KCl	−91.2	−87.9
$\dfrac{\tau_{CNS^-}^0}{\tau_{Cl^-}^0} = 4.42$	0.500 N KCNS	0.200 N KCl	−58.9	−56.8

brane, leads to an equation useful for the most generalized type of two-
ionic potential system in which both species of critical ions are present
in any arbitrary combination of concentrations on each side of the perm-
selective membrane. The system, a_1 KCl, a_2 LiCl | membrane | a_3 KCl,
a_4 LiCl, represents this general case.

The equation for the two-cationic potential can be expressed quantitatively by introducing transference numbers in the Planck-Henderson
equation

$$E = \frac{+RT}{F} \ln \frac{\tau_{K^+}^{(1)} + \tau_{Li^+}^{(1)}}{\tau_{K^+}^{(2)} + \tau_{Li^+}^{(2)}} \qquad (15)$$

$\tau_{K^+}^{(1)}$ and $\tau_{K^+}^{(2)}$, and $\tau_{Li^+}^{(1)}$ and $\tau_{Li^+}^{(2)}$, represent the contribution
of the K+ and Li+ ions originating in solutions 1 and 2, respectively, to
the virtual transportation of current within the membrane. Thus, the

quantity $\tau_{K^+}^{(1)}$ is analogous to $\dfrac{c_K^{(1)} u_{K^+}}{\Sigma c_i u_i}$ in the Planck or Henderson terminology for a liquid junction potential, and, similarly, $\tau_{K^+}{}^{(2)}$ corresponds to $\frac{c_{K^+}^{(2)}u_{K^+}}{\Sigma c_i u_i}$, $\tau_{Li^+}^{(1)}$ to $\frac{c_{Li^+}^{(1)}u_{Li^+}}{\Sigma c_i u_i}$, and $\tau_{Li^+}^{(2)}$ to $\frac{c_{Li^+}^{(2)}u_{Li^+}}{\Sigma c_i u_i}$.

According to the previously stated assumptions, we may write for the transference numbers within the membrane, τ_{K^+} and τ_{Li^+}

$$\tau_{K^+} = \frac{(a_{K^+}{}^{(1)} + a_{K^+}{}^{(2)})\tau_{K^+}{}^0}{(a_{K^+}{}^{(1)} + a_{K^+}{}^{(2)})\tau_{K^+}{}^0 + (a_{Li^+}{}^{(1)} + a_{Li^+}{}^{(2)})\tau_{Li^+}{}^0} \tag{16a}$$

and

$$\tau_{Li^+} = \frac{(a_{Li^+}{}^{(1)} + a_{Li^+}{}^{(2)})\tau_{Li^+}{}^0}{\Sigma a_i \tau_i{}^0} \tag{16b}$$

when $\sum a_i\tau_i^0$ denotes the same denominator as in equation (16a).

The transference numbers within the membrane can be split up into terms analogous to quantities in the Planck and Henderson equations

$$\tau_{K^+} = \tau_{K^+}{}^{(1)} + \tau_{K^+}{}^{(2)} \tag{17a}$$

and

$$\tau_{Li^+} = \tau_{Li^+}{}^{(1)} + \tau_{Li^+}{}^{(2)} \tag{17b}$$

where

$$\tau_{K^+}{}^{(1)} = \frac{a_{K^+}{}^{(1)}\tau_{K^+}{}^0}{\Sigma a_i\tau_i{}^0} \tag{18a}$$

$$\tau_{K^+}{}^{(2)} = \frac{a_{K^+}{}^{(2)}\tau_{K^+}{}^0}{\Sigma a_i\tau_i{}^0} \tag{18b}$$

$$\tau_{Li^+}{}^{(1)} = \frac{a_{Li^+}{}^{(1)}\tau_{Li^+}{}^0}{\Sigma a_i\tau_i{}^0} \tag{18c}$$

and

$$\tau_{Li^+}{}^{(2)} = \frac{a_{Li^+}{}^{(2)}\tau_{Li^+}{}^0}{\Sigma a_i\tau_i{}^0} \tag{18d}$$

Accordingly, the two-cationic potential, E, in any system can be expressed as

$$E = \frac{+RT}{F}\ln\frac{a_{K^+}{}^{(1)}\tau_{K^+}{}^0 + a_{Li^+}{}^{(1)}\tau_{Li^+}{}^0}{a_{K^+}{}^{(2)}\tau_{K^+}{}^0 + a_{Li^+}{}^{(2)}\tau_{Li^+}{}^0} \tag{19}$$

Table X compares in a few representative systems the values of the measured potentials with the values of the potentials calculated from equation (19) and its analogue for anionic systems.

The agreement in Table X between the calculated and the experimental data seems most satisfactory. By a single measurement of the bi-ionic potential with a pair of critical ions across a particular permselective membrane, it becomes possible to calculate the potentials that

TABLE X

A Comparison of Several Calculated and Experimental Two-Ionic Potentials With Mixed Electrolyte Solutions at Various Concentrations Across Two Representative Permselective Membranes (T = 25.0 ± 0.1° C)

Membrane	Solution 1		Solution 2		Two-ionic potential	
					Calcu-lated (mv)	Experi-mental (mv)
Sulfonated poly-styrene collodion $\rho^* = 260 \ \Omega\text{-cm}^2$ $\dfrac{\tau_{H^+}^0}{\tau_{Na^+}^0} = 64.5$	0.01250 0.0375	N NaCl N HCl	0.0500	N NaCl	+99.8	+100.0
	0.01485 0.0352	N NaCl N HCl	0.0477 0.00234	N NaCl N HCl	+62.6	+59.0
	0.01719 0.0328	N NaCl N HCl	0.0453 0.00469	N NaCl N HCl	+46.4	+44.5
	0.02188 0.02812	N NaCl N HCl	0.0406 0.00938	N NaCl N HCl	+26.8	+25.4
	0.02656 0.02344	N NaCl N HCl	0.0360 0.01406	N NaCl N HCl	+12.6	+11.6
Protamine collo-dion $\rho^* = 5450 \ \Omega\text{-cm}^2$ $\dfrac{\tau_{CNS^-}^0}{\tau_{Cl^-}^0} = 5.36$	0.1497 0.000275	N KCNS N KCl	0.000275 0.00911	N KCNS N KCl	−106.1	−104.5
	0.1489 0.001103	N KCNS N KCl	0.001103 0.00827	N KCNS N KCl	−98.2	−99.0
	0.1478 0.00220	N KCNS N KCl	0.00220 0.00717	N KCNS N KCl	−90.7	−93.1
	0.1456 0.00440	N KCNS N KCl	0.00440 0.00497	N KCNS N KCl	−80.0	−81.8
	0.1434 0.00662	N KCNS N KCl	0.00662 0.00276	N KCNS N KCl	−72.2	−73.3

arise across the same membrane if the two critical ions are distributed in the two solutions in any arbitrary combination of concentrations.

Two-ionic potentials, as shown by Marshall, may be used for the determination, with a fair degree of accuracy, of the activities of two coexisting species of ions of the same sign of charge in solution.[61] For this purpose it is necessary to determine the potentials that arise across two membranes of different, known $\tau_{A^+}{}^0/\tau_{B^+}{}^0$ ratios, which separate the "unknown" solution from a known reference solution, or to use the same membrane with two different reference solutions. The rapidly responding, low-resistance permselective membranes should turn out to be rather useful as membrane electrodes, both in mixed cationic and mixed anionic systems.

The use of membranes of well-defined and highly characteristic electrochemical properties in physicochemical investigations and in model studies of specific biological interest is still in its infancy. However, we may look forward with confidence to a rich harvest of answers to at least some of the questions which have motivated the old masters in this field—Höber, Donnan, Michaelis, and last but not least, Jacques Loeb, to whose memory this symposium is dedicated.

ACKNOWLEDGMENTS

The authors wish to thank the editors of the Journal of General Physiology, of the Journal of Physical (and Colloid) Chemistry, and of the Journal of the American Chemical Society for permission to quote freely from earlier papers, and to reproduce a number of graphs. We are particularly indebted to the Electrochemical Society and to the editors of the Journal of the Electrochemical Society, to the editors of the Annals of the New York Academy of Sciences, and to the editors and publishers of the Symposium on "Electrochemistry in Biology and Medicine" for kind permission to utilize verbatim lengthy sections of previous reviews.

REFERENCES

1. SOLLNER, K., J. Phys. Chem. **49,** 47 (1945).
2. SOLLNER, K., J. Electrochem. Soc. **97,** 139C (1950); Ann. N. Y. Acad. Sci. **57,** 177 (1953).
3. MICHAELIS, L., Bull. Natl. Research Council (U.S.) **69,** 119 (1929); Kolloid-Z. **62,** 2 (1933); MICHAELIS, L., and FUJITA, A., Biochem. Z, **158,** 28 (1925); **164,** 23 (1925); MICHAELIS, L., and DOKAN, S., Biochem. Z, **162,** 258 (1925); MICHAELIS, L., and HAYASHI, K., Biochem. Z, **173,** 411 (1926); MICHAELIS, L. and PERLZWEIG, W. A., J. Gen. Physiol. **10,** 575 (1926–27); MICHAELIS, L., McELLSWORTH, R., and WEECH, A. A., J. Gen. Physiol. **10,** 671 (1926–27); MICHAELIS, L., WEECH, A. A., and YAMATORI, A., J. Gen. Physiol. **10,** 685 (1927); MICHAELIS, L., and WEECH, A. A., J. Gen. Physiol. **11,** 147 (1927).
4. SOLLNER, K., J. Phys. Chem. **49,** 265 (1945).
5. ZSIGMONDY, R., "Kolloidchemie," 5th ed., vol. 1, p. 61. Leipzig, OTTO SPAMER, 1925.
6. JANDER, G., and ZAKOWSKI, J., "Membranfilter, Cella- und Ultrafeinfilter." Leipzig, Akademische Verlagsgesellschaft, OTTO SPAMER, 1929.
7. COLLANDER, R., Kolloidchem. Beih. **19,** 72 (1924); **20,** 273 (1925); Soc. Sci. Fennica Commentationes Biol. **2,** No. 6 (1926).
8. SOLLNER, K., Z. Elektrochem. **36,** 36, 234 (1930).
9. SOLLNER, K., and GROLLMAN, A., Z. Elektrochem. **38,** 274 (1932).

10. GROLLMAN, A., and SOLLNER, K., *Trans. Electrochem. Soc.* **61**, 477, 487 (1932).
11. SOLLNER, K., *J. Phys. Chem.* **49**, 171 (1945)
12. TEORELL, T., *Proc. Soc. Exptl. Biol. Med.* **33**, 282 (1935); *Proc. Natl. Acad. Sci. U.S.* **21**, 152 (1935); *Z. Elektrochem.* **55**, 460 (1951); *Progr. Biophys. and Biophys. Chem.* **3**, 305 (1953).
13. MEYER, K. H., and SIEVERS, J. F., *Helv. Chim. Acta* **19**, 649, 665 (1936).
14. MEYER, K. H., *Trans. Faraday Soc.* **33**, 1073 (1937).
15. CARR, C. W., and SOLLNER, K., *J. Gen. Physiol.* **28**, 119 (1944).
16. SOLLNER, K., ABRAMS, I., and CARR, C. W., *J. Gen. Physiol.* **25**, 7 (1941).
17. SOLLNER, K., and NEIHOF, R., *Arch. Biochem. and Biophys.* **33**, 166 (1951).
18. NEIHOF, R., Ph.D. Thesis, University of Minnesota, Minneapolis, 1950.
19. NEIHOF, R. *J. Phys. Chem.* (in press).
20. SOLLNER, K., and ABRAMS, I., *J. Gen. Physiol.* **24**, 1 (1940).
21. SOLLNER, K., ABRAMS, I., and CARR, C. W., *J. Gen. Physiol.* **24**, 467 (1941).
22. GIRARD, P., *Compt. rend.* **146**, 927 (1908).
23. BARTELL, F. E., Membrane potentials and their relation to anomalous osmosis, *in* Colloid Symposium Monograph (J. H. Mathews, ed.), Vol. 1, p. 120. Department of Chemistry, University of Wisconsin, Madison, 1923.
24. LOEB, J., *J. Gen. Physiol.* **1**, 717 (1919); **2**, 87, 173, 225, 387, 563, 577, 659, 673 (1920); **4**, 213, 463 (1922); **5**, 89 (1923); etc.
25. ABRAMS, I., and SOLLNER, K., *J. Gen. Physiol.* **26**, 369 (1943).
26. GREGOR, H. P., and SOLLNER, K., *J. Phys. Chem.* **50**, 53 (1946).
27. CARR, C. W., GREGOR, H. P., and SOLLNER, K., *J. Gen. Physiol.* **28**, 179 (1945).
28. GREGOR, H. P., and SOLLNER, K., *J. Phys. Chem.* **50**, 88 (1946).
29. WYLLIE, M. R. J., and PATNODE, H. W., *J. Phys. & Colloid Chem.* **54**, 204 (1950).
30. JUDA, W., and McRAE, W. A., *J. Am. Chem. Soc.* **72**, 1044 (1950); KRESSMAN, T. R. E., *Nature* **165**, 568 (1950); BONHOEFFER, K. F., MILLER, L., and SCHINDEWOLF, U., *Z. physik. Chem.* **198**, 270 (1951); BONHOEFFER, K. F., and SCHINDEWOLF, U., *Z. physik. Chem.* **198**, 281 (1951); MANECKE, G., *Z. Elektrochem.* **55**, 672 (1951); MANECKE, G., and BONHOEFFER, K. F., *Z. Elektrochem.* **55**, 475 (1951); CLARKE, J. T., MARINSKY, J. A., JUDA, W., ROSENBERG, N. W., and ALEXANDER, S., *J. Phys. Chem.* **56**, 100 (1952); etc.
31. SOLLNER, K., and GREGOR, H. P., *J. Phys. Chem.* **51**, 299 (1947).
32. SOLLNER, K., and GREGOR, H. P., *J. Phys. & Colloid Chem.* **54**, 330 (1950).
33. HARNED, H. S., and OWEN, B. B., "The Physical Chemistry of Electrolytic Solutions." Reinhold, New York, 1943.
34. BATES, R. G., *Chem. Rev.*, **42**, 1 (1948).
35. SOLLNER, K., AND GREGOR, H. P., *J. Colloid Sci.* **6**, 557 (1951); **7**, 37 (1952).
36. DUTROCHET, M., *Ann. chim. phys.* **60**, 337 (1835).
37. BERNSTEIN, J., "Elektrobiologie," Fridrich Vieweg & Sohn, Braunschweig, 1912.
38. HEYL, G. J., *Planta* **20**, 294 (1933).
39. HÖBER, R., "Physical Chemistry of Cells and Tissues." The Blakiston Co., Philadelphia, 1945.
40. KELLER, R., *Ergeb. Physiol.* **30**, 294 (1930).
41. LIFSON, N., and VISSCHER, M., Osmosis in Living Systems, *in* "Medical Physics" (O. Glasser, ed.) Yearbook Publishers, Chicago, 1944.
42. LOEB, J., *J. Gen. Physiol.* **2**, 173 (1920).

43. FREUNDLICH, H., "Colloid and Capillary Chemistry." Dutton and Co., New York. Transl. from 3rd German ed. by H. S. Hatfield, 1922.
44. TEORELL, T., *Ann. Rev. Physiol.*, **11**, 545 (1949).
45. GRIM, E., Ph.D. Thesis, University of Minnesota, Minneapolis, 1950.
46. GRIM, E., and SOLLNER, K., (in preparation).
47. VISSCHER, M. B., FETCHER, E., CARR, C. W., GREGOR, H., BUSHEY, S., and BARKER, D. E., *Am. J. Physiol.* **142**, 550 (1944).
48. BETHE, A., and TOROPOFF, TH., *Z. physik. Chem.* **88**, 686 (1914); **89**, 597 (1915).
49. PRAUSNITZ, P. H., and REITSTÖTTER, J., "Elektrophorese, Elektro-osmose, Elektrodialyse in Flüssigkeiten." Theodor Steinkopf, Dresden und Leipzig, 1931.
50. DONNAN, F. G., *Chem. Revs.*, **1**, 73 (1924).
51. DONNAN, F. G., and HARRIS, A. B., *J. Chem. Soc.* **99**, 1554 (1911); DONNAN, F. G., and ALLMAND, A. J., *J. Chem. Soc.* **105**, 1941 (1914); DONNAN, F. G. and GARNER, W. E., *J. Chem. Soc.* **115**, 1313 (1919).
52. BOLAM, T. R., "The Donnan Equilibria and their Application to Chemical, Physiological and Technical Processes." Bell, London, 1932.
53. SOLLNER, K., and GREGOR, H. P., *J. Am. Chem. Soc.* **67**, 346 (1945).
54. TAMAMUSHI, R., and SOLLNER, K., (in preparation).
55. SOLLNER, K., *J. Am. Chem. Soc.* **65**, 2260 (1943).
56. GREGOR, H. P., and SOLLNER, K., *J. Phys. Chem.* (1954) (in press).
57. HABER, F., *Ann. Physik* (4) **26**, 927 (1908); HABER, F., and KLEMENSIEWICZ, Z., *Z. physik. Chem.* **67**, 385 (1909).
58. NERNST, W., and RIESENFELD, E. H., *Ann. Phys.* (4) **8**, 600 (1902).
59. HOROWITZ, K., *Z. Physik.* **15**, 369 (1923); *Z. physik. Chem.* **115**, 424 (1925).
60. TENDELOO, H. J. C., *J. Biol. Chem.* **113**, 333 (1936).
61. MARSHALL, C. E., *J. Phys. Chem.* **43**, 1155 (1939); **48**, 67 (1944); *Soil Sci. Soc. Am. Proc.* **7**, 182 (1942); MARSHALL, C. E., and BERGMAN, W. E., *J. Am. Chem. Soc.* **63**, 1911 (1941); *J. Phys. Chem.* **46**, 52, 325 (1942); MARSHALL, C. E., and KRINBILL, C. A., *J. Am. Chem. Soc.* **64**, 1814 (1942); MARSHALL, C. E., and AYERS, A. D., *J. Am. Chem. Soc.* **70**, 1297 (1948); MARSHALL, C. E., and EIME, L. O., *J. Am. Chem. Soc.* **70**, 1302 (1948); etc.
62. SCATCHARD, G., *J. Am. Chem. Soc.* **75**, 2883 (1953).
63. CARR, C. W., *Arch. Biochem. and Biophys.* **40**, 286 (1952); **43**, 147 (1953); **46**, 417, 424 (1953).
64. CARR, C. W., and TOPOL, L., *J. Phys. & Colloid Chem.* **54**, 176 (1950).
65. SOLLNER, K., *J. Am. Chem. Soc.* **68**, 156 (1946).
66. SOLLNER, K., *Biochem. Z.* **244**, 370 (1932).
67. DOLEZALEK, F., and KRÜGER, F., *Z. Elektrochem.* **12**, 669 (1906).
68. NEIHOF, R., and SOLLNER, K., *J. Phys. & Colloid Chem.* **54**, 157 (1950).
69. NEIHOF, R., and SOLLNER, K., (in preparation).
70. MICHAELIS, L., *Bull. Natl. Research Council (U.S.)* **69**, 119 (1929); *Kolloid-Z.* **62**, 2 (1933).
71. MICHAELIS, L., and FUJITA, A., *Biochem. Z.* **161**, 47 (1925).
72. SOLLNER, K., *J. Phys. & Colloid Chem.* **53**, 1211, 1226 (1949).
73. HÖBER, R., *J. Cellular Comp. Physiol.* **7**, 367 (1936).
74. MOND, R., and HOFFMAN, F., *Pflügers Arch. ges. Physiol.* **220**, 194 (1928).
75. DRAY, S., Ph.D. Thesis (in preparation).
76. DRAY, S., and SOLLNER, K. (in preparation).

Theory of Protein Solutions[a]

TERRELL L. HILL

INTRODUCTION

In this paper we give a general discussion of two equilibrium problems which are obviously fundamental to a consideration of the role of proteins in ion transport across biological membranes, namely, the Donnan membrane equilibrium and the binding of ions or molecules by protein molecules in solution. The method used here is that due to McMillan and Mayer.

In 1945, McMillan and Mayer[1] published their very elegant general theory of solutions. The theory applies to any type of solution[b] and, in its quantum mechanical form, is formally exact if the forces between molecules of the solution are assumed known and if one accepts the general principles of quantum and statistical mechanics. The theory can be cast, in a very natural way, into the unsymmetrical form necessary if one wishes to distinguish "solutes" from "solvents" and to discuss properties such as the osmotic pressure (solute species impermeable to a membrane). This unsymmetrical approach is obviously the one of interest in protein solution theory.

An alternative but equivalent theory of solutions has been developed recently by Kirkwood and Buff.[2]

The McMillan-Mayer theory has already been applied to solutions of polymers and certain other large molecules by Zimm[3] and by Onsager.[4]

The properties of protein solutions are included in the general equations of McMillan and Mayer. In particular, interactions of protein molecules with small molecules or ions (including "binding") are taken care of *implicitly* by the inclusion of the appropriate forces. However, the binding of ions (especially hydrogen ions) and molecules on protein

---

[a] Sections III and IV were summarized at a Gordon Research Conference on Proteins and Nucleic Acids, New Hampton, N. H., August 25, 1953. A preliminary note has been published in *J. Chem. Phys.* **21**, 1395 (1953). The present version is a condensation of papers to be published elsewhere. A review of the McMillan-Mayer solution theory is available from the Naval Medical Research Institute, Bethesda, Md. as Report 54-2. See also *J. Chem. Phys.* **21**, 2242 (1953).

[b] Electrolyte solutions are mentioned explicitly at the beginning of Section III.

molecules is such an important property of these solutions that it is desirable to modify the theory in such a way that the binding referred to above appears *explicitly*. This modification is the main object of the present paper. With the explicit introduction of binding into the equations, it becomes possible, as we shall see, to discuss the formal interconnections between binding on proteins (e.g., titration curves), osmotic-pressure virial coefficients, forces between protein molecules, protein aggregation, protein distribution functions, etc.

To simplify an already sufficiently complicated notation, we shall restrict ourselves here to solutions containing only one protein species and one species of ion or molecule whose binding to the protein is considered explicitly.

The aggregation of protein molecules into pairs, triples, etc., is taken care of *implicitly* through protein-protein forces. Alternatively, as above for binding, aggregation can be treated *explicitly*, but this is not done here.

Actually, the present paper is not restricted to protein solutions. The discussion is equally applicable to any solution containing molecules of, say, type A, each of which can bind or combine with one or more molecules of type B. The treatment includes, therefore, the binding of hydrogen ions to polyelectrolytes, polybasic acids, amino acids, etc. The Kirkwood-Westheimer[5] theory, including the extension to molecules with internal rotation,[6, 7] is based on a particular model which is consistent with the more general formal equations of the present paper.

In Section II we shall summarize (without derivations) the notation and fundamental equations of the McMillan-Mayer solution theory in a form necessary for our later purposes. In Section III the McMillan-Mayer theory is illustrated, without the complication of binding, using the Debye-Hückel theory and the Donnan equilibrium. Section IV is devoted to the formal theory of protein solutions, including the binding of ions or molecules.

McMILLAN-MAYER SOLUTION THEORY

We present here the fundamental equations needed in the following sections. McMillan and Mayer treat all degrees of freedom classically or all quantum mechanically. For practical purposes in solution theory, we make the useful approximation here, at the outset, of assuming that vibrational degrees of freedom are separable. Although this approximation is not at all essential to the argument, it would presumably almost always be made in applications in the field of solution physical chemistry.

We begin by considering a *closed* system containing a set of molecules[c] $\mathbf{N} = N_1, N_2, \cdots N_\nu$; that is, N_1 molecules of species 1, etc. Each molecule has the usual three translational degrees of freedom and zero, two, or three "external" rotational degrees of freedom. The remaining degrees of freedom are classed either as vibrational or internal rotational; one of these degrees of freedom which is separable, to a sufficient approximation, is called "vibrational" and is (or, rather, may be) treated quantum mechanically; one which is not separable is called "internal rotational" and is treated classically. (The translational and external rotational degrees of freedom are also treated classically.) The internal rotational degrees of freedom include, in particular, angular coordinates associated with rotation about bonds. Internal rotation is, of course, important in polymers and proteins, and also in much simpler molecules.[6, 7] Because of internal rotation, molecules can take on different configurations and shapes. These may have different potential energies owing to interactions between groups, charges, etc., on the same molecule, and this is taken into account below.

In a strictly formal way, we could carry a *completely* quantum mechanical argument through the whole paper. This would be rigorous but useless (for our purposes).

The partition function in the canonical ensemble is written as

$$Q_{\mathbf{N}} = \frac{\prod_{s=1}^{\nu} q_{sv}^{N_s}}{\prod_{s=1}^{\nu} (N_s! h^{f_s N_s})} \int e^{-H_{\mathbf{N}}/kT} \, d\{\mathbf{N}\}_x \, d\{\mathbf{P}\}_x \, d''\{\mathbf{N}\}_\theta \, d\{\mathbf{P}\}_\theta \qquad (1)$$

where q_{sv} is the (separable) vibrational partition function of a molecule of species s, f_s is the number of translational and rotational (internal and external) degrees of freedom of an s molecule, $H_{\mathbf{N}}$ is the classical Hamiltonian function for translation and rotation, $\{\mathbf{N}\}_x$ refers to all the translational coordinates of the set $\mathbf{N}$ and $\{\mathbf{P}\}_x$ represents the conjugate momenta, and $\{\mathbf{N}\}_\theta$ and $\{\mathbf{P}\}_\theta$ have similar meanings for the rotational degrees of freedom. The double prime on d in equation (1) is introduced to distinguish the magnitude of this element of volume from the magnitudes of $d'\{\mathbf{N}\}_\theta$ and $d\{\mathbf{N}\}_\theta$ encountered below.

[c] The notation is that of McMillan and Mayer, except that we use Kirkwood's notation for distribution functions.

In q_{sv} the zero of energy is chosen at the bottom of the vibrational potential well. $H_{\mathbf{N}}$ includes the potential energy $U_{\mathbf{N}}$; the zero of potential energy for *inter*molecular interactions is chosen at infinite separation of all molecules, but the zero for *intra*molecular interactions is left arbitrary for each species (until Section IV).

We now integrate over the momenta in equation (1) and obtain

$$Q_{\mathbf{N}} = \frac{\prod_s q_{sv}^{N_s}}{\prod_s (N_s! \Lambda_{sx}^{N_s} \Lambda_{s\theta}^{N_s})} \int e^{-U_{\mathbf{N}}/kT} \, d\{\mathbf{N}\}_x \, d'\{\mathbf{N}\}_\theta \qquad (2)$$

where

$$\frac{1}{\Lambda_{sx}} = \left(\frac{2\pi m_s kT}{h^2} \right)^{3/2} \qquad (3)$$

The integration over $\{\mathbf{P}\}_\theta$ gives a constant, $1/\prod_s \Lambda_{s\theta}^{N_s}$ and also, in general, a function of rotational coordinates which, together with $d''\{\mathbf{N}\}_\theta$, is included in $d'\{\mathbf{N}\}_\theta$. For example, in the familiar case of a single rigid diatomic molecule of species s, we have[8]

$$\frac{1}{\Lambda_{s\theta}} = \frac{2\pi I_s kT}{h^2}$$

$$d''(i_s)_\theta = d\theta_{i_s} \, d\varphi_{i_s} \; ; \; d'(i_s)_\theta = \sin \theta_{i_s} \, d\theta_{i_s} \, d\varphi_{i_s}$$

where (i_s) is used to denote the coordinates of molecule i of species s. The symbolic subscript θ is, of course, not to be confused with the angle θ_{i_s}.

When N_s/V is very small for all s, we have a perfect gas mixture. $U_{\mathbf{N}}$ is then the sum of separate contributions from each molecule; these contributions arise from *intra*molecular interactions. We have in this case, from equation (2),

$$Q_{\mathbf{N}} = \frac{\left(\prod_s q_{sv}^{N_s} \right) \left(\prod_s V^{N_s} \lambda_{s\theta}^{N_s} \right)}{\prod_s (N_s! \Lambda_{sx}^{N_s} \Lambda_{s\theta}^{N_s})} \qquad (4)$$

where

$$\lambda_{s\theta} = \int \exp \left[-U_{i_s}((i_s)_\theta)/kT \right] \, d'(i_s)_\theta \qquad (5)$$

$U_{i_s} \equiv U_{N_s=1}$ is a function of the (internal) rotational coordinates of molecule i_s. For the rigid rotator above, $U_{i_s} = $ constant and

$$\lambda_{s\theta} = \exp(-U_{i_s}/kT) \int \sin \theta_{i_s} \, d\theta_{i_s} \, d\varphi_{i_s} = 4\pi \exp(-U_{i_s}/kT)$$

It is convenient to rewrite equation (2) in the form

$$Q_\mathbf{N} = \frac{Z_\mathbf{N}}{\prod_s (N_s! \Lambda_s^{N_s})} \tag{6}$$

where

$$\frac{1}{\Lambda_s} = \frac{q_{sv} \lambda_{s\theta}}{\Lambda_{sx} \Lambda_{s\theta}} \tag{7}$$

and

$$Z_\mathbf{N} = \prod_s \frac{1}{\lambda_{s\theta}^{N_s}} \int e^{-U_\mathbf{N}/kT} \, d\{\mathbf{N}\}_x \, d'\{\mathbf{N}\}_\theta \tag{8}$$

Or if we define $d(i_s)_\theta$ and $d\{\mathbf{N}\}_\theta$ by the equations

$$\frac{d'\{\mathbf{N}\}_\theta}{\prod_s \lambda_{s\theta}^{N_s}} = \prod_s \left[\frac{d'(1_s)_\theta}{\lambda_{s\theta}} \cdot \frac{d'(2_s)_\theta}{\lambda_{s\theta}} \cdots \frac{d'(N_s)_\theta}{\lambda_{s\theta}} \right]$$

$$= \prod_s [d(1_s)_\theta \cdot d(2_s)_\theta \cdots d(N_s)_\theta] \tag{9}$$

$$= d\{\mathbf{N}\}_\theta$$

then

$$Z_\mathbf{N} = \int e^{-U_\mathbf{N}/kT} \, d\{\mathbf{N}\} \tag{10}$$

where

$$d\{\mathbf{N}\} \equiv d\{\mathbf{N}\}_x \, d\{\mathbf{N}\}_\theta \tag{11}$$

Thus $Z_\mathbf{N}$, the configuration integral, is normalized in such a way that

$$Z_\mathbf{N} = \prod_s V^{N_s} \tag{12}$$

for a perfect gas mixture.

Distribution Functions in an Open System

In an *open* system, the grand partition function is

$$\Xi = e^{pV/kT} = \sum_{\mathbf{N} \geqq 0} \exp \left[(N_1 \mu_1 + \cdots + N_\nu \mu_\nu)/kT \right] Q_\mathbf{N} \tag{13a}$$

$$= \sum_{\mathbf{N} \geqq 0} \left(\prod_s \frac{z_s^{N_s}}{N_s!} \right) Z_\mathbf{N} \tag{13b}$$

$$= \sum_{\mathbf{N} \geqq 0} \left(\prod_s \frac{z_s^{N_s}}{N_s!} \right) \int e^{-U_\mathbf{N}/kT} \, d\{\mathbf{N}\} \tag{13c}$$

$$\rho^N g^N (r_1 \cdots r_N) = \frac{N!}{(N-m)!} \int_V \int e^{-u/kT} dr_{N+1} \cdots dr_N$$

where we have used equation (6) and

$$z_s = \frac{\exp\ (\mu_s/kT)}{\Lambda_s} \tag{14}$$

We shall call z_s the activity of the species s. As the gas becomes infinitely dilute, $z_s \rightarrow \rho_s (= \bar{N}_s/V)$.

The probability of the open system containing exactly the numbers of molecules $\mathbf{N}$ is

$$P_{\mathbf{N}} = \left(\prod_s \frac{z_s^{N_s}}{N_s!} \right) Z_{\mathbf{N}}/\Xi \tag{15}$$

Let $\rho_{\mathbf{n}}(\{\mathbf{n}\},\ \mathbf{z})\ d\{\mathbf{n}\}$ be the probability of observing any n_1 molecules of species $1, \cdots$, and any n_ν molecules of species ν in $d\{\mathbf{n}\}$ at $\{\mathbf{n}\}$, where $\mathbf{z}$ represents the activity set $z_1,\ \cdots,\ z_\nu$. Then one can show that the "distribution function" $\rho_{\mathbf{n}}$ has the property that

$$\frac{e^{pV/kT}\rho_{\mathbf{n}}(\{\mathbf{n}\},\ \mathbf{z})}{\prod_s z_s^{n_s}} = \sum_{\mathbf{m} \geqq 0} \left(\prod_s \frac{z_s^{m_s}}{m_s!} \right) \int e^{-U_{\mathbf{m}+\mathbf{n}}/kT}\ d\{\mathbf{m}\} \tag{16}$$

It would be preferable to write the $\mathbf{n}$ of $\rho_{\mathbf{n}}$ as a superscript in parentheses, following Kirkwood, but this is not generally practicable for the printer. We therefore follow the rule that in all distribution functions and potentials of average force, boldface letters representing the set of molecules are written as subscripts, but when the set can be represented by a lightface letter it is written as a superscript in parentheses. We define $g_{\mathbf{n}}(\{\mathbf{n}\},\ \mathbf{z})$ and $W_{\mathbf{n}}(\{\mathbf{n}\},\ \mathbf{z})$ in terms of $\rho_{\mathbf{n}}(\{\mathbf{n}\},\ \mathbf{z})$ by

$$g_{\mathbf{n}} = e^{-W_{\mathbf{n}}/kT} = \frac{\rho_{\mathbf{n}}}{\prod_s \rho_s^{n_s}} \tag{17}$$

If each member of this equation is integrated over $\{\mathbf{n}\}_\theta$, we obtain

$$g_{\mathbf{n}x}(\{\mathbf{n}\})_x = e^{-W_{\mathbf{n}x}(\{\mathbf{n}\}_x)/kT} = \frac{\rho_{\mathbf{n}x}(\{\mathbf{n}\}_x)}{\prod_s \rho_s^{n_s}} \tag{18}$$

where these functions are called "spatial" functions. That is

$$g_{\mathbf{n}x}(\{\mathbf{n}\}_x) = \int g_{\mathbf{n}}(\{\mathbf{n}\})\ d\{\mathbf{n}\}_\theta \tag{19}$$

etc. The special case $g_x^{(2)}$ is the well-known radial distribution function.

It is easy to prove that $W_{\mathbf{n}}$ has the physical significance of a potential of the average force acting on the set $\mathbf{n}$. That is, let $q_{\mathbf{n}}$ represent an arbitrary coordinate associated with one of the molecules of the set $\mathbf{n}$. When there are $\mathbf{N}$ molecules in the system in the configuration $\{\mathbf{N}\}$, including the set $\mathbf{n}$ in the configuration $\{\mathbf{n}\}$, the component of force along $q_{\mathbf{n}}$ is $-\partial U_{\mathbf{N}}/\partial q_{\mathbf{n}}$. Then $W_{\mathbf{n}}$ satisfies

$$-\frac{\partial W_{\mathbf{n}}}{\partial q_{\mathbf{n}}} = \left\langle -\frac{\partial U_{\mathbf{N}}}{\partial q_{\mathbf{n}}} \right\rangle_{\mathrm{Av}} \tag{20}$$

where the force is averaged properly over all configurations of the $\mathbf{N} - \mathbf{n}$ molecules not in the set $\mathbf{n}$, for a given $\mathbf{N}$, and also over all $\mathbf{N} \geqq \mathbf{n}$. Incidentally, $W_{\mathbf{n}} \rightarrow U_{\mathbf{n}}$ as the gas becomes infinitely dilute.

Osmotic Pressure

Equations (13c), (15), and (16) summarize the important properties (for our purposes) of a multicomponent gas in terms of integrals over $e^{-U_{\mathbf{N}}/kT}$. McMillan and Mayer proved, without approximation, that completely analogous equations hold in an osmotic system.

Suppose we have a membrane permeable to "solvent" species (subscript τ) but not to "solute" species (subscript σ). On one side of the membrane we have a solution containing solvent species only. Let the value of each z_τ in this solution be denoted by z_τ^* and each $z_\sigma = \rho_\sigma = 0$. We summarize this activity set by $\mathbf{z}_\tau^*$, $\mathbf{0}_\sigma$. The solution on the other side of the membrane contains both solute and solvent species and is in equilibrium with the first solution with respect to each solvent species. The second activity set is $\mathbf{z}_\tau^*$, $\mathbf{z}_\sigma$, since each z_τ must have the same value, namely z_τ^* , in the two solutions. The pressure difference across the membrane is by definition just the osmotic pressure

$$\Pi = p(\mathbf{z}_\tau^* , \mathbf{z}_\sigma) - p(\mathbf{z}_\tau^* , \mathbf{0}_\sigma) \tag{21}$$

The analogue of equation (13c) is

$$e^{\Pi V/kT} = \sum_{\mathbf{m}_\sigma \geqq 0} \left[\prod_\sigma \frac{(z_\sigma/\gamma_\sigma^0)^{m_\sigma}}{m_\sigma!} \right]$$
$$\cdot \int \exp\left[-W_{\mathbf{m}_\sigma}(\{\mathbf{m}_\sigma\}, \mathbf{z}_\tau^*, \mathbf{0}_\sigma)/kT\right] d\{\mathbf{m}_\sigma\} \tag{22}$$

and of equation (15)

$$\mathfrak{P}_{\mathbf{m}_\sigma} = \frac{1}{e^{\Pi V/kT}} \left[\prod_\sigma \frac{(z_\sigma/\gamma_\sigma^0)^{m_\sigma}}{m_\sigma!} \right]$$
$$\cdot \int \exp\left[-W_{\mathbf{m}_\sigma}(\{\mathbf{m}_\sigma\}, \mathbf{z}_\tau^*, \mathbf{0}_\sigma)/kT\right] d\{\mathbf{m}_\sigma\} \tag{23}$$

and, finally, of equation (16)

$$\frac{e^{\Pi V/kT}\rho_{n_\sigma}(\{n_\sigma\}, z_\tau^*, z_\sigma)}{\prod_\sigma (z_\sigma/\gamma_\sigma^0)^{n_\sigma}} = \sum_{m_\sigma \geqq 0} \left[\prod_\sigma \frac{(z_\sigma/\gamma_\sigma^0)^{m_\sigma}}{m_\sigma!} \right]$$

$$\cdot \int \exp\left[-W_{n_\sigma+m_\sigma}(\{n_\sigma + m_\sigma\}, z_\tau^*, 0_\sigma)/kT\right] d\{m_\sigma\}$$

(24)

where $\mathfrak{P}$, m_σ, and n_σ refer to sets of solute molecules only. The "activity coefficient" γ_s is defined by z_s/ρ_s. In particular, γ_σ^0 denotes the activity coefficient of the solute species σ in the solution with activity set z_τ^*, 0_σ; that is, in a solution which is infinitely dilute with respect to all solute species but not with respect to solvent species. Similarly, W_{m_σ} in equations (22)–(24) is the potential of average force associated with a fixed set of solute molecules m_σ in a solution which is infinitely dilute with respect to solute molecules; in other words, W_{m_σ} refers to a fixed set of solute molecules immersed in a medium which contains solvent species only (with activity set z_τ^*). Incidentally, although each solvent species has the same activity in the two solutions, in general the solvent will have a different composition on the two sides of the membrane.

Equations (22)–(24) are remarkable results. For example, equation (22) states that the osmotic pressure depends on z_σ/γ_σ^0 for solute species and on the potential of average force on solute molecules in an infinitely dilute solution in a way which is formally identical with the dependence of the pressure of a gas (equation (13c)) on z_s for all species and on the potential energy (which is the potential of average force when *all* species are infinitely dilute). Solvent species do not enter explicitly into equations (22)–(24). However, the solvent must be important, and in fact plays its role implicitly through γ_σ^0 and $W_{m_\sigma}(z_\tau^*, 0_\sigma)$.

Aside from the elegance of these results, for practical purposes these analogies make it possible to take over without modification the formal procedures familiar in the theory of the gaseous state (virial expansions, integral equations for distribution functions, etc.) and apply them to solutes in solution. To make real progress, however, the potential of average force and the activity coefficients for solute molecules at infinite dilution must be specified. This can usually be done only in an approximate way.

Virial Expansion of Osmotic Pressure

We consider here the virial expansion for a single[d, 9] solute (corresponding to the virial expansion of a one-component gas). The solvent

[d] McMillan and Mayer consider any number of solutes.

may consist of any number of different species. Denote the integral in equation (22) by (we can drop the subscript σ here)

$$Z_m^* = \int \exp\left[-W^{(m)}(\{m\}, z_\tau^*, 0)/kT\right] d\{m\} \qquad (25)$$

Then

$$e^{\Pi V/kT} = \sum_{m \geq 0} \frac{(z/\gamma^0)^m}{m!} Z_m^* \qquad (26)$$

We desire, first, an expansion of Π/kT in powers of z/γ^0

$$\frac{\Pi}{kT} = \sum_{j \geq 1} b_j^* (z/\gamma^0)^j \qquad (27)$$

where the coefficients b_j^* are functions of z_τ^* and T. By taking the logarithm of both sides of equation (26) we find that the b_j^* are given by

$$1! \ V b_1^* = Z_1^* = V \qquad (28a)$$

$$2! \ V b_2^* = Z_2^* - Z_1^{*2} \qquad (28b)$$

$$3! \ V b_3^* = Z_3^* - 3Z_1^* Z_2^* + 2Z_1^{*3} \qquad (28c)$$

etc. The average value of m is

$$\bar{m} = \sum_{m \geq 0} \mathfrak{P}_m m$$

or, from equations (23) and (27)

$$\rho = \frac{\bar{m}}{V} = (z/\gamma^0)\left[\frac{\partial \Pi/kT}{\partial(z/\gamma^0)}\right]_{z_\tau^*, \ T}$$

$$= \sum_{j \geq 1} j b_j^* (z/\gamma^0)^j \qquad (29)$$

The coefficients a_2, a_3, $\cdots$ in the inverted series

$$z/\gamma^0 = \rho + a_2 \rho^2 + a_3 \rho^3 + \cdots$$

are found by substituting it in equation (29) for z/γ^0. Having found the coefficients, the inverted series is then introduced in equation (27) with the result

$$\frac{\Pi}{kT} = \rho\left[1 - \sum_{k \geq 1} \frac{k}{k+1} \beta_k^* \rho^k\right] \qquad (30)$$

where

$$\beta_1^* = 2b_2^* \qquad (31a)$$

$$\beta_2^* = 3(b_3^* - 2b_2^{*2}) \qquad (31b)$$

etc. If B_n^* is the nth virial coefficient, that is, if

$$\frac{\Pi}{kT} = \rho[1 + B_2^* \rho + B_3^* \rho^2 + \cdots] \tag{32}$$

then

$$B_n^* = -\frac{n-1}{n} \beta_{n-1}^* \tag{33}$$

For example, the second virial coefficient is

$$B_2^* = -b_2^* = -2\pi \int_0^\infty \{\exp[-W_x^{(2)}(r, \mathbf{z}_r^*, 0)/kT] - 1\} r^2 \, dr \tag{34a}$$

$$= -\frac{2\pi}{3kT} \int_0^\infty r^3 \frac{\partial W_x^{(2)}}{\partial r} \exp(-W_x^{(2)}/kT) \, dr \tag{34b}$$

where r is the distance between the centers of mass of two solute molecules.

Superposition Approximation

It is convenient here to number the members of the set $\mathbf{n}$ from 1 to $n = n_1 + n_2 + \cdots + n_\nu$, and omit the boldface notation. The superposition approximation can be defined by stating that the probability $\rho^{(m)} \, d\{m\}$ is assumed expressible as a product of independent pair probabilities. That is

$$\frac{\rho^{(m)}}{\rho^{(1)}((1)) \cdots \rho^{(1)}((m))} = \frac{\rho^{(2)}((1), (2))}{\rho^{(1)}((1))\rho^{(1)}((2))} \cdots \frac{\rho^{(2)}((m-1), (m))}{\rho^{(1)}((m-1))\rho^{(1)}((m))} \tag{35}$$

or

$$W^{(m)} - \sum_{\alpha=1}^m W^{(1)}((\alpha))$$

$$= \sum_{1 \leqq \beta < \gamma \leqq m} [W^{(2)}((\beta), (\gamma)) - W^{(1)}((\beta)) - W^{(1)}((\alpha))] \tag{36}$$

$$= \sum_{1 \leqq \beta < \gamma \leqq m} w((\beta), (\gamma)) \tag{37}$$

where equation (37) defines w. In a fluid, w is a function of the intermolecular distance r, $(\beta)_\theta$, and $(\gamma)_\theta$; also, $w \to 0$ as $r \to \infty$. The superposition approximation is generally accepted as quite accurate in the potential energy (that is, when $\mathbf{z} = \mathbf{0}$), but it is certainly a much more serious approximation in the potential of average force ($\mathbf{z} \neq \mathbf{0}$).

A condensed form of the osmotic equation of state can be written if the superposition approximation is made in the potential of average force for solute molecules at infinite dilution. The general result is

$$\frac{\Pi}{kT} = \sum_\sigma \rho_\sigma - \frac{1}{6VkT} \sum_\sigma \sum_\sigma \int r \frac{\partial w_{\sigma\sigma'}(\mathbf{z}_\tau^*, \mathbf{0}_\sigma)}{\partial r} \rho_{\sigma\sigma'}^{(2)}(\mathbf{z}_\tau^*, \mathbf{z}_\sigma) d(1_\sigma)(1_{\sigma'}) \qquad (38)$$

where $w_{\sigma\sigma'}$ and $\rho_{\sigma\sigma'}^{(2)}$ refer to a pair of solute molecules, one of species σ and the other of species σ'. For monatomic solutes, equation (38) reduces to

$$\frac{\Pi}{kT} = \sum_\sigma \rho_\sigma - \frac{1}{6kT} \sum_\sigma \sum_{\sigma'} \rho_\sigma \rho_{\sigma'} \int_0^\infty r \frac{\partial w_{\sigma\sigma'}(\mathbf{z}_\tau^*, \mathbf{0}_\sigma)}{\partial r} g_{\sigma\sigma'}^{(2)}(\mathbf{z}_\tau^*, \mathbf{z}_\sigma) 4\pi r^2 dr \qquad (39)$$

In this case $w = W^{(2)}$ since $W^{(1)} = 0$ for a monatomic species in a fluid.

DEBYE-HÜCKEL THEORY AND DONNAN EQUILIBRIUM

In applying the equations of Section II to ionic solutions, the mean composition in the (open) systems on both sides of the semipermeable membrane will correspond to electroneutrality except for thermodynamically negligible deviations which, however, are responsible for the electrical potential difference across the membrane when it exists.[10] The chemical potentials μ_s of equation (13) for ionic species are so-called "electrochemical" potentials.[10]

No complications arise if the configuration integrals encountered in Section II converge. For example, convergence will be assured if the solvent (that is, the "infinitely dilute solution," the solution on the side of the membrane containing no solutes) is an ionic solution, for in this case the potential of average force between a pair of solute ions in the infinitely dilute solution will fall off with distance approximately as $e^{-\kappa r}/r$, $\kappa > 0$, because of the atmosphere of solvent ions surrounding each of the solute ions.[4, 11] This situation prevails in all or practically all protein solutions if the protein molecules are considered the only solute molecules.

If the solvent contains no ions, the potential of average force for a pair of solute ions in the infinitely dilute solution will fall off at least approximately as $1/r$. Divergence difficulties arise in configuration integrals involving this potential; for example, the virial expansion has to be abandoned. As an alternative, more complicated procedures[12-14] must be introduced. However, as will be illustrated below, no divergence problems present themselves in the application of equation (39) to ionic solutes with a nonionic solvent because $W^{(2)}$ (from $g^{(2)}$) in this equation refers to finite solute concentrations (instead of zero solute concentration as in the potentials of the virial expansion). Solute ions contribute to each other's ion atmospheres at finite solute concentrations and hence $W^{(2)}$ decreases approximately as $e^{-\kappa r}/r$, $\kappa > 0$, again.

We now discuss two examples (using the superposition approximation at infinite dilution).

Debye-Hückel Theory

Consider an electrolyte solution of monatomic ions, which we treat as point charges. The solvent is nonionic and has a dielectric constant D. We accept here the well-known relations of the Debye-Hückel theory for the potentials of average force, and merely show that equation (39) gives the correct osmotic pressure. For $w_{\sigma\sigma'}$ and $g_{\sigma\sigma'}^{(2)}$ in equation (39) we have

$$w_{\sigma\sigma'} = W_{\sigma\sigma'}{}^{(2)}(\mathbf{z}_\tau^*, \mathbf{0}_\sigma) = \frac{\bar{z}_\sigma \bar{z}_{\sigma'} \epsilon^2}{Dr} \tag{40}$$

and

$$g_{\sigma\sigma'}^{(2)}(\mathbf{z}_\tau^*, \mathbf{z}_\sigma) = \exp\left[-W_{\sigma\sigma'}{}^{(2)}(\mathbf{z}_\tau^*, \mathbf{z}_\sigma)/kT\right]$$

$$W_{\sigma\sigma'}^{(2)}(\mathbf{z}_\tau^*, \mathbf{z}_\sigma) = \frac{\bar{z}_\sigma \bar{z}_{\sigma'} \epsilon^2 e^{-\kappa r}}{Dr} \tag{41}$$

where $\epsilon = |$ electronic charge $|$, $\bar{z}_\sigma =$ algebraic valence of ion σ and

$$\kappa^2 = \frac{4\pi\epsilon^2}{DkT} \sum_\sigma \rho_\sigma \bar{z}_\sigma^2 \tag{42}$$

Neutrality requires that

$$\sum_\sigma \rho_\sigma \bar{z}_\sigma = 0 \tag{43}$$

If $\exp(-W_{\sigma\sigma'}^{(2)}/kT)$ in equation (41) is expanded, and equations (40) and (41) substituted into equation (39), then

$$\frac{\Pi}{kT} = \sum_\sigma \rho_\sigma + \frac{2\pi}{3} \sum_{\sigma,\sigma'} \rho_\sigma \rho_{\sigma'} \int_0^\infty r^3 \left(\frac{\bar{z}_\sigma \bar{z}_{\sigma'} \epsilon^2}{Dr^2 kT}\right)\left[1 - \frac{\bar{z}_\sigma \bar{z}_{\sigma'} \epsilon^2 e^{-\kappa r}}{DrkT} + \cdots\right] dr \tag{44}$$

The leading term in the series gives no contribution because of equation (43). Of the remaining terms, only the linear term in $1/kT$ is significant here as only linear terms in $1/kT$ were retained in deriving equation (41) in the Debye-Hückel theory. From the $1/kT$ term we find

$$\frac{\Pi}{kT} = \sum_\sigma \rho_\sigma - \frac{\kappa^3}{24\pi} \tag{45}$$

which is the correct result.

Donnan Membrane Equilibrium

On one side (the "outside") of a membrane we have an aqueous solution of a uni-univalent electrolyte at concentration c. On the other side (the "inside"), we have the positive ion of this electrolyte at concentration c_+, the negative ion at c_-, and an ion of valence $\bar{z}$ and concentration ρ which cannot pass through the membrane. All ions are considered as point charges. We treat this system from two different points of view: (a) the classical Donnan approach (but we introduce Debye-Hückel activity coefficients) and (b) the McMillan-Mayer method.

Donnan Method. Let κ and κ_i be the Debye-Hückel constants for outside and inside solutions, respectively

$$\kappa^2 = \frac{8\pi\epsilon^2 c}{DkT} \tag{46}$$

$$\kappa_i^2 = \frac{4\pi\epsilon^2}{DkT}(c_+ + c_- + \rho\bar{z}^2) \tag{47}$$

We now equate the inside and outside electrochemical potentials for each of the two diffusible ions, using Debye-Hückel activity coefficients and the membrane potential $\psi = \psi_{in} - \psi_{out}$

$$\ln c - \frac{1}{2}\frac{\epsilon^2\kappa}{DkT} = \ln c_+ + \frac{\epsilon\psi}{kT} - \frac{1}{2}\frac{\epsilon^2\kappa_i}{DkT} \tag{48a}$$

$$\ln c - \frac{1}{2}\frac{\epsilon^2\kappa}{DkT} = \ln c_- - \frac{\epsilon\psi}{kT} - \frac{1}{2}\frac{\epsilon^2\kappa_i}{DkT} \tag{48b}$$

On combining these equations, using the neutrality condition

$$c_- = c_+ + \bar{z}\rho \tag{49}$$

to eliminate c_-, we have

$$c_+ c_- = c_+(c_+ + \bar{z}\rho) = c^2 \exp\left\{\alpha\left[\left(\frac{c_+}{c} + \frac{\bar{z}\rho}{2c} + \frac{\rho\bar{z}^2}{2c}\right)^{1/2} - 1\right]\right\} \tag{50a}$$

$$= c^2\left\{1 + \alpha\left[\left(\frac{c_+}{c} + \frac{\bar{z}\rho}{2c} + \frac{\rho\bar{z}^2}{2c}\right)^{1/2} - 1\right]\right\} \tag{50b}$$

where

$$\alpha = \frac{\epsilon^2\kappa}{DkT} = \left(\frac{\epsilon^2}{DkT}\right)^{3/2}(8\pi c)^{1/2} \tag{51}$$

The Debye-Hückel theory is valid only when $\alpha \ll 1$, hence we can use equation (50b), which is linear in α. When $\alpha = 0$

$$c_+ = \tfrac{1}{2}[-\bar{z}\rho + (\bar{z}^2\rho^2 + 4c^2)^{1/2}]$$

so we write, for $0 \leqq \alpha \ll 1$,

$$\frac{c_+}{c} = \xi - \frac{\bar{z}\rho}{2c} + \left[\left(\frac{\bar{z}\rho}{2c}\right)^2 + 1\right]^{1/2} \tag{52}$$

where $\xi \to 0$ as $\alpha \to 0$. If equation (52) is substituted for c_+/c in equation (50b) and we keep only linear terms in α and ξ, we find

$$\xi = \frac{\alpha}{2\left[\left(\frac{\bar{z}\rho}{2c}\right)^2 + 1\right]^{1/2}} \left(\left\{\frac{\rho\bar{z}^2}{2c} + \left[\left(\frac{\bar{z}\rho}{2c}\right)^2 + 1\right]^{1/2}\right\}^{1/2} - 1\right) \tag{53}$$

Equation (53), when substituted in equations (49) and (52), gives c_+ and c_- as functions of ρ.

To obtain the osmotic pressure Π, we use

$$\Pi = \Pi_{\text{in}} - \Pi_{\text{out}} \tag{54}$$

where Π_{in} is the osmotic pressure for the system: inside solution—membrane permeable to water only—water. Π_{out} has an analogous meaning for the outside solution. From equations (45), (46), (47), (49), (52), and (53)

$$\frac{\Pi}{kT} = \left(c_+ + c_- + \rho - \frac{\kappa_i^3}{24\pi}\right) - \left(2c - \frac{\kappa^3}{24\pi}\right) \tag{55a}$$

$$= \rho + 2c\left[\left(\frac{\bar{z}\rho}{2c}\right)^2 + 1\right]^{1/2} - 2c$$

$$- \frac{\alpha c}{3}\left(\left\{\frac{\rho\bar{z}^2}{2c} + \left[\left(\frac{\bar{z}\rho}{2c}\right)^2 + 1\right]^{1/2}\right\}^{3/2} - 1\right)$$

$$+ \frac{\alpha c}{\left[\left(\frac{\bar{z}\rho}{2c}\right)^2 + 1\right]^{1/2}}\left(\left\{\frac{\rho\bar{z}^2}{2c} + \left[\left(\frac{\bar{z}\rho}{2c}\right)^2 + 1\right]^{1/2}\right\}^{1/2} - 1\right) \tag{55b}$$

In the limit $\alpha \to 0$, the last two terms drop out and we have the usual Donnan result. In the limit $c \to 0$, recalling that α contains $c^{1/2}$, we find

$$\frac{\Pi}{kT} \to \rho + |\bar{z}|\rho - \frac{1}{24\pi}\left[\frac{4\pi\epsilon^2}{DkT}(\rho\bar{z}^2 + \rho|\bar{z}|)\right]^{3/2} \quad (c \to 0) \tag{56}$$

This is the osmotic pressure of a solution containing the nondiffusible ions and their counter-ions, the outside solution in this case being pure

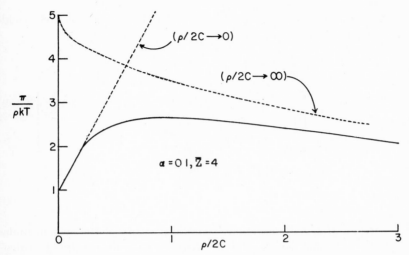

FIG. 1. Osmotic pressure in Donnan Equilibrium, using the Donnan method (equations (48) and (55a)).

water. At the other extreme, in the limit $\rho \to 0$, expansion of equation (55b) yields[e]

$$\frac{\Pi}{kT} \to \rho + \frac{\bar{z}^2 \rho^2}{4c} \left(1 - \frac{\alpha \bar{z}^2}{4} \right) \qquad (\rho \to 0) \qquad (57)$$

In the usual Donnan treatment ($\alpha = 0$), ρ is the contribution to Π/kT owing to the difference in concentration of the nondiffusible ion across the membrane, whereas $\bar{z}^2 \rho^2 / 4c$ is the contribution (when $\rho \to 0$) owing to the sum of the differences in concentrations of the diffusible ions, that is $c_+ + c_- - 2c$. The term in α is a Debye-Hückel correction.

According to equation (55b), $\Pi/\rho kT$ is a function of $\rho/2c$, $\bar{z}^2$, and α. The limiting behavior for $\rho/2c \to 0$ and ∞ has been discussed in equations (57) and (56), respectively. Figure 1 shows the full curve and the two limiting curves in the arbitrary numerical example $\alpha = 0.1$ and $\bar{z} = 4$.

To find the membrane potential ψ, we write equation (48b) in the form

$$e^{\epsilon \psi / kT} = \frac{c_-}{c} \exp \left[-\frac{1}{2} \frac{\epsilon^2}{DkT} (\kappa_i - \kappa) \right] \qquad (58)$$

[e] The term in ρ^2 is also contained in Hill, T. L., *Discussions, Faraday Soc.* **13,** 132 (1953), Equation 27b.

Substitution of equations (49), (52), and (53) in equation (58) yields (to linear terms in α)

$$e^{\epsilon\psi/kT} = \left\{\frac{\bar{z}\rho}{2c} + \left[\left(\frac{\bar{z}\rho}{2c}\right)^2 + 1\right]^{1/2}\right\}$$

$$\cdot\left[1 - \frac{\alpha}{2}\frac{\left(\left\{\frac{\rho\bar{z}^2}{2c} + \left[\left(\frac{\bar{z}\rho}{2c}\right)^2 + 1\right]^{1/2}\right\}^{1/2} - 1\right)\frac{\bar{z}\rho}{2c}}{\left[\left(\frac{\bar{z}\rho}{2c}\right)^2 + 1\right]^{1/2}}\right] \quad (59)$$

As $c \to 0$, $|\psi| \to \infty$. As $\rho \to 0$, we find, to terms in ρ^2, that

$$\frac{\epsilon\psi}{kT} \to \frac{\bar{z}\rho}{2c} - \frac{\alpha\bar{z}^3\rho^2}{16c^2} \quad (60)$$

McMillan-Mayer Method. The osmotic pressure of the system under consideration, expressed as a virial expansion, can in principle be calculated from equation (32) of the McMillan and Mayer theory provided only that the potential of average force at infinite dilution is known. In the present example we need, then, the potential of average force between an isolated pair of nondiffusible ions immersed in the "outside" solution. In the notation of section (a) above, this is, assuming the validity of the Debye-Hückel limiting law,

$$W^{(2)}(0) = \frac{\bar{z}^2\epsilon^2 e^{-\kappa r}}{Dr} \quad (61)$$

where κ is given by equation (46). It is not necessary here to consider at all quantities such as κ_i, c_+, c_-, ψ, etc.

To calculate the second virial coefficient B_2^*, we insert equation (61) in equation (34a) and expand the exponential in powers of $1/kT$ to $(1/kT)^2$. (Alternatively, equation (34b) may be used with an expansion of the exponential to $1/kT$). The retention of higher powers of $1/kT$ would be inconsistent with the use of the Debye-Hückel potential, equation (61) (see equation (44), *et seq.*). Writing, then,

$$\exp\left[-W^{(2)}(0)/kT\right] - 1 = -\frac{W^{(2)}(0)}{kT} + \frac{1}{2}\left[\frac{W^{(2)}(0)}{kT}\right]^2 \quad (62)$$

the first term on the right-hand side leads, in equation (34a), to a contribution to B_2^* of $\bar{z}^2/4c$. The second term contributes $-\bar{z}^4\alpha/16c$. This result for B_2^* agrees with the Donnan term in ρ^2 in equation (57). Thus, for example, instead of regarding the term $\bar{z}^2\rho^2/4c$ in equation (57) (with $\alpha = 0$) as a correction to the osmotic pressure arising from the unequal diffusible ion distribution, we may equally well attribute this term to the repulsive forces (equation (61)) between nondiffusible ions in the infinitely dilute solution. It is interesting that in the Donnan method the term $\bar{z}^2\rho^2/4c$ follows without use of the Debye-Hückel theory, whereas on the other hand, in the McMillan-Mayer method, the Debye-Hückel theory is definitely used (equations (61) and (62)). This may be regarded as a confirmation of the Debye-Hückel limiting law (equation (61)).

The third virial coefficient B_3^* can be expressed in terms of V, Z_2^*, and Z_3^* using equations (28), (31), and (33). It is then easy to verify that this expression for B_3^* is equivalent to the more familiar equation due to Mayer,[15]

$$B_3^* = -\frac{1}{3V} \int f_{12}f_{13}f_{23}\, d(1)_x\, d(2)_x\, d(3)_x \tag{63}$$

where

$$f_{ij} = \exp\left[-W^{(2)}(r_{ij}, 0)/kT\right] - 1 \tag{64}$$

Since $W^{(2)}(0) \geqq 0$ for all r (equation (61)), $f_{ij} \leqq 0$ for all r_{ij}, and hence B_3^* is positive (the same is true of B_2^*, of course).

The computation of B_3^* in equation (63) offers no difficulties using the method of Bird, Spotz, and Hirschfelder.[16] The first term on the right-hand side of equation (62) suffices for f_{ij} in order to obtain B_3^* to the linear term in α. One finds

$$B_3^* = \frac{\alpha \bar{z}^6}{96c^2} \tag{65}$$

Expansion of the Donnan equation, equation (55), to ρ^3 gives a result which differs from equation (65): $\bar{z}^6$ in equation (65) is replaced by $\bar{z}^6 - 6\bar{z}^4$. Although B_2^*, B_3^*, etc., calculated by the McMillan-Mayer method, are correct to linear terms in α *for the potential of equation* (61), it cannot be assumed that these virial coefficients are exact for a system of point charges, since, as Mayer has pointed out in another connection,[13] higher terms not included in equation (61) might affect higher virial coefficients. In fact, one can show[a] that the McMillan-Mayer third and higher virial coefficients from equation (61) are certainly not exact in this sense. In the Donnan method it is also certain that the third and higher virial coefficients are not exact in the sense mentioned since, for sufficiently small $|\bar{z}|$, the Donnan third virial coefficient is negative, which is impossible with strictly repulsive forces between nondiffusible ions.

In the case of a general diffusible electrolyte (concentration c_j in the outside solution and charge $\bar{z}_j$ for the jth species), the McMillan-Mayer method gives[a]

$$B_2^* = \frac{\bar{z}^2}{2\Sigma^{(2)}} - \frac{\alpha\bar{z}^4}{8\Sigma^{(2)}} \tag{66a}$$

whereas the Donnan method gives[a]

$$B_2^* = \frac{\bar{z}^2}{2\Sigma^{(2)}} - \frac{\alpha}{8\Sigma^{(2)}}\left(\bar{z}^2 - \bar{z}\frac{\Sigma^{(3)}}{\Sigma^{(2)}}\right)^2 \tag{66b}$$

where

$$\Sigma^{(n)} = \sum_j c_j \bar{z}_j^n$$

The first terms in equations (66a) and (66b) agree, as do also the second terms when $\Sigma^{(3)} = 0$. It is difficult to decide which second term, if either, is exact for a system of point charges when $\Sigma^{(3)} \neq 0$, without having available an exact extension of the Debye-Hückel theory to higher concentrations.

BINDING OF IONS OR MOLECULES ON PROTEIN MOLECULES

We consider a solution containing protein molecules P, ions or molecules a which can be "bound" by the protein molecules, and an arbitrary number of other types of molecules which are not "bound." There are important questions concerning the definition of "binding" which we bypass here. These are discussed in detail elsewhere.[a] We simply state that it proves to be possible to discuss *explicitly* the binding of one type of molecule, and not others, on P, without introducing any approximations. Of course it is only profitable to consider binding of a given species explicitly when the binding forces holding the species on P are strong.

Suppose there are B sites (not equivalent in general) on P for the binding of a. When s molecules of a are bound, there are $B!/s!(B-s)!$ different distributions (an arbitrary one of which we label ω_s) of the s molecules among the B sites. Let us consider each combination s, ω_s as a different species of protein molecule, P_{ω_s} (ω_s as a subscript implies s, ω_s). The number of molecules of P_{ω_s} is denoted by N_{ω_s}.

We introduce here the "absolute activity" of any component (see equation (14))

$$\mathfrak{z} = e^{\mu/kT} = z\Lambda$$

Consider a solution which contains **N** protein molecules at $\mathfrak{z}$(**N** represents the set of numbers N_{ω_s}, and $\mathfrak{z}$ the set $\mathfrak{z}_{\omega_s}$), $\mathfrak{N}_a$ unbound a molecules at the absolute activity $x \equiv \exp(\mu_a/kT)$, and an arbitrary number of other components q (number L_q and absolute activity $y_q \equiv \exp(\mu_q/kT)$). Let $Q_{\mathfrak{N}_a \mathbf{NL}}$ be the partition function at V and T. Then, from equation (13a),

$$\Xi = \sum_{\mathfrak{N}_a, \mathbf{N}, \mathbf{L}} (\prod_q y_q^{L_q}) x^{\mathfrak{N}_a} (\prod_{s, \omega_s} \mathfrak{z}_{\omega_s}^{N_{\omega_s}}) Q_{\mathfrak{N}_a \mathbf{NL}} \tag{67}$$

The x just introduced should not be confused with the symbolic subscript x.

Osmotic Pressure and Amount of Binding

Now consider an osmotic equilibrium in which the protein molecules P_{ω_s} cannot pass through the membrane, but all other molecules can. Let the "inside" solution contain solutes (P_{ω_s}) and solvents at absolute activities $\mathfrak{z}$, **y**, and x and the outside solution contain solvents at **y** and $x(\mathfrak{z} = \mathbf{0})$. Then, just as we passed from equation (13a) to equation (22) in Section II, in this special case we pass from equation (67) to

$$e^{\Pi V/kT} = \sum_{\mathbf{m} \geqq \mathbf{0}} \left[\prod_{s, \omega_s} \frac{(\mathfrak{z}_{\omega_s}/\Lambda_{\omega_s} \gamma_{\omega_s}^0)^{m_{\omega_s}}}{m_{\omega_s}!} \right]$$
$$\cdot \int \exp\left[-W_{\mathbf{m}}(\{\mathbf{m}\}, x, \mathbf{y}, \mathbf{0}_{\omega_s})/kT \right] d\{\mathbf{m}\} \tag{68}$$

where **m** represents a set of m_{ω_s}. Of course $\gamma_{\omega_s}^0$ is a function of x and **y** (and T). By virtue of the equilibria existing, we have

$$\mu_{\omega_s} = s\mu_a + \mu_{s=0}$$
$$\mathfrak{z}_{\omega_s} = x^s \mathfrak{z} \tag{69}$$

for all ω_s belonging to s, where $\mathfrak{z}$ is the absolute activity of a protein molecule with $s = 0$. Then

$$e^{\Pi V/kT} = \sum_{\mathbf{m} \geqq \mathbf{0}} \left[\prod_{s, \omega_s} \frac{(\mathfrak{z}x^s/\Lambda_{\omega_s} \gamma_{\omega_s}^0)^{m_{\omega_s}}}{m_{\omega_s}!} \right] \int e^{-W_{\mathbf{m}}(0)/kT} d\{\mathbf{m}\} \tag{70}$$

where we have used $W_{\mathbf{m}}(0)$ as shorthand for $W_{\mathbf{m}}(\{\mathbf{m}\}, x, \mathbf{y}, \mathfrak{z} = 0)$.

With the aid of equation (23) we can immediately write down expressions for the mean number of protein molecules $\bar{M}_P$ and the mean number of a molecules $\bar{M}_a$ bound to protein in the inside solution

$$\bar{M}_P = \langle \sum_{s, \omega_s} m_{\omega_s} \rangle_{\mathrm{Av}}$$
$$= \frac{1}{e^{\Pi V/kT}} \sum_{\mathbf{m} \geqq \mathbf{0}} (\sum_{s, \omega_s} m_{\omega_s}) \left[\prod_{s, \omega_s} \frac{(\mathfrak{z}x^s/\Lambda_{\omega_s} \gamma_{\omega_s}^0)^{m_{\omega_s}}}{m_{\omega_s}!} \right] \int e^{-W_{\mathbf{m}}(0)/kT} d\{\mathbf{m}\} \tag{71}$$

$$\bar{M}_a = \left\langle \sum_{s,\omega_s} s m_{\omega_s} \right\rangle_{\mathrm{Av}}$$

$$= \frac{1}{e^{\Pi V/kT}} \sum_{\mathbf{m} \geq 0} \left(\sum_{s,\omega_s} s m_{\omega_s} \right) \left[\prod_{s,\omega_s} \frac{(\mathfrak{z} x^s / \Lambda_{\omega_s} \gamma^0_{\omega_s})^{m_{\omega_s}}}{m_{\omega_s}!} \right] \int e^{-W_{\mathbf{m}}(0)/kT} d\{\mathbf{m}\} \tag{72}$$

We note that

$$\bar{M}_P = \mathfrak{z} \left(\frac{\partial \ln e^{\Pi V/kT}}{\partial \mathfrak{z}} \right)_{x,\mathbf{y},T,V} \tag{73}$$

and, formally,

$$\bar{M}_a = x \left(\frac{\partial \ln e^{\Pi V/kT}}{\partial x} \right)_{\mathfrak{z},T,V,\gamma,W} \tag{74}$$

where the subscripts γ and W signify that $\gamma^0_{\omega_s}$ and $W_{\mathbf{m}}(0)$ are held constant in the differentiation with respect to x.

In equation (70), let us replace $W_{\mathbf{m}}(0)$ by $\mathfrak{W}_{\mathbf{m}}(0)$, using

$$\mathfrak{W}_{\mathbf{m}}(0) = W_{\mathbf{m}}(0) - \sum_{s,\omega_s} [W^{(1)}((1_{\omega_s}), 0) + \cdots + W^{(1)}((m_{\omega_s}), 0)]$$

as the definition of $\mathfrak{W}_{\mathbf{m}}(0)$. Since each $W^{(1)}(0)$ depends only on rotational coordinates in a fluid, $\exp[-W^{(1)}(0)/kT]$ can be placed in front of the translational coordinate integral sign if we restrict ourselves to an infinitely dilute solution (solvent) which is a fluid. Thus we can write

$$e^{\Pi V/kT} = \sum_{\mathbf{m} \geq 0} \int d'\{\mathbf{m}\}_\theta \prod_{s,\omega_s} \left\{ \frac{(\mathfrak{z} x^s)^{m_{\omega_s}}}{m_{\omega_s}!} \prod_{(m_{\omega_s})} H_{\omega_s} \right\} \int e^{-\mathfrak{W}_{\mathbf{m}}(0)/kT} d\{\mathbf{m}\}_x \tag{75}$$

where

$$\prod_{(m_{\omega_s})} H_{\omega_s} = H_{\omega_s}((1_{\omega_s})_\theta) H_{\omega_s}((2_{\omega_s})_\theta) \cdots H_{\omega_s}((m_{\omega_s})_\theta) \tag{76a}$$

and

$$H_{\omega_s}((i_{\omega_s})_\theta) = \frac{\exp\left[-W^{(1)}((i_{\omega_s})_\theta), x, \mathbf{y}, \mathfrak{z} = 0)/kT\right]}{\gamma^0_{\omega_s} \Lambda_{\omega_s} \lambda_{\omega_s \theta}} \tag{76b}$$

Roughly speaking, H_{ω_s} is a partition function for a single molecule of species s, ω_s in a particular rotational configuration and includes interactions between a molecules bound to the same protein molecule. Actually, H_{ω_s} will depend only on the internal rotational configuration, and not the external. $\mathfrak{W}_{\mathbf{m}}(0)$ has the property that it approaches zero when the molecules of the set $\mathbf{m}$ are widely separated; also, $\mathfrak{W}^{(1)} = 0$ by definition.

We now introduce the notation

$$\sum_{(s)} = \sum_{s,\omega_s} \int d'(1_{\omega_s})_\theta \tag{77}$$

That is, $\sum_{(s)}$ is a sum over all values of s, over all distributions ω_s for each s, and over all rotational configurations for each s, ω_s. Using this notation, let us write equation (75) in the form of a power series in ζ

$$e^{\Pi V/kT} = 1 + \zeta C_1 + \frac{\zeta^2}{2!} C_2 + \frac{\zeta^3}{3!} C_3 + \cdots \tag{78}$$

where

$$C_1 = c_1 V; \; c_1 = \sum_{(s)} x^s H_{\omega_s} \tag{79a}$$

$$C_2 = \sum_{(s)} \sum_{(s')} (x^s H_{\omega_s})(x^{s'} H_{\omega_s'})$$
$$\cdot \int \exp\left[-\mathfrak{W}^{(2)}((1_{\omega_s}), (1_{\omega_s'}), 0)/kT\right] d(1_{\omega_s})_x \, d(1_{\omega_s'})_x \tag{79b}$$

$$C_3 = \sum_{(s)} \sum_{(s')} \sum_{(s'')} (x^s H_{\omega_s})(x^{s'} H_{\omega_s'})(x^{s''} H_{\omega_s''})$$
$$\cdot \int \exp\left[-\mathfrak{W}^{(3)}((1_{\omega_s}), (1_{\omega_s'}), (1_{\omega_s''}), 0)/kT\right] d(1_{\omega_s})_x \, d(1_{\omega_s'})_x \, d(1_{\omega_s''})_x \tag{79c}$$

etc., where the subscript ω_s' should be understood as s', ω_s' etc., and terms with $(s) = (s')$, etc., are included in the sums. If equation (78) is rewritten as

$$e^{\Pi V/kT} = 1 + (\zeta c_1)[V] + \frac{(\zeta c_1)^2}{2!}\left[\frac{C_2}{c_1^2}\right] + \frac{(\zeta c_1)^3}{3!}\left[\frac{C_3}{c_1^3}\right] + \cdots \tag{80}$$

the method of equations (26)–(28) gives immediately

$$\frac{\Pi}{kT} = \sum_{j \geq 1} \mathfrak{b}_j (\zeta c_1)^j \tag{81}$$

where

$$1!V\mathfrak{b}_1 = V \tag{82a}$$

$$2!V\mathfrak{b}_2 = \frac{C_2}{c_1^2} - V^2 \tag{82b}$$

$$3!V\mathfrak{b}_3 = \frac{C_3}{c_1^3} - 3V \frac{C_2}{c_1^2} + 2V^3 \tag{82c}$$

etc. Equations (73) and (81) then lead to

$$\rho = \frac{\bar{M}_P}{V} = \sum_{j \geq 1} j\mathfrak{b}_j (\mathfrak{z}c_1)^j \tag{83}$$

Following equations (29)–(33), we find

$$\mathfrak{z}c_1 = \rho - 2\mathfrak{b}_2\rho^2 + (8\mathfrak{b}_2^2 - 3\mathfrak{b}_3)\rho^3 + \cdots \tag{84}$$

and the virial expansion of the osmotic pressure

$$\frac{\Pi}{kT} = \rho + \mathfrak{B}_2\rho^2 + \mathfrak{B}_3\rho^3 + \cdots \tag{85}$$

where

$$\mathfrak{B}_2 = -\mathfrak{b}_2 \tag{86a}$$

$$\mathfrak{B}_3 = -2(\mathfrak{b}_3 - 2\mathfrak{b}_2^2) \tag{86b}$$

etc. From equations (79a), (79b), (82b), and (86a), the explicit expression for the second virial coefficient is

$$\mathfrak{B}_2 = -\frac{1}{2} \frac{\displaystyle\sum_{(s)} \sum_{(s')} [s, s'](x^s H_{\omega_s})(x^{s'} H_{\omega_s'})}{\left(\displaystyle\sum_{(s)} x^s H_{\omega_s}\right)^2} \tag{87}$$

where

$$[s, s'] = \int_0^\infty \{\exp\left[-\mathfrak{W}^{(2)}(r, (1_{\omega_s})_\theta, (1_{\omega_s'})_\theta, 0)/kT\right] - 1\} \, 4\pi r^2 \, dr \tag{88}$$

Equation (88) contains the conventional type of integral for the second virial coefficient (see equation (34a)), and equation (87) shows the proper type of averaging of this integral to use, for given x, with respect to the number of molecules bound, the distribution of bound molecules among sites, and the rotational configurations of the protein molecules. When x is small (x is proportional to the activity of a in solution), $\mathfrak{B}_2$ in equation (87) can be expanded[a] in powers of x. If $\mathfrak{W}^{(2)}(0)$ happens to be the same for all (s), (s'), equation (87) reduces to

$$\mathfrak{B}_2 = -\frac{1}{2} \int_0^\infty \{\exp\left[-\mathfrak{W}^{(2)}(0)/kT\right] - 1\} \, 4\pi r^2 \, dr \tag{89}$$

The amount of binding of a per protein molecule is, from equations (73), (74), and (78)

$$\frac{\bar{M}_a}{\bar{M}_P} = \frac{x(\partial e^{\Pi V/kT}/\partial x)_{\mathfrak{z},T,V,\gamma,w}}{\mathfrak{z}(\partial e^{\Pi V/kT}/\partial \mathfrak{z})_{x,y,T,V}}$$

$$= \frac{\dfrac{\mathfrak{z}E_1}{1!} + \dfrac{\mathfrak{z}^2 E_2}{2!} + \dfrac{\mathfrak{z}^3 E_3}{3!} + \cdots}{\mathfrak{z}C_1 + \dfrac{\mathfrak{z}^2 C_2}{1!} + \dfrac{\mathfrak{z}^3 C_3}{2!} + \cdots} \qquad (90)$$

where

$$E_1 = e_1 V; \qquad e_1 = \sum_{(s)} s x^s H_{\omega_s} \qquad (91a)$$

$$E_2 = \sum_{(s)} \sum_{(s')} (s + s')(x^s H_{\omega_s})(x^{s'} H_{\omega'_s})$$

$$\cdot \int \exp\left[-\mathfrak{W}^{(2)}((1_{\omega_s}), (1_{\omega'_s}), 0)/kT\right] d(1_{\omega_s})_x\, d(1_{\omega'_s})_x \qquad (91b)$$

$$E_3 = \sum_{(s)} \sum_{(s')} \sum_{(s'')} (s + s' + s'')(x^s H_{\omega_s})(x^{s'} H_{\omega'_s})(x^{s''} H_{\omega_s}'')$$

$$\cdot \int \exp\left[-\mathfrak{W}^{(3)}((1_{\omega_s}), (1_{\omega'_s}), (1_{\omega_s}''), 0)/kT\right] d(1_{\omega_s})_x\, d(1_{\omega'_s})_x\, d(1_{\omega_s}'')_x \qquad (91c)$$

etc. Equation (90) can also be written as

$$\frac{\bar{M}_a}{\bar{M}_P} = \frac{e_1}{c_1}\left[1 + \mathfrak{z}\left(\frac{E_2}{2E_1} - \frac{C_2}{C_1}\right) + \mathfrak{z}^2\left(\frac{E_3}{6E_1} - \frac{E_2 C_2}{2E_1 C_1} - \frac{C_3}{2C_1} + \frac{C_2^2}{C_1^2}\right) + \cdots\right] (92)$$

or, using equation (84),

$$\frac{\bar{M}_a}{\bar{M}_P} = \frac{e_1}{c_1}\left[1 + \frac{\rho}{c_1}\left(\frac{E_2}{2E_1} - \frac{C_2}{C_1}\right)\right.$$

$$\left. + \left(\frac{\rho}{c_1}\right)^2\left(\frac{E_3}{6E_1} - \frac{E_2 C_2}{E_1 C_1} - \frac{C_3}{2C_1} + \frac{2C_2^2}{C_1^2} + \frac{E_2 C_1}{2E_1} - C_2\right) + \cdots\right] (93)$$

In the limit $\rho \rightarrow 0$, the amount of binding

$$\frac{\bar{M}_a}{\bar{M}_P} = \frac{e_1}{c_1} = \frac{\displaystyle\sum_{(s)} s x^s H_{\omega_s}}{\displaystyle\sum_{(s)} x^s H_{\omega_s}} \qquad (\rho = 0) \quad (94)$$

is in a form which is familiar from the usual discussion of protein binding neglecting protein-protein interactions.[17-20] However, the present theory provides the precise statistical mechanical significance of H_{ω_s} in equation (94).

At finite protein concentrations, correction terms owing to the influence of protein-protein interactions must be considered in equation (93). The question of interest is: under what conditions is $(\rho/c_1)[(E_2/2E_1) - (C_2/C_1)]$ not negligible compared to unity? For the present, it can be stated that although no experimental data appear to be available to answer this question directly, there is some indirect evidence that indicates that under ordinary conditions in light scattering and osmotic pressure work the correction term is probably of the order of about 0.02 (2 % of the leading term). This tentative conclusion has been reached as follows. From equations (82b) and (86a) we observe that

$$\frac{-\rho(\partial \mathfrak{B}_2/\partial \ln x)_{T,\gamma,W}}{e_1/c_1} = \frac{\rho}{c_1}\left(\frac{E_2}{2E_1} - \frac{C_2}{C_1}\right) \tag{95}$$

Now the change of the second virial coefficient with concentration of the ion being bound (e.g., H^+) is available experimentally in several cases, but not under conditions which correspond exactly to the unusual derivative in equation (95). If we ignore this difference for order of magnitude purposes, four different sets of data[21-23] (H^+ on insulin, H^+ on insulin, CNS^- on insulin, and H^+ on serum albumin) were found to give of the order of 0.02 in equation (95). It seems reasonable, for the present at least, to expect that, except in unusual cases, the influence of protein-protein interactions on binding will be small, although of course the converse effect of binding on protein-protein interactions is certainly not small in many systems.

Distribution Functions and Potentials of Average Force

In equation (24) we replace $\mathbf{m} + \mathbf{n}$ by $\mathbf{m}$ and obtain for the distribution function of a set of protein molecules

$$\rho_n(\{\mathbf{n}\}, x, \mathbf{y}, \mathfrak{z})$$

$$= \frac{1}{e^{\overline{\Pi}V/kT}} \sum_{\mathbf{m} \geq \mathbf{n}} \left[\prod_{s,\omega_s} \frac{(\mathfrak{z}x^s/\Lambda_{\omega_s}\gamma^0_{\omega_s})^{m_{\omega_s}}}{(m_{\omega_s} - n_{\omega_s})!}\right] \int e^{-W_{\mathbf{m}}(0)/kT} d\{\mathbf{m} - \mathbf{n}\} \tag{96}$$

$$= \frac{1}{e^{\overline{\Pi}V/kT}} \sum_{\mathbf{m} \geq \mathbf{n}} \int d'\{\mathbf{m} - \mathbf{n}\}_\theta \prod_{s,\omega_s} \left\{\frac{(\mathfrak{z}x^s)^{m_{\omega_s}}\lambda^{n_{\omega_s}}_{\omega_s\theta}}{(m_{\omega_s} - n_{\omega_s})!} \prod_{(m_{\omega_s})} H_{\omega_s}\right\}$$

$$\cdot \int e^{-\mathfrak{W}_{\mathbf{m}}(0)/kT} d\{\mathbf{m} - \mathbf{n}\}_x \tag{97}$$

where $\mathbf{m}$ and $\mathbf{n}$ both refer to solute sets. Also, the spatial distribution function for the set $\mathbf{n}$ is

$$\rho_{nx}(\{\mathbf{n}\}_x, x, \mathbf{y}, \mathfrak{z}) = \int \rho_n \, d\{\mathbf{n}\}_\theta$$

$$= \frac{1}{e^{\Pi V/kT}} \sum_{\mathbf{m} \ge \mathbf{n}} \int d'\{\mathbf{m}\}_\theta \prod_{s,\omega_s} \left\{ \frac{(\mathfrak{z}x^s)^{m_{\omega_s}}}{(m_{\omega_s} - n_{\omega_s})!} \prod_{(m_{\omega_s})} H_{\omega_s} \right\} \qquad (98)$$

$$\cdot \int e^{-\mathfrak{W}\,\mathbf{m}\,(0)/kT} \, d\{\mathbf{m} - \mathbf{n}\}_x$$

In the limit ρ or $\mathfrak{z} \to 0$, we set $e^{\Pi V/kT} = 1$, $\mathfrak{z} = \rho/c_1$, and retain only the term $\mathbf{m} = \mathbf{n}$

$$\rho_n(0) = \left(\frac{\rho}{c_1}\right)^n \prod_{s,\omega_s} \{(x^s \lambda_{\omega_s \theta})^{n_{\omega_s}} \prod_{(n_{\omega_s})} H_{\omega_s}\} e^{-\mathfrak{W}\,\mathbf{n}\,(0)/kT} \quad (\rho = 0) \qquad (99)$$

$$\rho_{nx}(0) = \left(\frac{\rho}{c_1}\right)^n \int d'\{\mathbf{n}\}_\theta \prod_{s,\omega_s} \{x^{sn_{\omega_s}} \prod_{(n_{\omega_s})} H_{\omega_s}\} e^{-\mathfrak{W}\,\mathbf{n}\,(0)/kT} \quad (\rho = 0) \qquad (100)$$

where

$$n = \sum_{s,\omega_s} n_{\omega_s}$$

The quantity $\rho_n d\{\mathbf{n}\}$ is the probability of observing the set $\mathbf{n}$ in $d\{\mathbf{n}\}$ at $\{\mathbf{n}\}$. Of greater interest is a probability such as this for a set of n protein molecules irrespective of species s, ω_s. Especially important is the probability of finding any n protein molecules in the spatial volume element $d\{n\}_x$ (i.e., irrespective of species s, ω_s and also of rotational configurations). We denote this probability by $\rho_x^{(n)} \, d\{n\}_x$. It is clearly just the sum of the separate (spatial) probabilities for the various possible sets $\mathbf{n}$ obtained by letting each of the positions $(1)_x$, $(2)_x$, $\cdots (n)_x$ be occupied by every different species s, ω_s. That is,

$$\rho_x^{(n)}(\{n\}_x) \, d\{n\}_x = \sum_{2^{nB}} \rho_{nx}(\{\mathbf{n}\}_x) \, d\{\mathbf{n}\}_x \qquad (101)$$

or

$$\rho_x^{(n)}(\{n\}_x) = \sum_{2^{nB}} \rho_{nx}(\{n\}_x) \qquad (102)$$

where ρ_{nx} is given by equation (98) and the sum is over the

$$2^{nB} = \left[\sum_{s=0}^{B} \frac{B!}{s!(B-s)!} \right]^n$$

different assignments of 2^B species s, ω_s to n positions in space. Of these assignments, $n!/\prod_{s,\omega_s} n_{\omega_s}!$ will correspond to the same $\mathbf{n}$, but ρ_{nx} will in general be different because of its dependence on $\{\mathbf{n}\}_x$ (not just $\mathbf{n}$), for $n > 2$.

Distribution functions for other coordinates than just $\{n\}_x$ can be obtained by summing as in equation (101). But one is restricted to a set of coordinates belonging to every species s, ω_s. So in general one cannot use the complete distribution function $\rho_{\mathbf{n}}(\{\mathbf{n}\})$ for this purpose, since different species may have different choices for, or numbers of, rotational coordinates.

Returning to equation (102), we define $g_x^{(n)}$ and $W_x^{(n)}$ for the set of protein molecules by

$$g_x^{(n)} \;=\; \exp\;(-W_x^{(n)}/kT) \;=\; \frac{\rho_x^{(n)}}{\rho^n} \tag{103}$$

The quantity $g_x^{(2)}$ is the radial distribution function. We should now verify that $\rho_x^{(n)}$, $g_x^{(n)}$, and $W_x^{(n)}$ have the expected properties of one-component functions (i.e., these functions refer to the single protein species in the solution, irrespective of the sub-species classification s, ω_s).

(1). We recall from equation (101) that $\rho_x^{(n)}$ has the usual probability definition.

(2). At infinite separation of the n molecules

$$\rho_x^{(n)} \to \sum_{2^n B} \left(\prod_{s,\omega_s} \rho_{\omega_s}^{n_{\omega_s}} \right) = \left(\sum_{s,\omega_s} \rho_{\omega_s} \right)^n = \rho^n \tag{104a}$$

and

$$g_x^{(n)} \to 1 \tag{104b}$$

$$W_x^{(n)} \to 0 \tag{104c}$$

(3). As regards normalization

$$\int \rho_x^{(n)} \, d\{n\}_x = \sum_{2^n B} \left\langle \prod_{s,\omega_s} \frac{m_{\omega_s}!}{(m_{\omega_s} - n_{\omega_s})!} \right\rangle_{\mathrm{Av}}$$

$$= \left\langle \sum_{2^n B} \left[\prod_{s,\omega_s} \frac{m_{\omega_s}!}{(m_{\omega_s} - n_{\omega_s})!} \right] \right\rangle_{\mathrm{Av}} \tag{105}$$

It is not difficult to see that the sum in equation (105) exhausts all the ways of selecting $n = \sum_{s,\omega_s} n_{\omega_s}$ molecules from $M_P = \sum_{s,\omega_s} m_{\omega_s}$. That is

$$\int \rho_x^{(n)} \, d\{n\}_x = \left\langle \frac{M_P!}{(M_P - n)!} \right\rangle_{\mathrm{Av}} \tag{106}$$

(4) Finally, one can show that $W_x^{(n)}$ is the potential of the average force on protein molecules of the set n, including averaging over all rotational configurations and species s, ω_s.

Equations (98), (102), and (103) provide us with general expressions for $\rho_x^{(n)}$, $g_x^{(n)}$, and $W_x^{(n)}$ as functions of $\{n\}_x$, x, $\mathbf{y}$, and $\mathfrak{z}$. Expansions of these functions in powers of $\mathfrak{z}$ or ρ (using equation (84)) can be written out, but we omit them here. The leading terms in these series correspond to ρ or $\mathfrak{z} = 0$ and we now consider this special case. From equations (100), (102), and (103)

$$
g_x^{(n)}(0) = \frac{\rho_x^{(n)}(0)}{\rho^n} = \exp\left(-W_x^{(n)}(0)/kT\right)
$$

$$
= \frac{\displaystyle\sum_{(s)}\sum_{(s')}\sum_{(s'')}\cdots\sum_{(s^{(n)})}\cdot (x^s H_{\omega_s})(x^{s'} H_{\omega_s'})\cdots (x^{s^{(n)}} H_{\omega_s^{(n)}}) \cdot \exp\left[-\mathfrak{W}^{(n)}((1_{\omega_s}),(1_{\omega_s'}),\cdots(1_{\omega_s^{(n)}}),0)/kT\right]}{\left(\displaystyle\sum_{(s)} x^s H_{\omega_s}\right)^n} \tag{107}
$$

Equation (107) is closely related to equation (79)

$$
\int g_x^{(n)}(0)\, d\{n\}_x = \int \exp\left[-W_x^{(n)}(0)/kT\right] d\{n\}_x
$$

$$
= \frac{C_n}{c_1^n} \tag{108}
$$

which result should be compared with equations (25), (26), and (80). In particular, from equations (82b) and (108), the second virial coefficient can be written in the alternative form

$$
\mathfrak{B}_2 = -\mathfrak{b}_2 = -\frac{1}{2V}\left(\frac{C_2}{c_1^2} - V^2\right)
$$

$$
= -\frac{1}{2}\int_0^\infty [g_x^{(2)}(0) - 1]\, 4\pi r^2\, dr \tag{109}
$$

where $g_x^{(2)}(0)$ is given by equation (107). This is a standard form for the second virial coefficient (see equation (34a)), and we see that binding on a protein does not alter it.

Equation (107) also shows how to calculate the potential of average force $W_x^{(n)}(0)$ on a set of n isolated ($\rho = 0$) protein molecules in solution, taking into account binding.

Superposition Approximation

We introduce here the superposition approximation in the potential of average force for sets of protein molecules at infinite dilution. This means

$$\mathfrak{W}_m(0) = \sum_{\text{pairs in } m} w_{\omega_s \omega_s'}(0) \tag{110}$$

where

$$w_{\omega_s \omega_s'}(0) = \mathfrak{W}^{(2)}((1_{\omega_s}), (1_{\omega_s'}), x, \mathbf{y}, \mathfrak{z} = 0) \tag{111}$$

Equation (38) reads (in our protein notation)

$$\frac{\Pi}{kT} = \rho - \frac{1}{6VkT} \sum_{s,\omega_s} \sum_{s',\omega_s'} \int r \frac{\partial w_{\omega_s \omega_s'}(0)}{\partial r} \rho^{(2)}_{\omega_s \omega_s'}(\mathfrak{z}) \, d(1_{\omega_s}) \, d(1_{\omega_s'}) \tag{112}$$

where r is the intermolecular distance (regarding $w_{\omega_s \omega_s'}(0)$ as a function of r, $(1_{\omega_s})_\theta$ and $(1_{\omega_s'})_\theta$) and $\rho^{(2)}_{\omega_s \omega_s'}$ is the distribution function of equation (97) for a set of two protein molecules, one of species s, ω_s and the other of species s', ω_s'. An equivalent form, when the protein solution at $\mathfrak{z}$ (as well as at $\mathfrak{z} = 0$) is a fluid, is

$$\frac{\Pi}{kT} = \rho - \frac{\rho^2}{6kT} \int_0^\infty r \left\langle \frac{\partial w}{\partial r} \right\rangle_{\text{Av}} (\mathfrak{z}) g_x^{(2)}(\mathfrak{z}) 4\pi r^2 \, dr \tag{113}$$

where

$$\left\langle \frac{\partial w}{\partial r} \right\rangle_{\text{Av}} (\mathfrak{z}) = \frac{\displaystyle\sum_{s,\omega_s} \sum_{s',\omega_s'} \int \frac{\partial w_{\omega_s \omega_s'}(0)}{\partial r} \rho^{(2)}_{\omega_s \omega_s'}(\mathfrak{z}) \, d(1_{\omega_s})_\theta \, d(1_{\omega_s'})_\theta}{\displaystyle\sum_{s,\omega_s} \sum_{s',\omega_s'} \int \rho^{(2)}_{\omega_s \omega_s'}(\mathfrak{z}) \, d(1_{\omega_s})_\theta \, d(1_{\omega_s'})_\theta} \tag{114}$$

and $g_x^{(2)}(\mathfrak{z})$ is the pair (radial) distribution function of equation (103). Equation (112) agrees with equation (85) only as far as the second virial coefficient since the superposition approximation was not made in equation (85). That is, the leading term, $\rho^{(2)}_{\omega_s \omega_s'}(0)$, in the expansion of $\rho^{(2)}_{\omega_s \omega_s'}(\mathfrak{z})$ in equation (112) in powers of ρ or $\mathfrak{z}$ leads to the second virial coefficient.

Born-Green-Yvon Integro-Differential Equation

In this section we employ the superposition approximation introduced above to derive an integro-differential equation which is the analogue of the well-known Born-Green-Yvon equation for a one-component monatomic system. Let molecule 1 be a member of the set $\mathbf{n}$ in equation

(98). We take the gradient $\nabla_1\rho_{nx}$ of both sides of this equation[f] and use the notation

$$\mathfrak{W}_m(0) = \sum_{\text{pairs } i,j \text{ in } m} w(i,j) \tag{115}$$

$$\nabla_1\mathfrak{W}_m(0) = \sum_{i \text{ in } n, i\neq 1} \nabla_1 w(1,i) + \sum_{i \text{ in } m-n} \nabla_1 w(1,i) \tag{116}$$

instead of that of equations (110) and (111). It is understood that $w(i,j)$ refers to x, y, $\mathfrak{z} = 0$. After taking the gradient as indicated, the right-hand side of equation (98) breaks up into two parts corresponding to the two sums in equation (116). The first part (i in $\mathbf{n}$) can be written

$$-\frac{1}{kT}\frac{1}{e^{\Pi V/kT}} \int d\{\mathbf{n}\}_\theta [\sum_i \nabla_1 w(1,i)] \sum_{\mathbf{m}\geq\mathbf{n}} \int d'\{\mathbf{m}-\mathbf{n}\}_\theta \prod_{s,\omega_s}$$

$$\left\{ \frac{(\mathfrak{z}x^s)^{m_{\omega_s}}}{(m_{\omega_s}-n_{\omega_s})!} \lambda_{\omega_s\theta}^{n_{\omega_s}} \prod_{(m_{\omega_s})} H_{\omega_s} \right\} \int e^{-\mathfrak{W}_m(0)/kT} d\{\mathbf{m}-\mathbf{n}\}_x \tag{117}$$

$$= -\frac{1}{kT}\int [\sum_i \nabla_1 w(1,i)] \rho_n(\mathfrak{z}) d\{\mathbf{n}\}_\theta$$

There are $m_{\omega_s^0} - n_{\omega_s^0}$ identical contributions to the second part (i in $\mathbf{m}-\mathbf{n}$) as i runs through $n_{\omega_s^0}+1$, $n_{\omega_s^0}+2$, $\cdots m_{\omega_s^0}$ for each species s^0, ω_s^0. Thus the second part is

$$-\frac{1}{kT}\frac{1}{e^{\Pi V/kT}} \sum_{s^0,\omega_s^0} \int d\{\mathbf{n}+1_{\omega_s^0}\}_\theta \int \nabla_1 w(1,n_{\omega_s^0}+1) d(n_{\omega_s^0}+1)_x$$

$$\cdot\left[\sum_{\mathbf{m}\geq\mathbf{n}} \int d'\{\mathbf{m}-\mathbf{n}-1_{\omega_s^0}\}_\theta \prod_{s,\omega_s}\left\{ \frac{(\mathfrak{z}x^s)^{m_{\omega_s}}}{(m_{\omega_s}-n_{\omega_s})!} \lambda_{\omega_s\theta}^{n_{\omega_s}} \prod_{(m_{\omega_s})} H_{\omega_s} \right\} \right.$$

$$\left. \cdot\lambda_{\omega_s^0\theta}(m_{\omega_s^0}-n_{\omega_s^0}) \int e^{-\mathfrak{W}_m(0)/kT} d\{\mathbf{m}-\mathbf{n}-1_{\omega_s^0}\}_x \right] \tag{118}$$

$$= -\frac{1}{kT} \sum_{s^0,\omega_s^0} \int \nabla_1 w(1,n_{\omega_s^0}+1)\rho_{n+1_{\omega_s^0}}(\mathfrak{z}) d(n_{\omega_s^0}+1)_x d\{\mathbf{n}+1_{\omega_s^0}\}_\theta$$

The sum of equations (117) and (118) is $\nabla_1\rho_{nx}$. To obtain $\nabla_1\rho_x^{(n)}$, we sum $\nabla_1\rho_{nx}$ over the 2^{nB} different assignments of species to the n positions $(1)_x$, $(2)_x$, $\cdots (n)_x$ of the set, with the understanding that, in each set $\mathbf{n}$, "molecules 1" is the molecule, of whatever species s, ω_s, located at

[f] Only $\mathfrak{W}_m$ is a function of $(1)_x$ as the infinitely dilute solution is assumed a fluid. See equation 76b.

the same position $(1)_x$. Then

$$
-kT\, \nabla_1 \rho_x^{(n)} = \sum_{2^{nB}} \int \left[\sum_{i=2}^{n} \nabla_1 w(1, i) \right] \rho_\mathbf{n}(\mathfrak{z})\, d\{\mathbf{n}\}_\theta
$$

$$
+ \sum_{2^{nB}} \sum_{s^0, \omega_s^0} \int \nabla_1 w(1, n_{\omega_s^0} + 1) \rho_{\mathbf{n}+1_{\omega_s^0}}(\mathfrak{z})\, d(n_{\omega_s^0} + 1)_x\, d\{\mathbf{n} + 1_{\omega_s^0}\}_\theta
\tag{119}
$$

Equation (119) can also be written as

$$
-kT \nabla_1 \rho_x^{(n)} = \rho_x^{(n)} \sum_{i=2}^{n} \langle \nabla_1 w(1, i) \rangle_{\mathrm{Av}}
$$

$$
+ \int \langle \nabla_1 w(1, n+1) \rangle_{\mathrm{Av}}\, \rho_x^{(n+1)}(\mathfrak{z})\, d(n+1)_x
\tag{120}
$$

where

$$
\langle \nabla_1 w(1, i) \rangle_{\mathrm{Av}} = \frac{\displaystyle\sum_{2^{nB}} \int \nabla_1 w(1, i) \rho_\mathbf{n}(\mathfrak{z})\, d\{\mathbf{n}\}_\theta}{\rho_x^{(n)}(\mathfrak{z})}
\tag{121}
$$

and

$$
\langle \nabla_1 w(1, n+1) \rangle_{\mathrm{Av}} = \frac{\displaystyle\sum_{2^{(n+1)B}} \int \nabla_1 w(1, n+1) \rho_{\mathbf{n}+1}(\mathfrak{z})\, d\{\mathbf{n} + \mathbf{1}\}_\theta}{\rho_x^{(n+1)}(\mathfrak{z})}
\tag{122}
$$

Equation (120) has the same formal appearance as the simple Born-Green-Yvon equation, but average forces replace forces. Since $w(1, i)$ refers to $\mathfrak{z} = 0$, we see that the averages here are of the same "mixed" type with respect to $\mathfrak{z}$ already encountered in equations (113) and (114). To make appreciable further progress, a superposition approximation at $\mathfrak{z}$ (as well as at $\mathfrak{z} = 0$) must be introduced (as in the case of a monatomic fluid).

In deriving equation (120), we have used the fact that the solvent is a fluid (see equation (76b) and footnote f; $W^{(1)}(0)$ is taken independent of $(1)_x$. However, equation (120) does not exclude the possibility that the protein molecules themselves may have long-range order when $\mathfrak{z}$ is sufficiently large, as, for example, in gel formation or when the protein precipitates. The case $n = 1$ is then particularly important.[24, 25]

Relation to the Kirkwood-Shumaker Theory

The equations of this section are quite general and should be useful as a reliable point of departure in making detailed approximate calculations for special cases. However, we wish to point out here that one such calculation has already been carried out. Kirkwood and Shumaker[26] have made an explicit approximate evaluation of the potential of average force between two isolated protein molecules at a distance r apart, for a particular model, including averaging with respect to external rotational orientation and the number s and distribution ω_s of bound hydrogen ions. The precise nature of their averaging is exhibited in their equation (8). From this equation it is clear that the averaging is in fact the same as in our equation (107) with $n = 2$ (as modified to suit their special model). The Kirkwood-Shumaker V and W (see their equation (2)) are in our notation $\mathfrak{W}^{(2)}((1_{\omega_s}), (1_{\omega_s'}), 0)$ and $W_x^{(2)}(0)$, respectively. They use the method, in the calculation of $g_x^{(2)}(0)$ and $W_x^{(2)}(0)$, of expanding the exponential in the summation of equation (107) to the term[g] in $(1/kT)^2$.

The "fluctuation" origin of an average attractive force[26] between two isolated protein molecules at the isoionic point refers to the fact that every combination of rotational orientations $(1_{\omega_s})_\theta$, $(1_{\omega_s'})_\theta$, numbers of bound molecules s, s', and distributions of bound molecules ω_s , ω_s' , is represented by a term in the numerator of the right-hand side of equation (107), and that those terms with negative $\mathfrak{W}^{(2)}(0)$ will tend to predominate in the sum, making the weighted average value $W_x^{(2)}(0)$ negative (attraction). Negative values of $\mathfrak{W}^{(2)}(0)$ arise, for example, when s and s' are such that the two proteins have opposite charges, or when ω_s and ω_s' are such that both charge distributions are unsymmetrical, with the positively charged side of one protein molecule adjacent to the negatively charged side of the other. Away from the isoionic point, the net charge on the protein molecules predominates in determining the force; there will be a repulsion between identical protein molecules, reduced slightly in magnitude by the statistical favoring (equation (107)) of orientations and distributions with charges arranged so as to reduce the repulsion.

ACKNOWLEDGEMENTS

The author is indebted to Professors J. T. Edsall, I. M. Klotz, and G. Scatchard for helpful comments and criticisms, and to Dr. H. Gutfreund for many stimulating discussions. Most of this work was done while the author was a Fellow of the John Simon Guggenheim Memorial Foundation in the Department of Chemistry, Yale University.

---

[g] There appears to be a typographical error in their equation (2): $\langle V^2 \rangle_{Av}$ should be replaced by $\langle V^2 \rangle_{Av} - \langle V \rangle_{Av}^2$, with corresponding changes in equation (3) and (5) (replace f_{ikls} by $f_{ikls} - 1$ in $W^{00}(R)$).

REFERENCES

1. McMillan, W. G., and Mayer, J. E., *J. Chem. Phys.* **13,** 276 (1945).
2. Kirkwood, J. G., and Buff, F. P., *J. Chem. Phys.* **19,** 774 (1951).
3. Zimm, B. H., *J. Chem. Phys.,* **14,** 164 (1946).
4. Onsager, L., *Ann. N. Y. Acad. Sci.* **51,** 627 (1949).
5. Kirkwood, J. G., and Westheimer, F. H., *J. Chem. Phys.* **6,** 506, 513 (1938).
6. Hill, T. L., *J. Chem. Phys.* **11,** 545, 552 (1943); **12,** 56, 147 (1944).
7. Peek, H. M., and Hill, T. L., *J. Am. Chem. Soc.* **73,** 5304 (1951).
8. Rushbrooke, G. S., "Introduction to Statistical Mechanics," p. 87. Oxford University Press, New York, 1949.
9. Ono, S., *J. Chem. Phys.* **19,** 504 (1951).
10. Guggenheim, E. A., "Thermodynamics," pp. 331–334. North-Holland Publishing Co., Amsterdam, 1949.
11. Verwey, E. J. W., and Overbeeck, J. Th. G., "Theory of the Stability of Lyophobic Colloids," Elsevier Publishing Co., Amsterdam, 1948.
12. Kramers, H. A., *Proc. Acad. Sci. Amsterdam* **30,** 145 (1927).
13. Mayer, J. E., *J. Chem. Phys.* **18,** 1426 (1950).
14. Berlin, T. H., and Montroll, E. W., *J. Chem. Phys.* **20,** 75 (1952).
15. Mayer, J. E., and Mayer, M. G., "Statistical Mechanics." John Wiley & Sons, New York, 1940.
16. Bird, R. B., Spotz, E. L., and Hirschfelder, J. O., *J. Chem. Phys.* **18,** 1395 (1950), Equations 4–10.
17. Klotz, I. M., *in* "Modern Trends in Physiology and Biochemistry" (E.S.G. Barron, ed.). Academic Press, New York, 1952.
18. Scatchard, G., *Ann. N. Y. Acad. Sci.* **51,** 660 (1949).
19. Cohn, E. J., and Edsall, J. T., "Proteins, Amino Acids and Peptides," Chapter 20. Reinhold Publishing Corp., New York, 1943.
20. Hill, T. L., *J. Phys. Chem.* **57,** 324 (1953).
21. Cohn, E. J., and Edsall, J. T., "Proteins, Amino Acids and Peptides," p. 387. Reinhold Publishing Corp., New York, 1943.
22. Doty, P. M. and Edsall, J. T., *Advances in Protein Chem.* **6,** 35 (1951).
23. Steiner, R. F., *Arch. Biochem. and Biophys.* **39,** 333 (1952).
24. Kirkwood, J. G., *in* "Phase Transformation in Solids" (R. Smoluchowski, J. E. Mayer, and W. A. Weyl, eds.). John Wiley & Sons, New York, 1951.
25. Kirkwood, J. G., and Mazur, J., *Compt. rend réunion ann. union intern. phys. (Paris),* p. 143 (1952).
26. Kirkwood, J. G., and Shumaker, J. B., *Proc. Natl. Acad. Sci. U. S.* **38,** 863 (1952).

Interaction of Proteins and Ions With Special Reference to Mercury Derivatives of Mercaptalbumin

JOHN T. EDSALL

The interactions of proteins with ions are numerous and diverse in character. They may be primarily due to electrostatic forces without any direct combination between the protein and the smaller ion. They may, on the other hand, involve actual combination; the linkage formed may vary in character from a loose electrostatic attraction to a relatively strong bond of primarily covalent character. Moreover, if the ion attached to the protein is a complex organic ion, with a charged group at one point in the structure, the strength of binding depends not merely on the interaction of the charged group with the protein molecule, but also on the interactions which may arise with other polar and nonpolar groups, both in the attached ion and in the protein.

Electrostatic interactions not involving direct ion-protein combination. Under this heading we may include all those effects which are due to the electric field that surrounds ions or dipolar ions. In solutions containing simple ions such interactions are described by the changes in activity coefficient which may be calculated from the Debye-Hückel theory of interionic forces, or from some modified form of that theory. The logarithm of the activity coefficient (γ) of a dipolar ion is a linear function of the ionic strength ($\Gamma/2$) in dilute solution, and may be described by the equation

$$\lim_{\Gamma/2 \to 0} (-\log \gamma) = K_R \Gamma/2 \tag{1}$$

Here the coefficient K_R is positive for most dipolar ions, so that the activity coefficient decreases, and the solubility, therefore, increases, with increase of the ionic strength at low $\Gamma/2$. The presence of large nonpolar residues in the side chains attached to the dipolar ion—as, for instance, in leucine or tyrosine—decreases K_R and may even cause it to become negative. For a series of related molecules in which such side chain effects are relatively constant, K_R increases with the electric moment of the dipolar ion. For an ellipsoidal model with charges $+q$ and $-q$ at the foci of the ellipsoid, with a distance R between them,

Kirkwood[1] has calculated K_R as

$$K_R = \frac{2Nq^4 g(\lambda_0) R}{2303(DkT)^2} \qquad (2)$$

Here D is the dielectric constant of the medium, T the absolute temperature, N Avogadro's number, and k the Boltzmann constant. The function g depends on the eccentricity (λ_0) of the ellipsoid, and is nearly unity for elongated ellipsoids. Thus K_R is proportional to the dipole distance R for this model. It has also been found experimentally to be proportional to the calculated dipole moments of a number of amino acids and peptides, from solubility studies in alcohol-water mixtures.[2] The dipole moments (μ) ranged from 15 Debye units for glycine to 59 for lysylglutamic acid, and the corresponding K_R values ranged from 0.33 to 1.2. The ratio μ/K_R was in the range of 45 to 50 for all the compounds studied in this series.

The interactions of proteins with ions and dipolar ions, as evaluated from solubility measurements, are qualitatively similar to those of amino acids but quantitatively greater. Some typical examples are illustrated in Fig. 1. This shows the change in the logarithm of the solubility of several amino acids and proteins in the presence of varying concentrations of sodium chloride or of glycine. The general parallelism between the effects of ions and dipolar ions is striking, although an examination of the scale of the two diagrams in Fig. 1 indicates immediately that the effect of glycine, expressed on a molar basis, is far less than that of sodium chloride. The solubility of β-lactoglobulin increases very nearly a hundred-fold when the sodium chloride concentration increases from 0 to 0.1 M. It increases ten-fold when the glycine concentration increases from 0 to approximately 0.4 M. The effects on hemoglobin are less than on β-lactoglobulin, but far greater than those for the amino acids and peptides. All these effects may be considered as primarily electrostatic and can be explained without assuming any actual combination between the protein and the other components of the system. There may be some actual binding of sodium or chloride ions, or of glycine, in the systems illustrated in Fig. 1, but these effects are certainly small.

The logarithm of the activity coefficient $(-\log \gamma)$, at low ionic strengths, is a linear function of the square root of the ionic strength for an ion, and of the first power of the ionic strength for a dipolar ion. However, a protein, even at its isoionic point, may behave with respect to these interactions more like an ion than a dipolar ion, for the actual

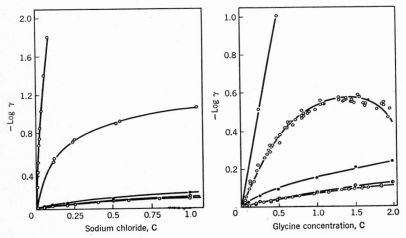

FIG. 1. Effects of sodium chloride and glycine on the solubility of certain proteins and amino acids. Note differences in scale of both abscissa and ordinate in the two halves of the figure. In each case, the steepest curve is for β-lacto-globulin, then below in descending order: horse carboxyhemoglobin, cystine, asparagine, and glycine. It was originally assumed in drawing this figure that $-\log \gamma$ is given by the change in the logarithm of the solubility with reference to the solubility in pure water as standard state. Concerning the limitations of this assumption, see discussion in the text.

state of an isoionic protein in solution is represented by a statistical distribution of the molecules among many microscopically different forms, some having zero net charge, others carrying a net positive or negative charge. In most proteins the latter forms outnumber those which are truly isoelectric; hence, the interactions may be more characteristic of ions than of dipolar ions. It should, of course, be understood that the state of charge on any individual molecule fluctuates from instant to instant, as protons (or other ions) are taken on or given off. The charge distribution in any individual molecule, if followed over a long period of time, should represent the same sort of statistical distribution that would be found among all the molecules in the solution at any given moment.[3, 4]

The significance of solubility measurements for the determination of activity coefficients in protein solutions should be clearly understood. If the composition of the solid phase remains constant as the composition of the solution in equilibrium with it is varied, then the change in solubility of the component under study can be taken as inversely proportional to the change in activity coefficient. This condition holds for most amino acids and peptides under most circumstances; the formation of a new solid phase, in the rare cases where it does occur, is recognizable either by direct observations of the crystals or by the appearance of discontinuities in the physical properties of the system— for instance, a discontinuity in the curve for the solubility of the amino acid or peptide when plotted as a function of the ionic strength. Protein crystals, however, are more complex; in equilibrium with an aqueous salt solution, they always contain both salt and water as well as protein, and the proportions of the three components vary continuously as the composition of the mother liquor is varied.[5] Hence the usual condition for calculating activity coefficients from solubility measurements is lacking. As salt is added to the mother liquor, it penetrates into the crystals also. If the salt lowers the activity coefficient of the protein in the liquid phase, it may also change it in the crystals, so that the measured solubility change depends upon effects occurring in both phases. In the case of ox hemoglobin in phosphate buffers, Adair[6] concluded that the effect of the buffer ions on the activity coefficient of the protein in the solid phase was large, and that the change in activity coefficient with change in the salt concentration, in the liquid phase, was, therefore, much larger than the observed change in solubility. Therefore, the true activity coefficient changes, for the protein systems portrayed in Fig. 1, may be much larger than those inferred from the solubility changes; they are unlikely to be less. Independent methods for the evaluation of activity coefficients of proteins in solution are available, for instance, by measuring the effect of the protein on the activity coefficients of the salts present, by any suitable method, and inferring the effect of the salt on the activity of the protein by the reciprocal relations between the components in a thermodynamic system. Here, however, we are concerned with emphasizing the general character, and the large magnitude, of these electrostatic effects in protein solutions.

Such interactions as these have served as the basis of many methods of protein fractionation. Electrostatic interactions increase in intensity as the dielectric constant of the solution is decreased, so that the "salting-in" effect, of the type portrayed in Fig. 1, increases as the dielectric constant decreases. On the other hand, the activity coefficient of an ion or a dipolar ion in the absence of salt is increased—and, therefore, its solubility is diminished—by decreasing the dielectric constant of the solvent. Thus, addition of a reagent such as ethanol or acetone precipitates proteins which are readily soluble in water, but in such a medium the solvent action of salts upon the precipitate is greater than it would be in water. Thus a molecule classed as an albumin in water may behave like a globulin in an ethanol-water mixture. In the case of proteins, with their numerous anionic and cationic groups, the effects can be enormous. These facts are fundamental, for instance, to the understanding of the use of ethanol at low temperatures for protein fractionation,[7a, b] although they are, of course, only a part of the whole story. The low temperature is important in the case of proteins because of the enormous temperature coefficient of protein denaturation and the great increase of the stability of the materials that is achieved by working at low temperatures.

These effects illustrated in Fig. 1 are for relatively low ionic strengths. At high ionic strengths, of course, the well known salting-out effect is observed, which has long been used as a basis of protein fractionation. Salting out depends largely on the general size and shape of the protein molecules and on the charge and radius of the ions of the salt. Here again salting-out effects are observed in solutions of simple dipolar ions such as cystine. Cystine is salted out by ammonium sulfate in concentrated solutions, the logarithm of the solubility being a linear function of the ionic strength, just as it is for proteins.[8] However, for such a small molecule as cystine, the slope of the salting-out curve is small, and salting out would not be an effective method of separating cystine from other amino acids. For proteins, on the other hand, the effect is enormous and it varies greatly from one protein to another, so that the power of the method as a practical technique of protein fractionation had already been recognized a century ago.

These general interactions between proteins and ions are not our chief concern in this discussion. However, they cannot be neglected, for the effects involved are very large and must be considered in any study of more specific interactions. If, in the course of an experiment, one makes any significant change in the dielectric constant or the ionic strength, the conditions governing all the interactions between ions and proteins will be altered; full account must be taken of these alterations if the properties of such systems are to be adequately understood.

Interactions describable in terms of the law of mass action. A great number of systems are now known in which proteins combine with smaller ions, the combination being describable in terms of the law of mass action. Dr. Gurd will further discuss such systems in this symposium and Dr. Klotz[9] has recently given an excellent general survey of the field. No extended comment, therefore, is required here. However, some points perhaps deserve a little added emphasis.

Certain ions combine with many proteins, and the combination is clearly associated with the presence of specific reactive groups in the protein molecule. However, even in such cases, it is probable that further research will uncover marked specific differences between different proteins and that no mere tabulation of protein composition, in terms of numbers of amino acid residues, will entirely explain the capacity or lack of capacity to bind a given ion. Such specific differences arise even in interactions with hydrogen ions. Thus the work of Crammer and Neuberger[10] on ovalbumin showed clearly that the tyrosine hydroxyl groups of this protein are unavailable to release protons to added hydroxyl ions until the protein has suffered alkaline denaturation at pH near 12; whereas the tyrosine hydroxyl groups in other proteins, such as insulin, are free to react, like simple phenols. Similarly, the studies of Steinhardt and Zaiser[11] have shown clearly the unavailability for reaction with acids or bases of approximately 36 groups per molecule of native hemoglobin, which become reactive on denaturation. The linkages in which these groups are bound are broken in acid solution, and they become available for reaction in the denatured molecule. More phenomena of this sort are sure to be uncovered in future, but the number and the chemical nature of such groups apparently vary greatly from protein to protein.

The reactivity of certain proteins, notably serum albumin, with anions appears to be highly characteristic. Presumably the groups within the protein which react with these anions are cationic groups, but it is still obscure why serum albumin has such a remarkable capacity for binding anions, even when the protein as a whole carries a negative net charge. Dr. Klotz has offered an interesting possible structural interpretation of this, but I am not convinced that it is adequate to explain all the facts, although it may well be part of the story. Anion binding has been studied far more with serum albumin than with any other protein; probably there are two major reasons for this. First, serum albumin is almost in a class by itself among the proteins hitherto studied because of its capacity for combining with many anions of most diverse structure. In the second place, bovine serum albumin has been made available on the market in purified form and is, therefore, accessible to many investigators who do not wish to prepare their own proteins. It is for these reasons, as well as for the inherent biochemical importance of serum albumin itself, that this protein has received far more attention in ion binding studies than any other. The emphasis so produced has in some respects been unfortunate, for serum albumin is not at all a typical protein, and generalizations based on its behavior can be very misleading.

The effects of ion binding on protein stability can be extremely various. As the studies of Luck and his collaborators[12, 13] have shown, the resistance of serum albumin to denaturation by heat and urea is greatly increased in the presence of fatty acid anions. The longer the hydrocarbon chain—at least up to a chain of 8 carbon atoms or so—the greater the stabilization achieved and, in general, the stronger the binding. On the other hand, the γ-globulins are not stabilized at all by the addition of these fatty acid anions. They appear indeed to become more susceptible to heat denaturation.[7b] The γ-globulins are stabilized against heat by glycine, although the effect is small compared to that of the fatty acid anions on serum albumin.

The addition of heavy metal ions to protein solutions has long been considered dangerous by protein chemists. Certainly the addition of such ions can lead to denaturation if they are added in excess, or under conditions of temperature or pH at which the protein is not particularly stable. On the other hand, such ions were long ago shown to be useful agents for protein fractionation when added judiciously and with care. Recently the systematic use of ions of heavy metals has made possible new methods of fractionation which promise to yield protein preparations of greater purity and stability than could be obtained by most earlier methods.[14, 15]

It is an interesting question whether the stability of proteins and their turnover rates in living tissues are significantly modified by the addition or removal of substances which are bound to them and markedly affect their stability. Such effects must certainly occur in pathological states, for instance in mercury poisoning. Whether such interactions are also a part of the normal physiological mechanisms for controlling the rates of metabolic transformation of proteins is, to my knowledge, an unanswered question at the present time. It certainly deserves to be explored.

Interaction of serum mercaptalbumin with mercurials. We may now turn from these general remarks to one highly specific type of interaction, intensively studied in this laboratory lately. It involves interactions between a protein and a small ion—in this case the mercuric ion—and also a particular kind of protein-protein interaction. The latter interaction involves two like protein molecules. It leads only to dimer formation, and no further, since it involves only one reactive group in each of the two protein molecules, which are linked by mercury or by an organic bifunctional mercurial. It is perhaps the only reversible association reaction between protein molecules for which both velocity and equilibrium constants have been determined over a considerable range of temperature and pH.

The discovery of the phenomenon, and the formulation of the fundamental reactions involved, are due to my colleague Dr. W. L. Hughes, Jr.[16] His insight has been indispensable at every step of the later researches, based on his discoveries, which other members of the laboratory have undertaken. He showed that total crystalline serum albumin, as ordinarily prepared from human or bovine plasma, contained approximately 0.7 titratable sulfhydryl groups per protein molecule. Addition of a mercuric salt in the proportion of one mercury to two albumin sulfhydryl groups led to the formation of albumin crystals under conditions where crystallization of albumin had never been obtained before. Analysis of the crystals showed a ratio of one mercury atom to two molecules of albumin, taking the molecular weight as approximately 69,000. The material remaining in the supernatant solution consisted largely of those albumin molecules which could not be shown to contain any titratable sulfhydryl groups, whereas the albumin molecules which entered into the crystals were found to contain one reactive sulfhydryl per molecule. The studies of Dr. Low[17] showed that these crystals were quite different from those obtained from decanol albumin as prepared earlier by Dr. Hughes. Moreover, when the crystals were redissolved in phosphate buffer, a new peak appeared in the ultracentrifuge, as shown by the measurements of Dr. Oncley. The sedimentation constant, s_{20}, was approximately 6.5 S as compared with the value for the albumin monomer of approximately 4.3–4.6 S. Moreover, the solutions containing the component with the larger sedimentation constant were more viscous than those containing only mercury-free albumin. Addition of cysteine or cyanide caused disappearance of the fast component and its reconversion to the monomer. All the available evidence then and since has fitted in with the view that the more rapidly sedimenting component consists of two molecules of mercaptalbumin linked together by a mercury atom, the linkage involving one reactive sulfhydryl group from each of the two albumin molecules.

The mercuric ion, of course, is highly reactive, so much so indeed that the concentration of free Hg^{++} in an aqueous solution is almost always very small. Many groups in proteins are capable of reacting with mercuric ion, including amino, imidazole, and carboxyl groups. However, the affinity of any of these groups for mercury is small compared to that of the sulfhydryl group. The most accurate measurements of the affinity of simple sulfhydryl compounds for mercuric ions are those of Stricks and Kolthoff[18] on the mercaptides of cysteine and glutathione. Their work shows that association constants for reactions of the type

$$Hg^{++} + 2RS^- \rightleftharpoons RSHgSR$$

in simple compounds are of the order of magnitude of 10^{41}–10^{45}, the exact values in the cases of cysteine and glutathione depending on the temperature and on the state of ionization of the adjoining amino and ammonium groups in the amino acid or peptide. For comparison, we may note that the corresponding equilibrium constant for the reaction[19]

$$Hg^{++} + 2Cl^- \rightleftharpoons HgCl_2$$

it is $10^{13.2}$, and for the reaction[20]

$$Hg^{++} + 2NH_3 \rightleftharpoons Hg(NH_3)_2^{++}$$

it is $10^{17.5}$.

The association constant between mercuric ion and an uncharged amino group for the reaction[20]

$$Hg^{++} + RNH_2 \rightleftharpoons Hg(NH_2R)^{++}$$

is of the order of 10^9. The value for imidazole groups may be of the same order of magnitude but is not definitely known. The association constant with an ionized carboxyl group appears to be of the order of 10^4, from the data recorded by Sidgwick.[21] All of these association constants are so small compared to that for interaction with the sulfhydryl group that any mercuric ion added to a protein solution reacts immediately with any available sulfhydryl groups in the protein. Only after these groups are saturated will other groups in the protein begin to interact with mercury.

Formulation of the reactions. For brevity we may denote the mercaptalbumin molecule with its sulfhydryl group by the symbol ASH, remembering that the radical denoted here by A— is an enormously complex structure, containing about 580 amino acid residues, including about 100 ionizable carboxyl groups, most or all of which are negatively charged in the pH range from 4 to 7; and an approximately equal number of positively charged residues including 16 histidine, 25 arginine, and 59 lysine residues,[22, 23] assuming a molecular weight of 69,000. If a mercuric salt HgX_2 is added to the system, the results of all our experiments can be described in terms of a series of reactions which may be written in three steps

$$ASH \ + \ HgX_2 \ \underset{k_{-1}}{\overset{k_1}{\rightleftharpoons}} \ ASHgX \ + \ H^+ \ + \ X^- \qquad (I)$$

$$ASHgX \ + \ ASH \ \underset{k_{-2}}{\overset{k_2}{\rightleftharpoons}} \ ASHgSA \ + \ H^+ \ + \ X^- \qquad (II)$$

$$ASHgSA \ + \ HgX_2 \ \underset{k_{-3}}{\overset{k_3}{\rightleftharpoons}} \ 2ASHgX \qquad (III)$$

The anion X, in our experiments, was generally acetate or chloride; bromide, iodide, and cyanide, which bind mercury much more strongly, have been added in some experiments to study their effects on the dissociation of the dimer. Dr. Hughes has shown by actual pH and titration measurements that hydrogen ion is released in reaction (I) and (II), as indicated, and in approximately the amounts to be expected.

Calculation of weight fraction dimer in solution from light scattering measurements. We have employed measurements of light scattering to determine the weight-average molecular weight of the protein in the system and thereby to calculate the weight fraction of dimer (D) in order to determine the rate of the reaction and the equilibrium constant. If c is the concentration of the protein in grams per milliliter and $R_{90,s}$ is the reduced intensity of scattering[24] at 90° to the incident beam, then the weight-average molecular weight $\bar{M}_w$ is given by the equation

$$\frac{Kc}{R_{90,s}} = \frac{1}{\bar{M}_w} + 2Bc \qquad (3)$$

Here the coefficient K is given by the relation

$$K = \frac{2\pi^2 n^2 (dn/dc)^2}{N\lambda_0^4} \qquad (4)$$

where n is the refractive index of the solution, dn/dc is the refractive increment of the solute, N is Avogadro's number, and λ_0 is the wavelength of the light *in vacuo*. The molecular weight of the monomer M is given from light scattering in a solution of pure monomer by an equation similar to (3), in which M instead of $\bar{M}_w$ appears on the right-hand side.

The coefficient B in equation (3) has been found to be zero or nearly zero in an isoelectric solution of serum albumin, but it becomes positive and of significant magnitude on either side of the isoelectric point.[25] Fortunately it has been found[26] that B is the same for monomer and dimer, within the limits of experimental error, in a solvent of given pH and ionic strength; we have every reason for believing that it will have the same value in a mixture of the two. Once B is known for pure monomer or pure dimer, we can, therefore, use this known value to extrapolate the light scattering measurements to zero concentration in any given solvent and obtain the weight-average molecular weight of a mixture of monomer and dimer. The weight fraction of dimer is then given by the simple relation

$$D = (\bar{M}_w/M) - 1 \tag{5}$$

In an isoelectric solution for which $B = 0$, D can thus be inferred directly from light scattering measurements on pure monomer and on a mixture of monomer and dimer at the same concentration

$$D_{B=0} = (R_{90,s}/R_{90,m}) - 1 \tag{6}$$

Here $R_{90,s}$ denotes the reduced intensity of scattering from the solution containing both monomer and dimer, and $R_{90,m}$ denotes the reduced intensity of scattering from the solution containing only monomer at the same protein concentration. If the protein is not isoelectric, one must extrapolate the measurements to zero concentration, as indicated above.

We may now consider the results obtained in terms of the three-step reaction formulated above. Step (I), involving the binding of mercury to the sulfhydryl group of a mercaptalbumin molecule, is extremely rapid; so fast indeed that we cannot yet determine its velocity. Step (II) involves the combination of ASHgX and ASH to form the dimer. It is the rate-determining step of the process as we have been able to show directly from light scattering measurements,[26] mixing the mercuric salt and the albumin in different proportions and at different times. We have been able to determine both the velocity constants k_2 and k_{-2} and also, independently, the equilibrium constant of the reaction at several values of pH and temperature. Step (III) is very rapid; if one increases the molar ratio of $(HgX_2)/(ASH)$ from 0.5 to 1, the light scattering drops immediately to the value characteristic of the monomer ASHgX, the molecular weight of which is, of course, indistinguishable from that of ASH.

232   JOHN T. EDSALL

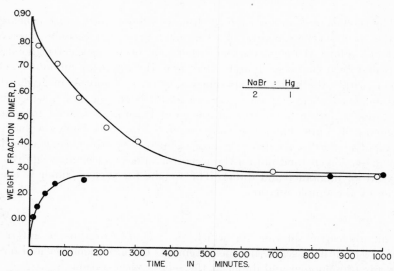

FIG. 2. Formation and dissociation of mercaptalbumin mercury dimer. Protein
concentration 0.01 gm/ml, pH 4.75, acetate buffer at ionic strength 0.05, temperature 25°. Two moles of bromide ion present per mole of mercury. Upper curve:
dissociation of freshly redissolved crystalline dimer; lower curve: association of
monomer in the presence of mercuric acetate, 1 mole Hg to 2 moles albumin.
[From Edelhoch, Katchalski, *et al.*, *J. Am. Chem. Soc.* **75**, 5058 (1953)].

First it should be made plain that step (II) represents a truly reversible
process. Evidence on this point is illustrated by Fig. 2, which is typical
of many other such experiments. Solutions of identical protein concentration, pH, and ionic strength, were prepared, and it was found that
the same equilibrium state was obtained, whether we started from the
pure mercury dimer and followed its dissociation or started with pure
monomer, adding mercuric acetate, and following the association
process. In the experiment shown in Fig. 2 at pH 4.75, the same equilibrium state was obtained from either direction in about 12 hours. The
association process at this pH was much faster than at more alkaline
values at which the protein carries a negative charge. In the lower
portion of Fig. 3, a plot is shown of the logarithm of the velocity constant
k_2 for this reaction in dilute acetate buffer as a function of pH. The rate
decreases approximately 60-fold between pH 4.75 and pH 6, the net
charge on the protein changing from 0 to approximately -10 over the
same range. Such a decrease in velocity with increase of charge is, at
least qualitatively, what would be predicted in terms of the theory

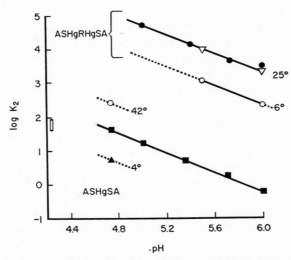

FIG. 3. The logarithm of the velocity constant of the dimerization reaction as a function of pH and temperature. Curve marked ASHgSA is for the formation of the mercury dimer at 25°. Points above and below show values for 4° and 42° at pH 4.75. The upper pair of curves represent the velocity constant of formation of the dimer with the bifunctional mercurial at two different temperatures. Note the general parallelism of the curves.

The solvent in all cases was acetate buffer, except at pH 6 where phosphate buffer was used. Ionic strength was generally 0.15 but was 0.05 at pH 4.75. [For further details see Edelhoch, Katchalski, *et al.*, *J. Am. Chem. Soc.* **75**, 5058 (1953); and Edsall, Maybury, Simpson, and Straessle, *ibid.* (in press).] May or June 1954.

developed by Bronsted, Christiansen, and Scatchard.[27] Since each of the reactants (ASH and ASHgX) carries the charge $-Z$, the charge on the critical complex—as on the dimer, the final product of the reaction —is $-2Z$, and the electrostatic work of forming the complex increases with the numerical magnitude of Z. Thus, as $-Z$ increases, the equilibrium between the reactants and the critical complex is shifted in favor of the reactants, and the rate decreases. We have made a rough calculation of the magnitude of the effect to be expected, treating the albumin molecule as a uniformly charged sphere (the charge being adjustable by adding H^+ or OH^- ions), and applying the Debye-Hückel theory. The results look reasonable, but the model is too crude to justify drawing any detailed conclusions.

It is, of course, reasonable that step (II) in the reaction scheme should proceed much more slowly than step (I). Actually, step (I) has

been written in somewhat condensed form. The formation of ASHgX
from ASH and HgX_2 must be preceded by a preliminary ionization of
ASH to AS^-, and of HgX_2 to HgX^+. These two ions then combine to
form ASHgX. All these reactions are ionic and should be rapid, particularly as HgX_2 and HgX^+ are very small particles compared to the
albumin, and their thermal motion is, therefore, relatively great. The
preliminary ionizations may occur in solution before reaction, or perhaps
within the critical complex; for our present purposes, it does not much
matter which picture is more nearly correct. Step (II), on the other
hand, involves combination between the two large molecules ASH and
ASHgX; their thermal motion is relatively slow, and they can react
only in a very narrow range of mutual relative orientations which will
permit the two SH groups to approach closely enough to be linked
through the mercury atom. Given these requirements, and the great
reactivity of mercury with sulfhydryl groups, it might have been
inferred that nearly every collision involving suitable relative orientations of the two mercaptalbumin molecules would result in reaction.
Such an inference, however, would be quite wrong, for it is shown below
that an analogous reaction involving a bifunctional organic mercurial
proceeds several thousand times as fast as the formation of ASHgSA;
and there is no reason to believe that this is an upper limit for the speed
of such reactions. Moreover, the rate of dimer formation, as measured
by the velocity constant k_2, has a large temperature coefficient, as is
shown by the experiment represented in Fig. 4. The energy of activation
is indeed of the order of 18–20 kcal/mole, a value which completely
excludes the hypothesis of a collision limited process.

   Calculation of association constants with mercuric ion. From equilibrium
data, such as those illustrated in Fig. 2, combined with other information, we can obtain an approximate estimate for the equilibrium constant
of the reaction between $ASHg^+$ and AS^- to form the dimer ASHgSA.
The argument is due largely to my colleague Dr. R. B. Simpson. We
may write for the equilibrium constant in question, which we denote as
K_A,

$$K_A = \frac{(ASHgSA)}{(ASHg^+)(AS^-)} = K_{A1} K_{A2} K_{ASH} \cong 10^{13.5} \qquad (7)$$

Here, if we are dealing with the equilibrium in a solution containing
bromide ion, as in the experiment shown in Fig. 2, we have

$$K_{A1} = \frac{(ASHgSA)(H^+)(Br^-)}{(ASHgBr)(ASH)} = 10^{-4.9} \qquad (8)$$

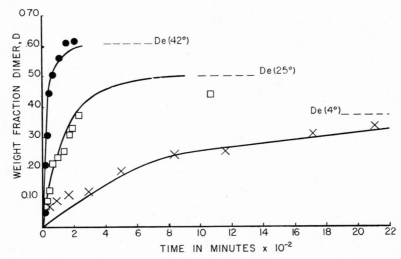

FIG. 4. Dimerization of mercaptalbumin at three temperatures to form the dimer ASHgSA. Albumin 0.01 gm/ml, pH 4.75, acetate buffer, ionic strength 0.05. The solid lines represent calculated curves, assuming second-order velocity constants $k_2 = 5$ 1-mole^{-1} min.$^{-1}$ at 4°, 40 at 25°, and 260 at 42°. The value of D_e at 4° is based on readings taken 3725 min after mixing albumin and mercury, but it is probably lower than the true equilibrium value at this temperature. [From Edelhoch, Katchalski, et al., J. Am. Chem. Soc. 75, 5058 (1953)].

In the experiment of Fig. 2, total albumin is 0.01 gm/ml (ASH = 1.4×10^{-4} M if no mercury were present) and the weight fraction of dimer at equilibrium (D_e) is 0.30. The total mercury equals (ASHgSA) + (ASHgBr) = 7.0×10^{-5}; the total bromide, (Br$^-$) + (ASHgBr) = 1.4×10^{-4}. Hence we obtain (ASHgX) = (ASH) = 4.9×10^{-5}; (ASHgSA) = 2.1×10^{-5}; (Br$^-$) = 9.1×10^{-5}. These values, together with (H$^+$) = $10^{-4.75}$, give the value of $10^{-4.9}$ for K_{A1} in equation (8). The true value for free bromide ion is probably somewhat less than the estimate given here, since some bromide is bound to sites on the protein other than the $-$SHg$^+$ group.[28, 29] Neglect of this factor may introduce an error of the order of 10 to 15 % into the calculation of K_A; but some of the other factors involved in equation (7) are subject to considerably more uncertainty than this.

K_{A2} is the equilibrium constant

$$K_{A2} = \frac{(ASHgBr)}{(ASHg^+)(Br^-)} = 10^{8.3} \qquad (9)$$

The value given here is derived by analogy, on the assumption that it is the same as the association constant for the reaction

$$HgBr^+ + Br^- \rightleftharpoons HgBr_2$$

which has been determined as $10^{8.3}$ at $25°$ in the very careful studies of Sillén[19] and his collaborators. The assumption is certainly not exact; the sulfur atom adjoining the mercury in $ASHg^+$ may well affect the affinity for Br^-, to say nothing of the influence of the rest of the albumin molecule. However, the value in equation (9) should be of the right order of magnitude.

The constant K_{ASH} in equation (7) is the association constant of the acid sulfhydryl group in mercaptalbumin

$$K_{ASH} = \frac{(ASH)}{(AS^-)(H^+)} \cong 10^{10} \qquad (10)$$

The value of 10^{10} is only an estimate of the order of magnitude; it has been inferred as reasonable from the data given by Cohn and Edsall,[30] by Ryklan and Schmidt,[31] and by Stricks and Kolthoff.[18] In this connection it should be noted that the assignment which I have previously given for cysteine,[32] attributing pK_2 to the $-NH_3^+$ and pK_3 to the $-SH$ group, is misleading. The titration constants for cysteine are hybrid constants—one must distinguish between the pK value of the $-SH$ group of cysteine, on the one hand when the neighboring amino group carries a positive charge, and on the other hand when it is uncharged. Similarly the pK of the ammonium group has one value when the adjoining $-SH$ group is uncharged, another when it is negatively charged. I have given the argument in more detail in a note published as part of the paper of Ryklan and Schmidt,[31] and their data give the necessary basis for calculating the individual constants. It should be noted that for glutathione the pK value of the $-SH$ group is not far from 9,[18] so that the estimate of 10^{10} for K_{ASH} in equation (10) may be too high. What is obviously needed, however, is a direct determination of the pK value of this group in mercaptalbumin, and this as yet we do not have.

As an independent check on the values of K_{A1} and K_{A2}, we may determine the corresponding constants for systems containing chloride ion instead of bromide. Thus from the data of Edelhoch, Katchalski, et al.,[26] (see their Table V) we find the weight fraction of dimer $D_e = 0.32$ when total $(Cl^-) = 7 \times 10^{-3}$ M. This gives $K_{A1} = 10^{-2.9}$ in the analogue of equation (8) for chloride ion. If we take $K_{A2} = [(HgCl_2)/$

$(HgCl^+)(Cl^-)] = 10^{6.5}$ from the data of Sillén at 25°, we then have $K_{A1}K_{A2} = 10^{3.6}$, as compared with the value $10^{3.4}$ from the figures for the bromide-containing systems given in equations (8) and (9).

The argument has been given in considerable detail, so that the sources of error and uncertainty may be plainly seen. The value of $K_A = 10^{13.5}$ given in equation (7) is uncertain perhaps to one power of 10. It is, in any case, very small when compared to the mean value of the association constant of mercuric ion with cysteine or glutathione in the form RS⁻.

$$K_{mean} = \left[\frac{([RS]_2 Hg)}{(Hg^{++})(RS^-)^2} \right]^{1/2} = 10^{20.5} \text{ to } 10^{22.5} \qquad (11)$$

from the figures given by Stricks and Kolthoff.[18] It will be seen that K_A for the mercury dimer is lower by a factor of 10^7 to 10^9. This difference is probably a reflection of the great steric obstacles to linking the two albumins together. The Hg—S covalent bond distance is not far from 2.5 Å, probably a little less, so that the two sulfur atoms in the sulfhydryl groups of the two albumin molecules cannot be more than 5 Å apart. The problems involved in such close fitting of two large molecules are discussed further below, in relation to the entropy of activation of the reaction.

Studies with a bifunctional organic mercurial. Dimerization of mercaptalbumin should also be possible by interaction with organic bifunctional mercurials of the general formula XHgRHgX, giving the dimer ASHgRHgSA and the intermediate compound ASHgRHgX, with a reaction sequence exactly analogous to that already formulated for the mercury dimer in equations (I), (II), and (III). This possibility has as yet been realized with only one organic mercurial. Straessle[33] employed the compound called, in the terminology used by Chatt,[34] 3,6-bis(acetatomercurimethyl)-dioxan

$$\text{XHgCH}_2 \cdot \text{HC} \underset{\text{O—CH}_2}{\overset{\text{CH}_2\text{—O}}{\diagup \diagdown}} \text{CH} \cdot \text{CH}_2\text{HgX} \quad (\text{X = acetate})$$

which for brevity we denote by XHgRHgX, as above. This had already been prepared 50 years earlier.[35] Fortunately it was easy to prepare and to purify. Moreover the two mercury atoms, being separated by a dioxan ring and two methylene groups, are about 10 Å apart, as inferred from the dimensions of a space model. Therefore, the extremely close approach of the two ASH molecules, which is necessary for the formation of the mercury dimer, is not required here; the coupling between the components of the dimer is considerably looser. This difference of structure has a profound influence both on the equilibrium and the velocity constants. Beginning with the early work of Straessle, numerous studies have been made in our laboratory on the interaction of this compound with mercaptalbumin, especially by R. B. Simpson and R. H. Maybury. The results have recently been reported in detail.[36]

Kinetic studies. In Fig. 5 the rate of dimerization is shown for two different pH values and for each at two different temperatures. The reaction goes to completion, within the experimental error, at both pH values; thus, in considering the kinetics of the process, we do not have to allow for the back reaction as is necessary in the case of the mercury dimer. Three points are immediately obvious from Fig. 5: (1). The reaction is extremely rapid compared with that of mercury dimer formation. At pH 5.5 and at 23–25°, the second-order velocity constant k_2 (in liters per mole per minute) is less than 5 for the reaction between ASHgX and ASH, and is 9800 for the reaction between ASHgRHgX and ASH. (2). The velocity constant k_2 falls with increasing pH, as it does for the mercury dimer. Indeed a plot of log k_2 as a function of pH, which is seen in Fig. 3, has nearly the same slope for both dimers, although at any given pH the values of k_2 differ by a factor of the order of 2000 or more. Below pH 5 the rate of dimerization with the bifunctional mercurial is too rapid to measure by the techniques we have employed. (3). The temperature coefficient of the reaction is large in both types of dimer formation, the energy of activation being of the order 18–22 kcal/mole in all cases.

The rate of dimerization with the bifunctional mercurial is remarkably rapid for a reaction between two large molecules; yet at the same time it has a large temperature coefficient and, therefore, a high energy of activation. The combination of these facts implies a high entropy of activation. The standard entropy of activation may be calculated from the energy of activation (E_{exp}) and the logarithm of the observed velocity constant by the equation[27]

$$\ln(k_2/60) = 1 + \ln(kT/h) + \Delta S\ddagger/R - E_{exp}/RT \qquad (12)$$

(Here we have divided k_2 by 60 to convert from units of liters per mole per minute to liters per mole per second.) Using the values of k_2 at 25° shown in Fig. 5, and the values of E_{exp} derived from the temperature coefficients of the data shown in that figure ($E_{exp} = 18$ kcal/mol at

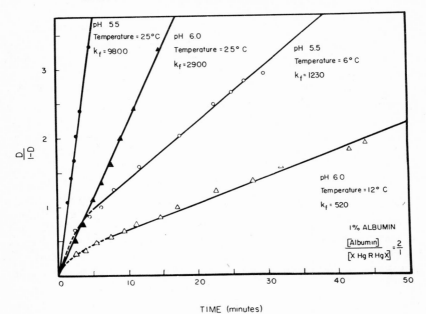

TIME (minutes)

FIG. 5. Rate of dimer formation with the bifunctional mercurial at two pH values and two temperatures. For an irreversible second-order reaction, the quantity $D/(1-D)$, where D is weight fraction of dimer, should be a linear function of time. This relation is fitted satisfactorily for the two curves at 25°. The increased rate of the reaction during the first few minutes in the low-temperature curves was probably due to difficulties in cooling the solution immediately after mixing the reagents. The symbol k_f in this figure denotes the velocity constant which is referred to as k_2 in the text. [From Edsall, Maybury, Simpson, and Straessle, *J. Am. Chem. Soc.* (in press).] May or June 1954.

pH 5.5, and 23 at pH 6) the estimated value of $\Delta S\ddagger$ is near 13.5 cal-deg^{-1} mole^{-1} at pH 5.5, and 26 at pH 6. The corresponding value for the mercury dimer, taking $k_2 = 40$ liter-mol^{-1}min^{-1} at pH 4.75, is near zero, of the order of 1 or 2 cal-deg^{-1}mole^{-1}. These figures are certainly not of high accuracy; the remarkable thing about all of them is that they are in striking contrast to the values obtained in most dimerization reactions, which are commonly large and negative, of the order of -50 cal-deg^{-1} mole^{-1}. Such negative values are to be expected in general on account of the decrease in translational and rotational degrees of freedom accompanying the linking of two molecules together. The values obtained for the reactions studied here are, by contrast, extraordinarily large in the positive direction. We have suggested two possible explanations for such an effect:[36] (1). The albumin molecules may be unable to combine in their native state, and a partial unfolding, in the neighborhood of the reactive centers, may be a necessary prelude to the linkage of the two sulfhydryl groups. This would be analogous to a partial denaturation—a process well known to involve a large positive entropy of activation. It must be remembered, however, that the over-all process is completely reversible. (2). The union of the two albumin molecules may involve a large surface of contact between them, with an accompanying dehydration of the charged groups on each molecule over this portion of the molecular surface. Since the hydration of charged groups, with the accompanying electrostriction, is accompanied by a large decrease in entropy, a dehydration process will yield a corresponding increase. This is the mechanism already proposed by Doty and Myers[37] to explain certain entropy effects found in the reversible polymerization of insulin in acid solution. Whether either of these two effects, or both in combination, may be adequate to explain the observed effects, is a question that must be left to the future.

Equilibrium measurements. The dimerization process involving the bifunctional mercurial goes practically to completion if two moles of ASH are mixed with one of XHgRHgX. However, it is possible to estimate roughly the equilibrium constant of the reaction [*cf.* equation (7)]

$$K_A = \frac{(ASHgRHgSA)}{(ASHgRHg^+)(AS^-)} \tag{13}$$

by measuring the degree of dissociation of the dimer in the presence of an added reagent with a high affinity for mercury. Figure 6 shows the effect of added cyanide at pH 4.75 and $\Gamma/2 = 0.05$ acetate buffer. It will be seen that the addition of one mole of cyanide per mole of the dimer ASHgRHgSA produces only a partial dissociation of the dimer according to the reaction

$$ASHgRHgSA + HCN \rightleftharpoons ASHgRHgCN + ASH$$

Three moles of cyanide per mole of dimer produce a further dissociation, and five moles lead to something approaching complete dissociation. An analysis of the data gives for the equilibrium constant K_{A1} a value close to unity

$$K_{A1} = \frac{(ASHgRHgSA)(HCN)}{(ASHgRHgCN)(ASH)} \cong 1 \tag{14}$$

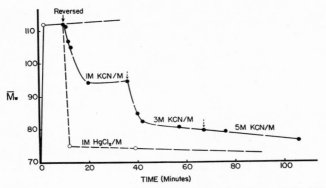

Fig. 6. Effect of cyanide in dissociating the albumin dimer of the bifunctional mercurial. The effects of several successive additions of cyanide are shown. The very rapid dissociation of the dimer following the addition of one equivalent of mercuric chloride is shown for comparison. [From Edsall, Maybury, Simpson, and Straessle, *J. Am. Chem. Soc.* (in press).] May or June 1954.

We must also make use of an estimate of K_{A2}

$$K_{A2} = \frac{(ASHgRHgCN)}{(ASHgRHg^+)(CN^-)} \cong 10^{17.5} \qquad (15)$$

By analogy with the argument used in connection with equation (9), we take K_{A2} as approximately equal to the square root of the association constant for the two step reaction $Hg^{++} + 2\ CN^- \rightleftharpoons Hg(CN)_2$ which is recorded by Bjerrum;[20] this is the value recorded in equation (15). To derive K_A in equation (13) we also need the association constant for HCN as an acid, $K_{HCN} = 10^{9.3}$ according to Sidgwick;[38] and the value of K_{ASH}, already taken as 10^{10} in equation (10). Thus we finally obtain for K_A

$$K_A = K_{A1}K_{A2}K_{ASH}/K_{HCN}$$
$$= 1 \times 10^{17.5} \times 10^{10}/10^{9.3} = 10^{18.2} \qquad (16)$$

This gives a rough quantitative measure of the stability of the dimer of the bifunctional mercurial as compared with that of the mercury dimer. From equations (7), (13), and (16) we may write

$$\frac{K_A(\text{for bifunctional mercurial})}{K_A(\text{for mercury dimer})} = \frac{10^{18.2}}{10^{13.5}} = 50,000 \qquad (17)$$

This estimate of the ratio of the two K_A values should be more reliable than either individual value, since the uncertainty in the assumed

K_{ASH} value cancels out, and the possible errors in the assumptions concerning the K_{A2} values in equations (9) and (15) are also largely cancelled. The standard free energy of formation of ASHgSA is larger than that of ASHgRHgSA by 2.303 RT log 50,000 = 6.4 kcal/mole. This is essentially the molar free energy increase involved in bringing the two albumin molecules closer by a distance of about 10 Å—from an S . . . . S distance of approximately 15 Å in ASHgRHgSA to one of approximately 5 Å in ASHgSA.

From the kinetic data already discussed it appears that the second-order constant k_2 for dimer formation is about 2000 times as great, at any given pH, for ASHgRHgX and ASH as for ASHgX and ASH. Combining this with the equilibrium constant in equation (17), it would appear that the first-order dissociation rate constant for ASHgSA is about 25 times as large as for ASHgRHgSA.

Effect of the removal of fatty acids from mercaptalbumin. Crystalline serum albumin preparations commonly contain some tightly bound fatty acid, of the order of one to three moles fatty acid per mole albumin.[39] Such acids are not removed by recrystallization, and only to a minor degree by electrodialysis. However, by suitable treatment, involving passage over a column of a mixed-bed ion-exchange resin, Dintzis[40] has been able to remove this fatty acid from both human and bovine mercaptalbumin almost quantitatively. The velocity constants for ASHgSA formation, plotted in Fig. 3, were obtained using preparations of human mercaptalbumin from which the attached fatty acids had not been removed. Dr. R. H. Maybury, on studying preparations purified by the method of Dintzis, found k_2 values that were distinctly lower—of the order of 13 l-mol^{-1} min^{-1}, at pH 4.75, instead of near 40, as in the earlier experiments of Drs. Edelhoch and Katchalski. Moreover, the curves were in general complex and could not be fitted by a single second-order velocity constant. Approximately the first 15% of the albumin that reacted to form dimer gave an apparent k_2 near 25; then the reaction slowed up, and proceeded the rest of the way, following a brief transition period, with a velocity constant of the order of 13. The description in terms of two velocity constants is somewhat arbitrary, but it does give a reasonable approximation to the observed facts. Furthermore Maybury found that the addition of oleate ion (3 moles per mole of albumin) to the protein from which fatty acid had been removed by the method of Dintzis caused a marked increase, by a factor of the order of 2, in the measured values of k_2; the region of the curve in which the transition to a lower velocity constant occurred was displaced to about 50 % of dimer formation instead of 15. It appears that bound fatty acid in albumin increases the rate of dimerization by a mechanism that is still far from clear. It cannot be due to the alteration of net charge on the albumin molecule; for if isoelectric albumin is given a negative charge by the addition of OH⁻ ion, the reaction rate is decreased, as shown in Fig. 3. A negative charge added to the albumin in the form of oleate ion, on the other hand, increases the reaction rate. The amount of dimer formed at equilibrium is also slightly increased by the addition of 3 moles of oleate, from a weight fraction near 0.55 to near 0.61, in a 1 % albumin solution at 25°. Presumably some at least of the bound oleate must be attached to a portion of the molecule not far from the reactive sulfhydryl group, but the mechanism of its action is quite unknown.[41]

Bovine mercaptalbumin. Not long ago, Dr. H. M. Dintzis, working in Dr. Oncley's laboratory, achieved the crystallization of bovine mercaptalbumin in high purity and excellent yield. Studies by Dr. Maybury, using the light scattering technique, showed that the equilibrium constant for the formation of the mercury dimer was considerably larger than in the case of human mercaptalbumin. At pH 4.75–5.0 and 25°, in a 1 % albumin solution, the weight fraction of dimer at equilibrium was 0.87–0.90 for the bovine as against 0.55–0.60 for the human material. Moreover, the velocity constant of dimerization, k_2, for the material carefully freed of fatty acid by the exchange resin treatment, was near 40, about 3 times as great as for the human albumin freed of fatty acid in a comparable manner. Moreover, the entire curve for the rate of dimerization in bovine albumin could be fitted with high accuracy by a single second-order constant. This appears to indicate greater purity and homogeneity of the bovine material. As yet few data have been obtained on these preparations, but they clearly deserve the most careful and thorough study.

This discussion of the interaction of mercaptalbumin with mercury and organic mercurials is confined to a very special type of reaction— to a single type of protein and a single type of ion. The dimerization reaction, however, is a unique and remarkable process, and the data discussed here provide evidence which, in conjunction with other studies on serum albumin, may ultimately serve to illuminate the detailed pattern of molecular structure for this particular protein, and thereby to advance our knowledge of the finer details of protein structure in general. As yet there is no evidence to indicate any particular biological or medical significance for the dimerization reaction, but even here future developments may surprise us. Knowledge of the nature of the interactions of proteins with the mercuric ion is certainly of potential importance for the pharmacologist and pathologist; but the method of approach is more important than the results achieved, and the future harvests to be reaped in this field should be far greater than any that have yet been gathered in.

ACKNOWLEDGMENTS

This work, although reported by one individual, is the product of many experimenters and many minds. The foundations of these studies on albumin dimerization were laid by Dr. Hughes, who made the fundamental discoveries and laid the entire basis of the main lines of the interpretations offered here. The progress of the light scattering work has been due to Harold Edelhoch, Ephraim Katchalski, Richard B. Simpson, Rudolf Straessle, and Robert H. Maybury, who between them have carried out nearly all of the experimental work and contributed a large part of the thinking.

REFERENCES

1. KIRKWOOD, J. G., *in* "Proteins, Amino Acids and Peptides" (E. J. Cohn and J. T. Edsall, eds.), Chapt. 12. Reinhold Publishing Corp., New York, 1943.
2. COHN, E. J., and EDSALL, J. T., "Proteins, Amino Acids and Peptides," Chapt. 11. Reinhold Publishing Corp., New York, 1943.
3. EDSALL, J. T., *in* ref. 2, Chapt. 20, pp. 460–468.
4. KIRKWOOD, J. G., and SHUMAKER, J. B., *Proc. Natl. Acad. Sci. U. S.* **38**, 855, 863 (1952).
5. MCMEEKIN, T. L., and WARNER, R. C., *J. Am. Chem. Soc.* **64**, 2393 (1942); also J. Lewin, *ibid.* **73**, 3906 (1951).
6. ADAIR, G. S., *in* "Haemoglobin" (F. J. W. Roughton and J. C. Kendrew, eds.), p. 183. Butterworth Scientific Publications, London; Interscience Publishers, New York, 1948.
7a. COHN, E. J., *et al.*, *J. Am. Chem. Soc.* **68**, 459 (1946); **72**, 465 (1950).
7b. EDSALL, J. T., *Advances in Protein Chem.* **3**, 383 (1947).
8. See the discussion by E. J. Cohn, *in* ref. 2, Chapter 11, p. 242 ff.
9. KLOTZ, I. M., *in* "The Proteins" (H. Neurath and K. Bailey, eds.), Vol. IB, Chapt. 8. Academic Press, New York, 1953.
10. CRAMMER, J. L., and NEUBERGER, A., *Biochem. J.* **37**, 302 (1943).
11. STEINHARDT, J., and ZAISER, E. M., *J. Biol. Chem.* **190**, 197 (1951); ZAISER, E. M., and STEINHARDT, J., *J. Am. Chem. Soc.* **73**, 5568 (1951).
12. BOYER, P. D., LUM, F. G., BALLOU, G. A., LUCK, J. M., and RICE, R. G., *J. Biol. Chem.* **162**, 181 (1946).
13. BOYER, P. D., BALLOU, G. A., and LUCK, J. M., *J. Biol. Chem.* **162**, 199 (1946).
14. See for instance "Blood Cells and Plasma Proteins" (J. L. Tullis, ed.). Academic Press, New York, 1953.
15. SURGENOR, D. M., "Blood," Scientific American, Feb. 1954.

16. HUGHES, W. L. JR., *J. Am. Chem. Soc.* **69,** 1836 (1947); *Cold Spring Harbor Symposia Quant. Biol.* **14,** 79 (1950).
17. LOW, B. W., *J. Am. Chem. Soc.* **74,** 4830 (1952).
18. STRICKS, W., and KOLTHOFF, I. M., *J. Am. Chem. Soc.* **75,** 5673 (1953).
19. SILLÉN, L. G., *Acta Chem. Scand.* **3,** 539 (1949).
20. BJERRUM, J., *Chem. Revs.* **46,** 381 (1950).
21. SIDGWICK, N. V., "The Chemical Elements and Their Compounds," p. 325. Oxford University Press, New York, 1950.
22. BRAND, E., and EDSALL, J. T., *Ann. Rev. Biochem.* **16,** 223 (1947).
23. TANFORD, C., *J. Am. Chem. Soc.* **72,** 441 (1950).
24. DOTY, P. M. and EDSALL, J. T., *Advances in Protein Chem.* **6,** 35 (1951).
25. EDSALL, J. T., EDELHOCH, H., LONTIE, R., and MORRISON, P. R., *J. Am. Chem. Soc.* **72,** 4641 (1950).
26. EDELHOCH, H., KATCHALSKI, E., MAYBURY, R. H., HUGHES, W. L. JR., and EDSALL, J. T., *J. Am. Chem. Soc.* **75,** 5058 (1953).
27. See for instance, GLASSTONE, S., LAIDLER, K. J., and EYRING, H., "The Theory of Rate Processes." McGraw-Hill Book Company, New York, 1941.
28. SCATCHARD, G., and BLACK, E. S., *J. Phys. & Colloid Chem.* **53,** 88 (1949).
29. SCATCHARD, G., SCHEINBERG, I. H., and ARMSTRONG, S. H. JR., *J. Am. Chem. Soc.* **72,** 535 (1950).
30. See ref. 2, Chapts. 4 and 5.
31. RYKLAN, L. R., and SCHMIDT, C. L. A., *Arch. Biochem.* **5,** 89 (1944).
32. See ref. 2, p. 85.
33. STRAESSLE, R., *J. Am. Chem. Soc.* **73,** 504 (1951).
34. CHATT, J., *Chem. Revs.* **48,** 7 (1951).
35. BIILMANN, E., *Ber.* **33,** 1641 (1900); HOFMANN, K. A., and SAND, J., *ibid.* **33,** 2692; SAND, J., *ibid.* **34,** 2906 (1901); SAND, J., and HOFMANN, K. A., *ibid.* **33,** 1358 (1900).
36. EDSALL, J. T., MAYBURY, R. H., SIMPSON, R. B., and STRAESSLE, R., *J. Am. Chem. Soc.* (in press). May or June, 1954.
37. DOTY, P. M., and MYERS, G. E., *Discussions Faraday Soc.* **13,** 51 (1953).
38. See ref. 21, p. 670.
39. COHN, E. J., HUGHES, W. L. JR., and WEARE, J. H., *J. Am. Chem. Soc.* **69,** 1753 (1947).
40. DINTZIS, H. M., PH.D. Thesis, Harvard University, 1952; ONCLEY, J. L., and DINTZIS, H. M., *Abstr. 122nd Meeting Am. Chem. Soc. Atlantic City,* p. 19C (Sept. 1952).
41. EDSALL, J. T., MAYBURY, R. H., and SIMPSON, R. B., *Abstr. 124th Meeting Am. Chem. Soc., Chicago,* p. 17C (Sept. 1953); also MAYBURY, R. H., and DINTZIS, H. M., *ibid.* p. 18C.

The Specificity of Metal-Protein Interactions[a]

FRANK R. N. GURD

INTRODUCTION

The interactions of proteins with metals may be divided into two classes. In the first class are those in which the protein possesses unique sites which combine firmly with one or more kinds of metallic ion. The site of binding may be a prosthetic group, as in the heme proteins, or it may involve a special arrangement of the amino acid units, as appears to be the case with the metal-combining protein of plasma.[1, 2] There are no obvious correlations between the number of binding sites and the number of the various amino acids contained in the protein, and the binding sites are unique in the same sense as the "active centers" of enzymes. Indeed, in the metal-activated enzymes the binding sites of this class are themselves part of the "active centers."[3]

A second class of metal-protein interactions is the subject of this review. Many proteins combine more or less reversibly with a variety of metallic cations irrespective of whether they are isolated in combination with metals or require metals for their physiological activity. This second class of metal-protein interaction is also of great physiological interest. Perhaps the best known physiological example is the reversible binding of calcium ion to the serum proteins.[4] It has recently become apparent that many such interactions exhibit specificities as to the classes of reactive groups on a protein to which a given metallic ion may bind; the relative affinities of a given reactive group for a series of metallic ions; the number of each class of reactive groups in a protein that is actually free to bind metallic ions; and the effect of the various metallic ions on the general properties of a protein, particularly solubility.

INTERACTIONS WITH REACTIVE GROUPS IN PROTEINS
Binding to Specific Classes of Groups

The most direct method of establishing whether a given class of reactive groups in a protein (e.g., sulfhydryl, ϵ-amino, imidazole, carboxyl)

[a] This work has been supported by funds of Harvard University and the Eugene Higgins Trust, by grants from the Rockefeller Foundation and the National Institutes of Health, and by contributions from industry.

246

is capable of combining with a certain metallic ion is to show that the metallic ion will block some specific reaction characteristic of the groups in question. For example, Hughes found that the addition of one equivalent of mercuric ion per mole of human serum mercaptalbumin abolished the positive nitroprusside test for the sulfhydryl group.[5] Another useful technique is that of modifying the groups in question in such a way as to reduce or abolish the affinity of the protein for the metal. Hughes showed that the oxidation of the sulfhydryl group in human serum mercaptalbumin nearly abolished binding of methyl-mercury iodide.[5]

Frequently a suitable test or modification procedure is not available. In this case advantage may be taken of the fact that most of the types of groups in a protein which are capable of binding metallic ions also react with hydrogen ions.[6] Therefore, a study of the extent of binding of the metallic ion as a function of pH may be useful in indicating which groups are responsible for the binding of the metallic ion.[7, 8] A detailed study of the competition between zinc and hydrogen ions for common sites in human serum albumin led Gurd and Goodman to conclude that the imidazole groups of the 16 histidine residues were the principal sites of binding of zinc ions by this protein.[8] They found that the intrinsic association constant for zinc ions with imidazole groups in serum albumin was nearly identical with the first association constant for zinc ions with imidazole itself. They also concluded that each zinc ion combined with only one imidazole group at a time, rather than with two or more as would be conceivable if the spatial arrangement in the protein molecule would permit such combination.

The study of hydrogen ion competition has recently indicated that, unlike zinc ions, plumbous ions bind in large part to the carboxylate groups in human serum mercaptalbumin.[9] The contrast in specificity of these two metallic ions is brought out in Fig. 1. The ordinate is $\bar{\nu}$, the number of moles of metal bound per mole of mercaptalbumin; the abscissa is pH. The data for lead ion are taken from Gurd and Murray,[9] those for zinc ion were obtained on the same protein preparation by Dr. Charlotte Fitting in the course of a separate investigation.[10] The equilibrium concentrations of lead ion were about 0.05 M, of zinc about 0.016 M. The experimental techniques have been described.[8, 9]

That zinc and lead ions combine specifically with different classes of reactive groups is supported by measurements of the binding of each ion in the presence of the other. Table I, taken from Gurd and Murray,[9] shows the values of $\bar{\nu}$ for zinc and lead ions after both metals had

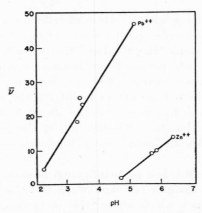

FIG. 1. Binding of lead perchlorate[9] and of zinc nitrate[10] by human serum mercaptalbumin. Variation of $\bar{\nu}$ with pH at 0°.

TABLE I

BINDING OF ZINC AND LEAD IONS TO HUMAN SERUM MERCAPTALBUMIN*

Experiment number	Order of addition	Hours of final equilibration	Concentration in supernatant solution ($M \times 10^3$)		Moles metal bound per mole protein	
			Zn	Pb	$\bar{\nu}_{Zn^{++}}$	$\bar{\nu}_{Pb^{++}}$
1	Zn, Pb	1	5.76	6.50	5.5	20.7
2	Zn, Pb	24	5.64	6.35	6.5	25.6
3	Pb, Zn	1	5.75	6.36	5.6	21.1
4	Pb, Zn	24	†	6.50	†	23.5
5	Pb	24		7.07		25.9
	Zn		5.5		5.0	

* Taken from Gurd and Murray.[9]
† Not measured.

been mixed with serum mercaptalbumin. In experiments 1–4, the order of addition of the metals and the time of final equilibration were varied. It may be seen that the binding of lead in experiments 2 and 4 was practically the same as in experiment 5 in which zinc was omitted, and that the binding of zinc was comparable to that in the absence of lead, as shown in the last line.

Lead and zinc ions have quite different complex-forming properties,[6] and it is not surprising that they do not appear to compete for common sites in serum mercaptalbumin. Such similar ions as cadmium and zinc, on the other hand, may be expected to compete with each other, and

TABLE II

COMPETITION BETWEEN ZINC AND CADMIUM IONS FOR BINDING SITES IN
HUMAN SERUM MERCAPTALBUMIN

Micromoles metal added		Concentration total un-		
Cd	Zn	bound metal ($M \times 10^3$)	pH	$\bar{\nu}_{Total}$
0	140	4.5	6.6	8.5*
125	0	3.96	6.48	11.4
250	0	8.27	6.32	14.5
125	140	9.07	6.25	12.5
250	140	13.33	6.12	15.0

* Value from interpolation, taken from results of C. Fitting on the same preparation of mercaptalbumin.[10]

evidence for such competition is presented in Table II. The dialysis equilibrium technique was employed.[8, 9] Concentrations of Cd^{++} and $Cd^{++} + Zn^{++}$ were measured by method A of Schwarzenbach, Biedermann, and Bangerter.[11] The isoionic protein was mixed with 16 moles of NaOH per mole protein before the equilibration with the cadmium and zinc nitrates. The temperature of the equilibration was 0°. Some fine precipitation of the protein occurred in the last three experiments summarized in Table II, and the contents of the dialysis bags were stirred before sampling.

From Table II it is clear that the number of moles of metal bound when zinc and cadmium ions are both present is much less than the sum of the values for the two ions measured separately. These results indicate that zinc and cadmium ions bind for the most part to the same class of sites in human serum mercaptalbumin, presumably to the 16 imidazole groups.

Affinities of Metallic Ions for a Given Class of Groups

The foregoing discussion has shown that cadmium, zinc, and lead show an affinity for the imidazole groups of human serum mercaptalbumin which decreases in the order named. The results of Tanford[7] indicate that thallous ions do not bind appreciably to bovine serum albumin and that cupric ions bind more strongly to imidazole groups than do cadmium or zinc ions.

Klotz, Urquhart, and Fiess[12] have compared spectrophotometrically the ability of various metallic acetates to displace cupric ions from combination with the sulfhydryl group of bovine serum albumin. The protein preparation used contained slightly less than one sulfhydryl group per protein molecule. The copper complex showed an absorption maximum at 375 mμ. Addition of zinc ion up to a concentration equal to that of the cupric ion reduced the height of the absorption band by about 30 %. Mercuric acetate abolished the 375-mμ band completely, silver nitrate almost completely. The order of affinity for the sulfhydryl group as measured by the displacement of cupric ion appeared to be $Hg^{++} > Pb^{++} > Cd^{++} > Zn^{++}$.

Many of the metallic ions which bind most strongly to proteins also combine strongly with various anions and uncharged molecules.[13] The presence of an anion with a strong tendency to form complexes will generally reduce the apparent affinity of the metallic ion for the groups in the protein. In certain cases, an anion may be found which competes so effectively that only the groups in the protein having the highest affinity are able to bind the metallic ion. Hughes[5] has made use of the high affinity of I^- for methylmercury to limit the reaction of methylmercury with serum mercaptalbumin to the sulfhydryl group alone. If the poorly-competing nitrate ion is substituted for iodide, a large number of methylmercury ions are able to combine with the protein.[6] Edelhoch and co-workers[14] have drawn a parallel between the effects of Cl^-, Br^-, and I^- on the rate of decomposition of mercaptalbumin mercury dimer and the affinities of these anions for mercury.

Although under favorable circumstances the addition of appropriate anions may serve to direct the specificity of a metal-protein interaction, it must not be overlooked that the presence of certain anions may obscure the results. It is particularly important to be aware of any possible effects due to buffers, the use of which should be avoided whenever possible.[6]

Availability of Groups in the Protein

The affinity of a protein molecule for a given metallic ion may be expected to depend not only upon the numbers of the various reactive groups in the protein, as represented in the amino acid analysis, but also upon the availability of such groups for the metallic ion. Many studies comparing the reactivity of groups in native and denatured proteins have shown that in the native configuration certain groups in many proteins are far less reactive than would be expected if they were freely available.[15, 16] For example, Anson[17] found that the sulfhydryl groups of egg albumin were able to react with the organic mercurial, p-chloromercuribenzoate, only after denaturation of the protein. Similar limitations on reactivity may apply in other metal-protein interactions: it has recently been found that human serum mercaptalbumin has an increased affinity for zinc ions following certain types of denaturation.[10] The greatest care must be exercised in interpreting such studies with metals, since the more random arrangement of the denatured protein might permit chelation of the metallic ion by groups which are not able to come into juxtaposition in the native molecule.

The extensive studies by Klotz,[18] Karush,[19] and Scatchard[20] have done much to bring out the subtlety of the binding of anions by proteins, particularly serum albumins. Klotz and Ayers[21] have drawn attention to the contrast between egg albumin, which binds anions much more strongly after heat denaturation, and serum albumin, which loses affinity for anions on being heated to 100°. Denaturation by other agents also shows specific differences.

Even when two similar proteins possess the same number of reactive groups of a given class, the groups may show differences in reactivity towards metallic ions. Both human and bovine serum mercaptalbumin possess a single reactive sulfhydryl group and form dimers by the sharing of a single mercuric ion between two protein molecules.[14, 22, 23] Despite these similarities in the reaction mechanisms, the equilibrium constants and rate constants are markedly different for the dimerization of the two proteins,[23, 24] indicating specific differences in the relation of the free cysteine residue to the rest of the molecular structure. The subtlety of these phenomena is pointed up by the discovery of a considerable increase in the rate of dimerization of human mercaptalbumin when a few moles of fatty acid are added.[24]

Perhaps more immediately dependent on the structure of the protein molecule adjacent to the sulfhydryl group is the difference in the ultraviolet absorption spectra of the copper complexes of bovine and human serum albumins.[12] The band at 375 mμ found in the bovine complex is not seen in the human. Klotz et al.[12] have drawn attention to the similarity between this absorption band and that shown by hemocyanin. Hughes[25] has suggested that some second group in the bovine albumin molecule shares the cupric ion with the sulfhydryl group and that the color is due to the whole chelate structure. Whether or not such a difference in neighboring groups would influence the behavior of the mercury derivatives of the two proteins is not certain, since mercuric and cupric ions form complexes of distinctly different steric properties.[26]

THE SOLUBILITY OF METAL-PROTEIN COMPLEXES

The property of a protein which is most obviously affected by combination with metallic cations is solubility. Indeed, far more striking examples of the specificity of metal-protein interactions are provided by observations on solubility than by the small number of binding studies made up to now. The study of protein solubility in the presence of metallic cations may appear at first sight to be a needless compounding of the uncertainties of two very complicated fields. Such studies have, nevertheless, two broad areas of application. One is in the separation and purification of proteins.[27, 28] The other is in the understanding of living systems, in which the proteins are normally exposed to metallic cations and may show the solubility behavior of the metal-protein complexes rather than of the proteins alone.

Many of the physico-chemical factors affecting the solubility of proteins[29] also play a part in determining the solubility of metal-protein complexes. For example, ethanol reduces the solubility of many such complexes.[27] Low concentrations of indifferent electrolytes generally tend to increase solubility. Temperature is an important variable from the points of view both of solubility and of stability.[10]

The following discussion of the solubility of metal-protein complexes is divided into five sections. First, solubility and metal binding studies are correlated for the case of a single purified protein, human serum albumin. Second, the specific differences between various proteins in their response to metallic ions are described. Third, the specific effects of anions on metal-protein interactions are taken into account. Fourth, the nature of the precipitates is discussed. Lastly, some general conclusions are drawn about the solubility of metal-protein complexes.

Solubility and Metal-Binding

The effects of different metallic ions on the solubilities of various proteins may be expected to depend in part on whether or not the specific requirements for binding are fulfilled. For instance, the specific effects of zinc and lead ions on the solubility of human serum mercaptalbumin appear only when the pH is raised above 4 (ref. 30, see especially Fig. 1) and 2,[9] respectively, in keeping with the results of the binding studies shown in Fig. 1.

The effect of zinc ions on the solubility of serum albumin is greatest in the pH range about 6.5–7.0, rather than near 5 as is found with sodium salts (ref. 30, Fig. 1). The higher pH of minimum solubility accords both with the greater zinc binding in this range (Fig. 1) and with the prediction that the positively charged zinc ions should form the least soluble complexes with albumin at a pH above the isoionic range, under conditions in which the protein itself bears a net negative charge. Qualitative observations indicate that the solubility minimum is likewise shifted to higher pH values when cupric and cadmium ions are employed, in keeping with their binding behavior discussed previously.

Although the metallic ion must bind if it is to affect solubility by mechanisms other than salting-in or salting-out, binding of a metallic cation does not necessarily affect the solubility of a protein markedly. Methylmercury nitrate has been found to interact very strongly with human serum albumin: for example, at $0°$ in 0.16 M sodium nitrate solution at pH 4.75 it was found that 49.4 moles of methylmercury were bound per mole of albumin when the concentration of unbound methylmercury was only 6.84×10^{-4} M.[31] Nevertheless, when a similar methylmercury-albumin mixture was compared with albumin that did not contain methylmercury, it was found that both solutions required the addition of the same quantities of ethanol for onset of precipitation or for comparable levels of solubility at $-5°$. Under similar conditions of pH, ionic strength, and concentration of unbound metallic ion, lead ion was bound to albumin to a somewhat smaller degree ($\bar{\nu}$ about 15–20) but caused extensive precipitation even in the absence of ethanol.[9]

Between these extremes of precipitating action for serum albumin shown by lead and by methylmercury ions fall the effects of cupric, cadmium, zinc, and nickelous ions. In the absence of other salts, 0.005–0.01 M cupric, cadmium, and zinc nitrates will cause decreasing amounts of precipitation when added at $0°$ to a 1 or 2% solution of salt-free human serum albumin adjusted with sodium hydroxide to pH 7.0–7.1. Nickelous nitrate does not cause precipitation under the same conditions. If the ionic strength is raised by the addition of a relatively indifferent electrolyte such as sodium nitrate, zinc ions no longer cause precipitation of the serum albumin. Cadmium ions still have some effect in 0.15 M sodium nitrate. If an organic solvent such as ethanol is added, all four of the cations under discussion cause precipitation of the albumin in the pH range 6–7. In alcohol-water mixtures, neutral salts seem to have much less solvent power for metal-protein complexes of this type than they have for albumin in the absence of such metals. This fact has made possible the complete precipitation of albumin by a combination of zinc ions and ethanol during plasma fractionation, without requiring large volumes of solvent in order to attain a low ionic strength.

The relative efficiencies of cupric, cadmium, zinc, and nickelous salts in precipitating human serum albumin in the pH range 6–7 are to some extent independent of differences in binding affinity. From the experiments on cadmium, summarized in Table II, and studies on the interaction of zinc ions with the same preparation of mercaptalbumin[10] it is established that cadmium ions are more effective precipitants than zinc ions when the two are compared at similar values of $\bar{\nu}$, ionic strength, and pH. Precise comparisons linking solubility with binding studies on cupric ions cannot yet be drawn. M. J. Hunter has observed that under conditions (at pH 6.3) in which nickelous ions were bound more extensively than zinc ions, albumin was precipitated by the latter but not by the former.[32]

Mercuric ion cannot be compared with the cations which have been discussed because of its strong tendency to hydrolyze. Mercuric nitrate solutions, for example, are unstable if the pH is appreciably greater than 2. Therefore, only poorly-dissociated salts such as the halides, which have already been discussed, or glycinate[30] may be studied, and the full effect of the ion cannot be manifested. Mercuric chloride affects the solubility of mercaptalbumin only slightly. If dimerization occurs, the solubility of the $Hg(SAlb.)_2$ dimer in alcohol-water mixtures is somewhat less than that of the monomer.[22]

Mercuric diglycinate reduces the solubility of albumin more effectively than mercuric chloride, but the most striking effect is found when mercuric diglycinate is added to a solution of albumin containing zinc diglycinate.[30] When human plasma is brought at 0° to 0.02 M zinc diglycinate at pH 7.0 many of the proteins are rendered insoluble, but the albumin remains almost completely soluble. Addition of mercuric diglycinate to 0.02 M (without changing the pH) causes very nearly complete precipitation of the albumin and of other proteins soluble in zinc diglycinate.[28, 30] The effect does not depend upon the order of addition of the metals. In an experiment with W. H. Batchelor it was found that such a precipitate, even after being washed with 0.010 M zinc diglycinate solution, contained considerable quantities of both metallic ions. The protein consisted of approximately 85 % serum albumin; calculated in terms of the same weight of pure albumin, the value of $\bar{\nu}$ for zinc was 19.6; for mercury, 24.5. The concentrations of the two metals in the wash solution were 1.01×10^{-2} M and 1.45×10^{-4} M, respectively. The principles of the analyses and the dithizone titration procedures have been described;[9] mercury was titrated in the presence of zinc after the addition of excess ethylenediaminetetraacetate, and zinc was determined from the difference between this value and that for the total metal. Protein was determined by dry weight.

Since methylmercury hydroxide is soluble in aqueous solutions,[b] it is possible to study the combined action of zinc and methylmercury without complications due to the presence of glycine. The precipitating action of zinc ions is not reinforced by methylmercury. Human serum albumin was adjusted at 0° to pH 7.0–7.1 in the presence and absence of 21–22 moles CH_3HgOH per mole of the protein. Samples of the two solutions were brought to 1.5 % protein concentration and 0.006 M zinc nitrate at 0°. The sample containing methylmercury remained clear and required the addition of about 5 % by volume of ethanol to reach a turbidity comparable to that of the mixture that did not contain methylmercury. Studies of the simultaneous binding of methylmercury and zinc have shown that each is bound almost independently of the other,[31] in keeping with the results described above with mixtures of zinc and mercuric diglycinates.

The qualitative observations on the effect of zinc ions on the solubility of albumin in the presence or absence of methylmercury were repeated using cupric and cadmium nitrates. Methylmercury again was observed to have no striking influence on the effect of the other metallic ions on the solubility of the protein.

The failure of methylmercury to reinforce or diminish the strong precipitating action of plumbous ions also has been observed in some preliminary experiments.[31] About 5 moles of lead perchlorate per mole of protein were mixed with 2 % human serum albumin at about pH 6 and dialyzed against methylmercury hydroxide solutions in a medium of 0.3 M sodium perchlorate at 0°. Although both metals bound to a considerable extent to the protein (for example, about 4 moles of lead and 12 moles of methylmercury), it remained soluble. When a sufficient concentration of lead was present to cause precipitation of the albumin, the lead was equally effective whether or not methylmercury was present.

In the studies on the binding of zinc and lead ions by human serum albumin,[8, 9, 31] the solubility of the protein has usually decreased with increasing $\bar{v}$.[c] A few attempts to measure $\bar{v}$ separately in both the pre-

[b] In the absence of halides or other ions which combine strongly with it, methylmercury forms a soluble hydroxide as the pH is raised from 3.5 to 5.5.[31] In a sense, methylmercuric ion is akin to hydrogen ion, and under certain conditions may be expected to affect the solubility of a given protein in much the same way as hydrogen ion.

[c] In certain cases the increase in ionic strength required to raise $\bar{v}$ may cause the protein to become more soluble.

cipitated and soluble protein fractions[33] have shown no marked differences in degree of binding. Very narrow ranges of conditions were studied, however, and the subject deserves more investigation.

Differences Between Proteins

The discussion of the relations between solubility and the degree of binding of metallic cations necessarily has been limited to the case of the most carefully studied protein, human serum albumin. The differences between the interactions of various proteins with metallic cations are well illustrated by simple observations on solubility alone, even when the amount of metal bound is not measured. In the following discussion some observations on the effects of certain cations on the solubility of fibrinogen, β-lipoprotein, γ-globulin, and some glycoproteins, all isolated from human plasma, will be used to illustrate the specific differences between various proteins in their response to the metallic cations.

Unlike albumin, many other proteins in plasma are almost completely precipitated on the addition of zinc diglycinate solution of pH 7.0–7.5.[30] The degree of dilution of the plasma (i.e., protein concentration and ionic strength) is not an important variable if the zinc concentration is made about 0.02 M. Among the proteins that are rendered almost completely insoluble under these conditions, fibrinogen, β-lipoprotein, and γ-globulin are present in greatest amount. W. B. Dandliker has shown that purified human fibrinogen may be precipitated by zinc at a concentration as low as 0.001 M.[34]

The effect of pH on the solubility of purified β-lipoprotein in the presence of certain acetate buffers is shown in Fig. 2. The preparation of the lipoprotein and method of determining solubility have been described.[35] The ionic strength was 0.04; in each case 0.01 was contributed by sodium acetate and 0.03 by the acetate salt under study. Water was the solvent for the experiments with zinc acetate, and 0.033 mole fraction ethanol was used for the other experiments. The temperatures were 0° and −3° for the two solvent systems, respectively. Dilute acetic acid was used to adjust the pH. The total lipoprotein concentration was 16 gm/liter. The precipitates were all soluble in ethylenediaminetetraacetate solution at pH near 6. Measurements of pH were made on the supernatant solutions at 25°.[35]

The results in Fig. 2 show that the pH dependence of the solubility in the presence of zinc ions is similar to that already discussed for serum albumin. The strong decrease in solubility as the pH approaches 6 is

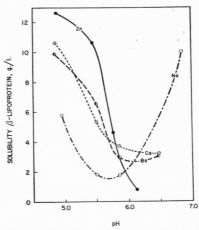

FIG. 2. Effect of pH on solubility of β-lipoprotein in acetate buffers. Ionic strength 0.01 contributed by sodium acetate, 0.03 by acetate salt under study. Zinc acetate experiments at 0° in water, all others at −3° in 0.033 mole fraction ethanol.

in marked contrast to the effect in sodium acetate alone. The curve for lithium acetate was so close to that for sodium acetate that it was omitted from the figure. The curves for calcium and barium ions have some resemblance to that for zinc, but neither of the alkaline earth metals compares quantitatively with zinc in precipitating power.

In sodium acetate buffers, the solubility of β-lipoprotein in the presence of the other proteins in plasma appears to be reduced by interaction with γ-globulin.[36] To test whether zinc acetate affected the coprecipitation of β-lipoprotein and γ-globulin, the experiments described in Table III were performed. The preparation of γ-globulin used was Fraction II-1, 2 (Lot L-413), the same material as was used for the earlier investigation;[36] this preparation was used for all studies reported here. The procedure for the spectrophotometric determination of the two proteins has been described.[36] The conditions were chosen so that a small amount of coprecipitation occurred in the absence of zinc acetate (Table III, first line). Each protein was soluble by itself in the absence of zinc acetate; in the presence of the concentration of zinc acetate employed, the γ-globulin remained soluble if the lipoprotein was not added.

The results in Table III show that a) the presence of zinc acetate caused the precipitation of *both* proteins in the mixture, and b) the

TABLE III

EFFECT OF ZINC ACETATE ON INTERACTION BETWEEN β-LIPOPROTEIN
AND γ-GLOBULIN

Total β-lipoprotein: 12.7 gm/liter in all tubes
Total γ-globulin: 12.3 gm/liter when present
Sodium acetate: 0.02 M; pH: 6.6–6.8; Temperature: 0°

γ-globulin present	Conc. zinc acetate ($M \times 10^3$)	Concentration dissolved proteins (gm/liter)	
		β-lipoprotein	γ-globulin
present	0.0	10.2	10.0
present	0.1	6.6	8.3
present	1.0	1.1	3.2
absent	0.1	11.0	—
absent	1.0	4.0	—

precipitation of β-lipoprotein by zinc acetate was accentuated by the
presence of γ-globulin. Apparently the β-lipoprotein–γ-globulin complexes are more sensitive than the separate proteins to the action of
zinc ions.

As will be shown below, under certain conditions barium acetate is a
relatively poor precipitating agent for γ-globulin. It was conceivable
that barium acetate might promote differentially the solubility of
γ-globulin in the presence of β-lipoprotein and zinc acetate. Therefore,
the two salts and two proteins were mixed together in different orders
with the results shown in Table IV. The looked-for effect was not
found; increasing the concentration of barium acetate affected both
proteins in the same way. The independence of the system of the order
of mixing was notable. In the last experiment in the table, the γ-globu-
lin–β-lipoprotein–zinc acetate mixture was stirred for an hour before
the barium was added. The mixture cleared noticeably as the barium
was added. In the absence of zinc, the 0.004 M barium acetate appeared
to make the β-lipoprotein–γ-globulin complexes slightly more soluble
than in the absence of both divalent metals.

The experiments described in Tables III and IV show that, under
conditions that allow β-lipoprotein and γ-globulin to interact in the
absence of heavy metallic cations, the presence of such cations does
not disrupt the interaction profoundly. Instead, the proteins continue
to influence each others' solubility behavior, even though the over-all
solubility is markedly changed by the addition of the metallic cations.

Human γ-globulin bears a positive net charge in the pH range 5–6.
The addition of salts to solutions of γ-globulins under these conditions

TABLE IV

Interaction Between β-Lipoprotein and γ-Globulin in the Presence of Barium and Zinc Acetates

Total β-lipoprotein: 12.7 gm/liter
Total γ-globulin: 12.3 gm/liter
Sodium acetate: 0.02 M; Zinc acetate: 0.001 M
Temperature: 0°; pH: 6.5–6.6

Conc. Barium acetate ($M \times 10^3$)	Order of addition to γ-globulin*	Concentration dissolved proteins (gm/liter)	
		β-lipoprotein	γ-globulin
4	Zn β Ba	2.8	7.8
4	Ba β Zn	2.8	7.3
4	(Zn Ba) β	3.2	7.6
4	β (Zn Ba)	3.2	7.9
4	β Zn Ba	2.7	7.8
4	β Ba Zn	2.7	7.8
10	Ba β Zn	5.9	10.0
10	β Zn Ba	5.9	9.8

* Symbols in parentheses indicate that Zn and Ba were mixed together beforehand.

decreases the solubility of the protein.[37] Of the sodium salts which have been studied, acetates and other short-chain fatty acids are the least effective in promoting precipitation of γ-globulin.[38] Acetates were accordingly chosen in a search for any possibly specific effects of metallic cations on the solubility of γ-globulins. That such effects do exist, even when the protein bears the same net charge as the metallic ion, is shown by the results illustrated in Fig. 3. Barium, zinc, sodium, and lithium

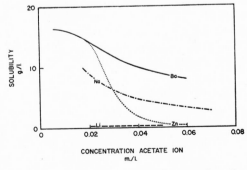

Fig. 3. Solubility of γ-globulin in acetate buffers as a function of concentration of acetate ion. Mole fraction ethanol 0.091; pH 5.4–5.7; temperature −5°.

acetates were compared. Solubility measurements were made in 0.091 mole fraction ethanol at −5°. The pH in all cases was adjusted to 5.4–5.7 with dilute acetic acid, and measured on an aliquot of the suspension at 25°. The total protein concentration was 18 gm/liter.

The salt concentrations are expressed in Fig. 3 in terms of acetate ion concentration, in deference to the very strong effects of the anions on the solubility of γ-globulin. The results show some striking specificities, with barium, zinc, sodium, and lithium each showing distinctive behavior. These results call to mind the surprising effects of various salts on the solubility of edestin.[39]

Barium and zinc acetates appear to differ from each other quantitatively and qualitatively in much the same way for γ-globulin (Fig. 3) as for β-lipoprotein (Fig. 2). However, γ-globulin distinguishes sharply between sodium and lithium, whereas, as mentioned above, β-lipoprotein does not. At a lower ethanol concentration, mole fraction 0.051, the effect of lithium acetate on γ-globulin follows a curve similar to that for zinc in Fig. 3.

A broader survey of the effects of various metallic acetates on the solubility of γ-globulin is summarized in Table V. The concentration of γ-globulin was determined spectrophotometrically and checked by biuret determination; agreement was almost always within 2%, except

TABLE V

SOLUBILITY OF HUMAN γ-GLOBULIN IN SOLUTIONS OF METALLIC ACETATES IN 0.091 MOLE FRACTION ETHANOL

Total Protein: 16 gm/liter; Temperature: −5°
Ionic strength: 0.0325 (composed of 0.02 M sodium acetate + 0.0125 ionic strength added metal acetate)

Cation	pH*	Solubility γ-globulin (gm/liter)
NH_4^+	5.43	6.65
Na^+	5.46	5.79
Li^+	5.51	4.75
Ba^{++}	5.45	15.8
Cd^{++}	5.63	11.0
Co^{++}	5.49	7.87
Ca^{++}	5.47	7.80
Cu^{++}	5.23	7.73
Mg^{++}	5.48	7.45
Ni^{++}	5.28	7.31
Zn^{++}	5.45	5.69

* Measured on the suspension at +25°.

that the biuret value was about 30% too high in the presence of cobalt. Sodium acetate formed the bulk of the electrolyte in each case, so that the specific effects are not as accentuated as they might be if the sodium acetate were omitted. Besides the effects of barium, zinc, and lithium ions, it is noteworthy that cadmium and cupric ions did not show any special tendency to reduce solubility, in marked contrast to their behavior towards serum albumin. These studies were carried out during the development of procedures for the precipitation of γ-globulins in which it was desirable to maintain the pH near 5.4.[27] It would be very helpful to extend the investigations to higher ranges of pH.

The α_1-glycoprotein, the final example chosen here to illustrate the diversity of solubility behavior of metal-protein complexes, is the most soluble protein in plasma under the usual conditions of study.[40] It remains in solution when even serum albumin is rendered almost totally insoluble by media containing both zinc salts and ethanol.[27] At pH 6.2 in 0.136 mole fraction ethanol at $-8°$ containing 0.01 M zinc acetate it is soluble to the extent of about 10 gm/liter. In barium acetate and, especially, cadmium acetate solutions it is less soluble under the same conditions.[40]

To render the glycoprotein insoluble in 0.066 mole fraction ethanol at pH 6.2 at $-5°$ (conditions under which zinc salts suffice to precipitate serum albumin) it is necessary to employ ions of such heavy metals as silver, lanthanum, thallium, and lead.[40] It is worth noting that the precipitation of serum albumin by lead salts requires no ethanol whatever.[9] By contrast, Tanford has reported negligible binding of thallous ion by bovine serum albumin.[7] The glycoprotein was crystallized by Schmid as a lead salt under the following conditions: 6.3% protein, 0.0072 M lead acetate, pH 5.4, 0 to $-8°$ C, 10.6% methanol, 10.6% acetone. More recently, other glycoproteins have been isolated which show distinctive behavior towards zinc, barium, and lead salts.[41]

Specific Effects of Anions

Up to now we have given little attention to the specific effects of anions on the solubility behavior of metal-protein complexes. With the exception of any strong chelating agent (which simply prevents the metal-protein interaction from occurring at all), the anion with the most influence on the solubility of metal-protein complexes is the hydroxyl ion. The role of the hydroxyl ion is multiple. The indirect effect of the addition of hydroxyl ions, the removal of hydrogen ions from combination with the protein, has two consequences which have already been discussed. One is the exposure of the reactive groups in the protein to the action of the metallic ion; the other is the neutralization, in whole or in part, of the net positive charge imparted to the protein particles by the bound metallic cations. The main direct effect of the hydroxyl ion is due to its high affinity for many of the cations which bind most strongly to proteins.

Depending somewhat on the concentration of zinc ion and on the temperature,[8, 42] appreciable hydrolysis of zinc ion begins to occur as the pH approaches 7.0. The pH range of the onset of hydrolysis of zinc ions in the presence of serum albumin[43] or β-lipoprotein[31] is at most 0.2 to 0.3 pH unit above that found in the absence of the protein, and the usual narrow range of pH is found for the uptake of the first two equivalents of hydroxyl ion.[42] This same pH range is critical from the point of view of solubility; the minimum solubility at 0° in the presence of zinc has been found to be near pH 7.0 for almost all the plasma proteins studied in this laboratory.

The increase in solubility between pH 7 and 8 could be due either to the removal of zinc ions as zinc hydroxide (competition for the metallic ions between hydroxyl ions and groups in the protein) or to the hydrolysis of zinc ions that remain combined with the protein. According to the latter alternative, the forms $ZnOH^+$ and $Zn(OH)_2$ and, ultimately, $Zn(OH)_3^-$, might be bound to the protein. In order to distinguish between these two alternatives, some preliminary experiments[31] have been carried out in which human serum albumin was equilibrated at pH 8.2–8.5 with the soluble zinc glycinate complexes formed by mixing the proportions of 1 mole of zinc nitrate with 3 moles of glycine and 2 moles of sodium hydroxide. No precipitation occurred, but it was found that zinc was bound strongly to the protein. For example, in one experiment, $\bar{\nu}$ for zinc was 19.5, and for glycine, 7.7.

It is clear from these results that the high pH did not cause the disruption of the zinc-albumin complexes. On the contrary, the binding of zinc was about maximal. Furthermore, a large fraction of the bound zinc was unattended by glycine, and so could have been in the forms Zn^{++}, $ZnOH^+$, or $Zn(OH)_2$, bound to imidazole groups[d] in the protein. The formation of mixed complexes of zinc ions with hydroxyl ions and imidazole molecules has been known for some time, and was employed in classical procedures for the preparation of imidazole derivatives.[44]

[d] Although there is no evidence to suggest the idea, it is possible that as the pH rose the zinc ions became distributed on new sets of sites in the protein, and hence that hydrolysis of the zinc ions was not the only change occurring as the pH increased.

As stated previously, the point of minimum solubility of a protein in the presence of a zinc salt may be expected to coincide with the pH at which the net charge on each protein molecule is close to zero. The net charge is perhaps controlled by the balance between a) charge due to the usual dissociation of hydrogen ions from groups in the protein, b) the charge due to the bound metal, and c) the charge due to hydrolysis of the bound metal. If appreciable numbers of zinc ions are bound, the balance between a and b at a pH just below 7.0 would be towards a positive net charge for a protein such as human serum albumin. With a small increment in pH, c would balance this effect, and the solubility minimum should be very close to pH 7. Some preliminary electrophoretic studies[45] of serum albumin in a zinc glycinate buffer at pH about 7.3 have confirmed that the protein complexes bore an appreciable negative charge under these conditions. The similarity of the pH range of the solubility minimum of most of the plasma proteins in the presence of zinc is explained by this hypothesis, because differences in the sum of a and b for different proteins would be compensated by c at the expense of very small differences in pH.[e] It should be interesting to examine whether or not the point of minimum solubility with other cations, such as cadmium and copper, is determined by the pH values of the onset of hydrolysis of these metallic ions.

The above interpretation of the pH dependence of the solubility of metal-protein complexes is applicable only to systems in which no appreciable precipitation of metallic hydroxide occurs. The phenomenon of precipitation of proteins by metallic hydroxides has been known for a long time and has recently been applied extensively to the separation of certain plasma proteins.[40] The binding of the protein molecule to the particles of metallic hydroxide may depend on essentially the same bonds as have been postulated above to bind the molecules of zinc hydroxide to the protein particles. The difference is that here the metallic hydroxide forms a matrix connecting zinc-protein bonds on one protein molecule with those on a neighboring protein molecule. Much more effective metallic hydroxides are prepared by adjusting the pH with ammonia buffers[40] than with sodium hydroxide.[32]

[e] The pH of minimum solubility of serum albumin in the presence of glycine (ref. 30, see Fig. 1) is slightly lower than in its absence. It is possible that this effect is due to some binding of zinc glycinate rather than of zinc ions. Perhaps more important are the suggestions (*vide infra*) that less zinc is bound by the protein in the presence of glycine (for a given total zinc concentration) and that in the absence of glycine some zinc hydroxide is precipitated and carries the protein with it.

In addition to hydroxyl ions, many other anions have specific effects on the solubility of metal-protein complexes. The anion and the protein may compete with each other for the cation. Such competition undoubtedly plays some role in the metal-hydroxide-protein system, but a more striking example that has already been discussed is the ability of halides to compete for mercuric ion with all groups in serum albumin except sulfhydryl.

Another very striking specific effect of an anion is shown in the ability of molar sodium acetate buffers to dissolve the precipitates formed on mixing serum albumin with lead perchlorate. Comparable or even higher concentrations of sodium perchlorate hardly affect the solubility of such complexes at all.[9] Relatively speaking, zinc-albumin precipitates are less sensitive to acetate ion, in keeping with the smaller affinity of acetate for zinc ions.[13] Cohn and co-workers have drawn attention to other anionic reagents which show specific effects upon cation-protein interactions.[28, 30]

Glycine, by forming complexes with zinc ions,[46, 47] reduces somewhat the binding of zinc to human serum albumin at about pH 6.4.[48] The results mentioned previously of the studies on more alkaline zinc-glycinate-albumin mixtures indicated that glycine as well as zinc was bound to the protein. Since control experiments showed very little binding by glycine in the absence of zinc, it seems very likely that the glycine was bound to the protein through a zinc ion bridge. This finding calls to mind the suggestions of Smith concerning the mode of action of peptidases.[3] Similar observations have been reported by Klotz and Loh Ming on the formation of mixed complexes in which a metallic ion mediated the interaction of a protein with a small molecule.[49] Such complexes in which the cation-protein complex is in turn modified by the combination with an anion presumably have special solubility characteristics of their own.

Anions bind of their own accord to certain proteins[6] and in some cases markedly affect solubility. For example, in Method 10 of plasma fractionation the reprecipitation of γ-globulin is completed by the addition of sodium sulfate in conjunction with zinc acetate.[50] The sulfate ion was chosen from among a number of anions which reduce the solubility of γ-globulin in the presence or absence of ions such as zinc.

In summary, anions may change the solubility of metal-protein complexes either by a) affecting the degree of cation binding by the protein, b) combining with the cation *in situ* on the protein, or c) by some effect peculiar to the anion in question and not necessarily directly related to the presence of the metallic ion. Such a classification is perhaps too rigid, since it implies that one could discriminate sharply between one factor or another. In any case, the specific effects of anions on the solubility of metal-protein complexes may be interpreted in terms of these factors, taken either singly or together.

Nature of the Precipitates

The nature of the precipitates formed by proteins in the presence of metallic cations such as those of zinc, mercury, and lead should be of interest to anyone who wishes to separate proteins by these methods. Such precipitates also may serve as models for some of those formed in biological systems and involving, for example, calcium ions.

One of the most striking properties of the metal-protein precipitates studied in this laboratory is the large volume that they occupy. For example, when zinc and mercury diglycinates caused the precipitation of the albumin-rich fraction of the plasma proteins, as described in an earlier section, it was found that, even after centrifugation, the precipitate occupied approximately the same volume as the plasma from which it was derived and contained only 4.7 % protein. By contrast, the same protein precipitated by ethanol would usually pack under equivalent centrifugal force to a concentration of 15 % or more. When both metallic reagent and ethanol were used simultaneously, as in the precipitation of the similar Fraction IV + V in Method 10,[27] the precipitate was also voluminous.

The bulkiness of the metal-protein precipitates means that, under certain conditions, precipitation has more the form of a gelation than of the separation of a precipitate from a supernatant solution. By adding alternately small volumes of solutions containing metallic reagents or chelating agents such as citrates, it is possible repeatedly to form and redisperse the massive precipitates. If similar phenomena in living systems also involve metallic ions, it is intriguing to consider that the supply of chelating agent (for example, citrate) could be controlled by metabolic processes.

Serum albumin crystals, in which the molecules are well oriented and intermolecular distances are relatively small, contain about 45 % protein.[51] The metal-protein precipitate containing only 5 % protein must have a very open structure, with relatively small areas of contact between the protein molecules. In keeping with this picture is the extreme rapidity with which solids form on the addition of the metallic ions, and also the rapid resolution on the addition of agents that reverse the process. More important is the accessibility of the groups in the protein molecule in such solid phases. The titration of insoluble proteins[52] has shown that the usual groups are accessible to hydrogen ions. And, as shown in Table I, the lead-albumin precipitate has been found to be freely reactive with zinc ions.[9]

One point of difference between the protein precipitates formed by the action of ethanol and of metallic reagents is that precipitation with ethanol is normally carried out when the protein is nearly isoelectric. The metallic reagents, on the other hand, are such effective precipitating agents that in this laboratory they have been employed successfully over wide ranges of pH. Normally it is not necessary to arrive at conditions under which solubility is truly minimal because precipitation remains almost complete even when the average net charge on the protein complexes is not essentially zero.

Such charge effects are particularly likely in the case of the precipitates of serum albumin formed on the addition of both perchloric acid and lead perchlorate.[9] Here precipitation was complete over a wide range of conditions in which the isoionic protein was found to have combined with sufficient hydrogen and lead ions to supply a positive charge of about 100 to each albumin molecule. Much of this charge may have been neutralized by binding of perchlorate ion, but the individual protein molecules still must have carried appreciable net charges, calling to mind an analogy between such precipitates and cross-linked polyelectrolytes.

Many observers in this laboratory and elsewhere have noticed that, on standing, metal-protein precipitates become less easy to redissolve by addition of minimal quantities of chelating agents such as glycine. The phenomenon seems to be related to structural changes in the precipitate; once the precipitate is redissolved, it is no easier than before to cause precipitation again. An extreme expression of this phenomenon is the observation of F. M. Richards[53] that crude casein precipitated by zinc glycinate was insoluble in much lower concentrations of zinc than were required to cause the initial precipitation. After resolution and addition of more zinc reagent, the same observations were repeated. In this system the hysteresis effects seemed to become more pronounced the longer the precipitate was allowed to stand, although they were striking no matter how rapidly the manipulations were carried out.

General Conclusions

Several general conclusions stand out from the preceding description of the solubility behavior of metal-protein complexes: a) The study of the interrelationships between solubility and binding with human serum albumin shows that metallic ions (e.g., cadmium and zinc) which bind to the same sites in the protein affect solubility in a qualitatively similar but quantitatively different way. b) Metallic ions which do not bind to the same sites may have very different effects both qualitatively and quantitatively (lead and zinc) and may even show what appear to be additive effects (mercury and zinc). c) An ion, such as methylmercury, which lacks more than one strong coordinative valence may not affect the solubility of a protein, either by itself or in the presence of effective ions. d) Different proteins interact in specific ways with certain metallic ions, although points of similarity with respect to pH dependence may reflect similarities in the underlying mechanisms. e) Interactions between different proteins need not be disrupted by the introduction of ions which affect the solubility of each protein in the absence of the other. f) The effects of anions may be explained under the headings of affecting the degree of cation-binding by the protein, combining with the cation *in situ* on the protein molecule, or showing some specific effect not necessarily related to the metal-protein interaction. g) The precipitates are voluminous, the individual groups in the protein molecules are readily accessible to certain solutes,

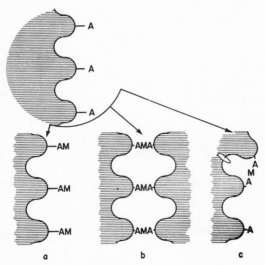

Fig. 4. Diagram showing postulated types of metal-protein complexes. a: Binding of metal (M) to individual groups (A) in a protein molecule. b: Cross-linking in an intermolecular complex. c: Cross-linking in an intramolecular complex.

and there seems to be a tendency for some intermolecular rearrangements to occur during aging.

Some alternative types of metal-protein interaction are summarized diagramatically in Fig. 4. In the simplest type shown in Fig. 4a each metallic ion, M, is bound to a single group, A, in the protein. This appears to be the most common type of binding in the case of zinc ions and human serum albumin in solution.[8] Presumably methylmercury also binds in this way.

In Fig. 4b is shown a cross-linked structure in which the metallic ion, M, is combined with a group in each of two protein molecules. Cross-linking has been clearly demonstrated in the case of serum mercaptalbumin mercury dimer.[5, 14] Binding of more than one ligand group at a time to a metallic ion is well known.[6, 13] Of the metallic ions which have been discussed here, only methylmercury appears to be incapable of combining with more than one ligand group at a time. The failure of methylmercury to affect the solubility of serum albumin might be taken to support the idea that the "multivalent" character of metallic ions is a primary factor in the formation of insoluble metal-protein complexes.[f] Tanford and Epstein[54] have shown that the transition of amorphous zinc insulin into crystalline zinc insulin involves the displacement of bound hydrogen ion and have taken this as evidence of intermolecular cross-linking. It would be interesting to find out whether or not the binding of zinc ion also changes.

A third general type of metal-protein interaction is illustrated in Fig. 4c. This is the case of intramolecular cross-linking or chelation. The possible importance of chelate binding in metal-protein interactions has been discussed by Schwarzenbach.[55] As mentioned previously, it is possible that cupric ion enters into a chelate complex with the sulfhydryl group and another (unspecified) group in bovine serum albumin.[12, 25]

Of the three types of interaction depicted in Fig. 4, intermolecular cross-linking is the one most obviously likely to render the protein insoluble. The effect of the simple type (a) of binding is not predictable at present. In general, binding of this type should affect the dipole moment and solvation of the protein. Furthermore, it is unlikely that the group A in the protein is without influence on its neighbors in the

[f] This point applies equally to intermolecular cross-linking (Fig. 4b) and intramolecular cross-linking (Fig. 4c). The effect of bond formation with one ligand group on the affinity of the metallic ion for a second group[13] may be important in influencing the tendency of a metallic ion to form cross-linkages.

protein molecule, and the combination with M may cause some subtle rearrangements, even swelling or shrinking. Laskowski and Scheraga[56] recently proposed a formal theory concerning internal hydrogen bonds linking together reactive groups in the side-chains of proteins.

It is equally difficult to predict the effects on solubility which might result from the intramolecular cross-linking type of structure (Fig. 4c). Here both groups (A) attached to the metal (M) need not be identical, and one of them could be a group to which the metallic ion would not normally show measurable affinity.[55] Since many metallic ions have more than two coordinative valences, it is possible for a metallic ion to take part simultaneously in both intramolecular and intermolecular cross-linking. The drawing in Fig. 4c illustrates a further possible consequence of intramolecular cross-linking; the protein molecule may be constrained to a certain configuration that shows characteristic solubility properties. How subtle the effects of bound ions may be is shown by the marked influence of fatty acids and other small molecules on the ease of crystallization of serum albumins,[57, 58] as well as on the rate of formation of the mercury dimer.[23, 24]

We have seen that there is evidence that each of the alternatives in Fig. 4 actually occurs in some particular metal-protein interaction. In any metal-protein precipitate the distribution of bound metallic ions between the possible forms symbolized in Fig. 4 should be statistically determined by the location, number and nature of the specific A groups in the protein molecule, the concentration of the protein, and the properties and activity of the metallic ion. Even if intermolecular cross-linking is the main mechanism which renders the protein insoluble, relatively few cross-linkages may be needed. This is implied by the stability of the albumin mercury dimer,[5] the small number of lead ions required to precipitate serum albumin,[9] and the small number of barium ions necessary to cause the formation of oriented gels of serum albumin under certain conditions.[59] Indeed, the rigidity of the protein molecules and the steric properties of the metal-ligand bonds[26] should be expected to limit the number of intermolecular cross-linkages. In the insoluble lead-serum albumin complexes, most metal-protein bonds appear to be of type 4a.[9] In the pH range where hydrolysis of the metallic ion occurs, the cross-linkages may be formed of particles of metallic hydroxide (see section on specific effects of anions, above). In this case many more groups (A) in the protein molecules might be interconnected. Such structures would very likely show hysteresis of the type already mentioned in the section on nature of the precipitates.

One would expect that at full saturation with metallic ions all linkages would be of the type illustrated in Fig. 4a. In none of the studies considered here has there been any sign of increased solubility as the degree of binding increased. It might be concluded, therefore, that the insoluble forms are of the type of Fig. 4a or 4c rather than of Fig. 4b. Experimentally, however, it is difficult to achieve full saturation. For example, there is no reason to believe that some binding of zinc ions to amino groups in serum albumin may not occur as the imidazole groups approach saturation.[8] Indeed, the results with zinc glycinate mixtures described earlier could well be interpreted in such a way. Very few metallic bridges connecting each protein molecule with its neighbor would be sufficient to maintain a three-dimensional structure.

ACKNOWLEDGMENT

I wish to acknowledge the help of all my colleagues in the University Laboratory whose work and ideas I have drawn on freely. Many of the ideas expressed here came out of discussions with the late Dr. Edwin J. Cohn. I am indebted to Drs. G. Scatchard, J. T. Edsall, J. L. Oncley, and M. J. Hunter for their criticisms of the manuscript.

REFERENCES

1. SURGENOR, D. M., KOECHLIN, B. A., and STRONG, L. E., *J. Clin. Invest.* **28**, 73 (1949).
2. LAURELL, C. B., *Pharmacol. Revs.* **4**, 371 (1952).
3. SMITH, E. L., *in* "Enzymes and Enzyme Systems" (J. T. Edsall, ed.), p. 47. Harvard University Press, Cambridge, 1951.
4. MCLEAN, F. C., and HASTINGS, A. B., *J. Biol. Chem.* **108**, 285 (1935).
5. HUGHES, W. L., JR., *Cold Spring Harbor Symposia Quant. Biol.* **14**, 79 (1950).
6. SCATCHARD, G., HUGHES, W. L., JR., GURD, F. R. N., and WILCOX, P. E., *in* "Chemical Specificity in Biological Interactions" (F. R. N. Gurd, ed.), Chap. XI, Academic Press, New York, 1954.
7. TANFORD, C., *J. Am. Chem. Soc.* **74**, 211 (1952).
8. GURD, F. R. N., and GOODMAN, D. S., *J. Am. Chem. Soc.* **74**, 670 (1952).
9. GURD, F. R. N., and MURRAY, G. R., JR., *J. Am. Chem. Soc.* **75**, 187 (1954).
10. GURD, F. R. N., and FITTING, C., unpublished results.
11. SCHWARZENBACH, G., BIEDERMANN, W., AND BANGERTER, F., *Helv. Chim. Acta* **29**, 811 (1946).
12. KLOTZ, I. M., URQUHART, J. M., AND FIESS, H. A., *J. Am. Chem. Soc.* **74**, 5537 (1952).
13. BJERRUM, J., *Chem. Revs.* **46**, 381 (1950).
14. EDELHOCH, H., KATCHALSKI, E., MAYBURY, R. H., HUGHES, W. L., JR., and EDSALL, J. T., *J. Am. Chem. Soc.* **75**, 5058 (1953).
15. ANSON, M. L., *Advances in Protein Chem.* **2**, 361 (1945).
16. PUTNAM, F. W., *in* "The Proteins" (H. Neurath and K. Bailey, eds.), Vol. IB, p. 893. Academic Press, New York, 1953.

17. ANSON, M. L., *J. Gen. Physiol.* **24,** 399 (1941).

18. KLOTZ, I. M., *in* "The Proteins" (H. Neurath and K. Bailey, eds.), Vol, IB, p. 727. Academic Press, New York, 1953.

19. KARUSH, F., *J. Am. Chem. Soc.* **72,** 2705, 2714 (1950).

20. SCATCHARD, G., SCHEINBERG, I. H., AND ARMSTRONG, S. H., JR., *J. Am. Chem. Soc.* **72,** 535, 540 (1950).

21. KLOTZ, I. M., and AYERS, J., *Discussions Faraday Soc.* **13,** 189 (1953).

22. HUGHES, W. L., JR., *J. Am. Chem. Soc.* **69,** 1836 (1947).

23. MAYBURY, R. H., and DINTZIS, H. M., *Abst. 124th Meeting Am. Chem. Soc., Chicago,* p. 18C (Sept., 1953).

24. EDSALL, J. T., accompanying chapter in this volume.

25. HUGHES, W. L., JR., personal communication.

26. WELLS, A. F., "Structural Inorganic Chemistry, Chapter 16. Oxford University Press, New York, 1945.

27. COHN, E. J., GURD, F. R. N., SURGENOR, D. M., BARNES, B. A., BROWN, R. K., DEROUAUX, G., GILLESPIE, J. M., KAHNT, F. W., LEVER, W. F., LIU, C. H., MITTELMAN, D., MOUTON, R. F., SCHMID, K., and UROMA, E., *J. Am. Chem. Soc.* **72,** 465 (1950).

28. COHN, E. J., *in* "Blood Cells and Plasma Proteins" (J. L. Tullis, ed.), Section I, Chapter 3, p. 29. Academic Press, New York, 1953.

29. COHN, E. J., and EDSALL, J. T., "Proteins, Amino Acids and Peptides, pp. 569–622. Reinhold Publishing Corp., New York, 1943.

30. COHN, E. J., SURGENOR, D. M., SCHMID, K., BATCHELOR, W. H., ISLIKER, H. C., and ALAMERI, E. H., *Discussions Faraday Soc.* **13,** 176 (1953).

31. GURD, F. R. N., unpublished results.

32. HUNTER, M. J., personal communication.

33. GURD, F. R. N., and MURRAY, G. R., JR., unpublished results.

34. DANDLIKER, W. B., personal communication.

35. ONCLEY, J. L., GURD, F. R. N., and MELIN, M., *J. Am. Chem. Soc.* **72,** 458 (1950).

36. ONCLEY, J. L., ELLENBOGEN, E., GITLIN, D., and GURD, F. R. N., *J. Phys. & Colloid Chem.* **56,** 85 (1952).

37. ONCLEY, J. L., MELIN, M., RICHERT, D. A., CAMERON, J. W., and GROSS, P. M., JR., *J. Am. Chem. Soc.* **71,** 541 (1949).

38. ONCLEY, J. L., GORDON, F. H. GURD, F. R. N., and LONTIE, R. A., *Abst. 119th Meeting Am. Chem. Soc., Boston,* p. 28C (April, 1951).

39. OSBORNE, T. B., and HARRIS, I. F., *Am. J. Physiol.* **14,** 151 (1905).

40. SCHMID, K., *J. Am. Chem. Soc.* **75,** 60 (1953).

41. SCHMID, K., *J. Am. Chem. Soc.* **75,** 2532 (1953).

42. FEITKNECHT, W., and HÄBERLI, E., *Helv. Chim. Acta* **33,** 922 (1950).

43. WILCOX, P. E., personal communication.

44. WINDAUS, A., and KNOOP, F., *Ber.* **38,** 1166 (1905).

45. GURD, F. R. N., and THOMPSON, T. E., unpublished observations.

46. GREENWALD, I., *J. Phys. Chem.* **47,** 607 (1943).

47. FLOOD, H., and LORAS, V., *Tidsskr. Kjemi, Bergvesen Met.* **6,** 83 (1945).

48. GOODMAN, D. S., Thesis for A. B. degree with Honors, Harvard College, 1951.

49. KLOTZ, I. M., and LOH MING, W.-C., *Abstr. 123rd Meeting Am. Chem. Soc. Los Angeles*, p. 35C (March, 1953).

50. LEVER, W. F., GURD, F. R. N., UROMA, E., BROWN, R. K., BARNES, B. A., SCHMID, K., and SCHULTZ, E. L., *J. Clin. Invest.* **30,** 99 (1951).

51. LOW, B. W., *J. Am. Chem. Soc.* **74,** 4830 (1952).

52. STEINHARDT, J., *Ann. N. Y. Acad. Sci.* **41,** 287 (1941).

53. RICHARDS, F. M., personal communication.

54. TANFORD, C., and EPSTEIN, J., *Abstr. 124th Meeting Am. Chem. Soc. Chicago,* p. 31C (Sept., 1953).

55. SCHWARZENBACH, G., *in* "Chemical Specificity in Biological Interactions" (F. R. N. Gurd, ed.), Chap. X, Academic Press, New York, 1954.

56. LASKOWSKI, M., JR., and SCHERAGA, H. A., *Abstr. 124th Meeting Am. Chem. Soc. Chicago*, p. 31C (Sept., 1953).

57. COHN, E. J., HUGHES, W. L., JR., and WEARE, J. H., *J. Am. Chem. Soc.* **69,** 1753 (1947).

58. ONCLEY, J. L., and DINTZIS, H., *Abstr. 122nd Meeting Am. Chem. Soc., Atlantic City*, p. 19C (Sept., 1952).

59. LOW, B. W., and WEICHEL, E. J., *J. Am. Chem. Soc.* **73,** 3911 (1951).

Equilibrium and Sedimentation of Uncharged Particles in Inhomogeneous Electric Fields

P. DEBYE

In a recent "Letter to the Editor"[a] experiments have been described, showing that polymer solutions adjust the concentration distribution of the solute when subjected to the influence of inhomogeneous electric fields. In this note the more quantitative aspects of this effect will be discussed.

GENERAL CONSIDERATIONS AS TO THE ORDER OF MAGNITUDE OF THE EFFECT

A particle of positive polarizability α in an electric field E will be driven to places of increasing electric energy density, since its potential energy can be represented by the expression

$$-\frac{\alpha}{2} E^2$$

The well known method of P. Curie for measuring magnetic susceptibilities makes use of the analogous force in a magnetic field. If the particle is a molecule of a solute surrounded by solvent molecules, α is the effective polarizability, the value of which can be derived from the change of dielectric constant with concentration. If the original dielectric constant is ϵ_0 and if, by dissolving n solute molecules per cubic centimeter, it changes to a value ϵ, the relation is

$$\epsilon - \epsilon_0 = 4\pi n \alpha \tag{1}$$

in which, for nonpolar molecules, ϵ can be identified with the square of the refractive index.

The order of magnitude of α, which by the way has the dimensions of a volume, is the volume of the molecule. Now if we want to obtain appreciable effects it will be necessary for the electrical energy to be comparable with the thermal energy. This leads to the condition that

[a] P. Debye, P. P. Debye, B. H. Eckstein, W. H. Barber, and G. J. Arquette, *J. Chem. Phys.* **22**, 152 (1954).

we should use field strengths of an order of magnitude to be derived from the equation

$$\frac{\alpha}{2} E^2 = kT \tag{2}$$

Substituting 10^{-24} cm^3 for α and 4×10^{-14} ergs for kT at room temperature, it follows that

$$E = 2 \times 10^5 \text{ esu} = 60 \times 10^6 \text{ volts/cm}$$

This is the order of magnitude of the fields active in the vicinity of ions. It cannot be doubted that salting-out is primarily due to the action of these strong and inhomogeneous electrical fields which surround all ions. However, such forces act only over short distances and other forces of the same order of magnitude are active at the same time. As a result of this the actual activity of nonelectrolytes in ionized salt solutions has rather more complicated features.[b] Anyway, it would be impossible to subject ordinary nonconductive liquids to artificial fields of several million volts per centimeter without breakdown. As soon, however, as we go over to polymer molecules, α can be considerably increased. A 1 % solution of polystyrene in benzene, for instance, increases the refractive index over that of pure benzene by about one unit in the third decimal. From this it follows by using equation (1) that the average monomer in the polymer chain has under these circumstances an effective polarizability $\alpha = 2 \times 10^{-24}$. Therefore if we should experiment with a polymer of molecular weight 500,000, the polarizability of this molecule will be 10,000 times larger than the value used in the foregoing calculation. This means that in this case our estimate of the necessary field strength is 100 times smaller, namely 600,000 volts/cm. We may suspect that in order to succeed it will be sufficient if the electrical energy is only a fraction of the thermal energy, say for instance 1 %. This would mean that the estimated necessary field strength is 60,000 volts/cm and fields of this order of magnitude can certainly be sustained in insulating liquids.

The expected change in concentration is determined by Boltzmann's relation, according to which the number of particles n per cubic centimeter at the place where the field equals E divided by the number of particles n_0 at the place where $E = 0$ is

$$\frac{n}{n_0} = \exp\left(\frac{\alpha E^2}{2kT}\right) \tag{3}$$

[b] See, for instance: F. A. Long and W. F. McDevit, *Chem. Revs.*, **51**, 119 (1952).

This shows that as long as the effect is small the fractional change in concentration equals the electrical energy divided by thermal energy. This relation is of course correct only for ideal solutions. Later on we will see what the correction is in the nonideal case.

EXPERIMENTAL ARRANGEMENT USING A CYLINDRICAL CONDENSER

The first requirement is that the solution be influenced by an inhomogeneous field. This was obtained in our experiments by the use of a cylindrical condenser, the inner cylinder being a wire of a diameter of 0.1 mm and the outer cylinder with a diameter of 5 cm approximately.

The potential ϕ in this arrangement at a distance r from the center is

$$\Phi = \frac{Q2}{L} \int_r^A \frac{dr}{\epsilon r} \tag{4}$$

in which Q/L is the charge per unit length of the inner wire, ϵ is the dielectric constant of the medium, and A is the radius of the outer cylinder. The potential is supposed to be zero at this cylinder. If ϵ is constant throughout, this means that

$$\phi = \frac{2Q}{\epsilon L} \ln \frac{A}{r} \tag{5}$$

which makes the field strength E equal to

$$E = \frac{2Q}{\epsilon L} \frac{1}{r} \tag{6}$$

Taking the radius of the inner wire to be $r = a$ and the total applied potential V, it follows from equation (5) that

$$Q = \frac{\epsilon L}{2 \ln \dfrac{A}{a}} V \tag{7}$$

which shows that the capacity C is

$$C = \frac{\epsilon L}{2 \ln \dfrac{A}{a}} \tag{8}$$

From (6) and (7) it follows now that

$$E = \frac{V}{a \ln \dfrac{A}{a}} \frac{a}{r} \tag{9}$$

If in our case we apply, for example, a potential of 7,000 volts, the field strength at the surface of the wire becomes 225,000 volts/cm.

Under the influence of the inhomogeneous field that has an electrical energy density which increases proportionally to $1/r^2$ with decreasing distance from the center, solute will move to the center (at least if, as in our example, it has a positive effective polarizability). After equilibrium is established we shall have a condenser in which the concentration of the solution increases with decreasing r and therefore the dielectric constant of the medium will no longer be constant but also increase with diminishing distance. Equation (4) still holds. If we now write

$$\epsilon = \bar{\epsilon} \, (1 + \sigma) \tag{10}$$

in which the fractional variation σ of $\bar{\epsilon}$ is a function of r, and treat this variation σ as small, it follows immediately that the capacity has changed from C to $C + \Delta C$ and we find

$$\frac{\Delta C}{C} = \frac{1}{\ln \dfrac{A}{a}} \int_a^A \sigma \, \frac{dr}{r} \tag{11}$$

We now consider the case in which the concentration changes are relatively small, i.e., the case in which Boltzmann's exponential function e^x can be approximated by $1 + x$. In this case the fractional change in concentration is proportional to E^2, and since E is proportional to $1/r$ we can take it that

$$\sigma = \sigma_0 \, \frac{a^2}{r^2}$$

where we indicate by σ_0 the fractional change in dielectric constant at the surface of the wire. With this assumption we find from (11)

$$\frac{\Delta C}{C} = \frac{\sigma_0}{2 \ln \dfrac{A}{a}} \left(1 - \frac{a^2}{A^2} \right) \tag{12}$$

in which the second term in brackets can of course be neglected.

Now in our example we had at the surface of the wire a field $E_0 = 225,000$ volts/cm $= 750$ esu. Suppose we consider the case of polystyrene, of molecular weight 1,000,000, in benzene and let us accept the value of $\alpha = 2 \times 10^{-24}$ cm^3 for the average monomer of the chain. Since the molecular weight of the average monomer is about 50, the polarizability of the polymer molecule will be $\alpha = 4 \times 10^{-20}$ cm.^{3} Under these circumstances the fractional concentration change at the surface of the wire will be

$$\frac{\Delta n}{n} = \alpha \frac{E_0^2}{2kT} = 0.28$$

We know that for a 1% solution of polystyrene in benzene the corresponding increase of the refractive index is 0.001 unit over that of benzene. Taking for the index of refraction of benzene the value $\mu = 1.5$ and remembering that the dielectric constant is equal to the square of the refractive index, it now is easily calculated that for such a solution and at the surface of the wire the fractional change of the dielectric constant is

$$\sigma_0 = 3.7 \times 10^{-4}$$

Substituting this value of σ_0 in equation (12) we see that for our condenser the application of 7,000 volts should lead to an increase in capacity ΔC, which follows from

$$\frac{\Delta C}{C} = 3 \times 10^{-5}$$

It is this change in capacity which is being measured by the beat-method in our experiment. Supposing that no other additional capacity exists and that the induction has been arranged so as to give a frequency of 5 megacycles, the calculated change in capacity would correspond to 75 beats per second.

It can easily be seen that, in the approximation we have been using, the number of beats to be observed is directly proportional to the molecular weight. For a substance with a distribution of molecular weights the average observed is the weight average.

Actually the number of beats per second is less than the calculated value. One reason for this is that additional capacity is present in the circuit. Another more important reason is that the solutions which have been used cannot be considered as ideal.

Nonideal Solutions

Solutions of coiling polymers of high molecular weight already show deviations from ideality at rather low concentrations. This is due to the fact that the molecular coil extends over a large volume of the solvent and therefore interaction occurs when the centers of those coils are still relatively far apart. Light-scattering experiments have shown that the diameter of the coil for a polystyrene of 1,000,000 molecular weight in benzene is roughly 1000 Å. In order to obtain an average distance of the molecular centers of 1000 Å we need only 10^{15} molecules/cm^3 and this corresponds to a concentration of only 1.7×10^{-3} gm/cm^3.

How interaction affects the concentration changes in electrical fields can easily be calculated if osmotic pressure or light scattering has been measured as a function of concentration.

According to the definition of osmotic pressure P we shall have equilibrium when

$$n \operatorname{grad}\left(\frac{\alpha}{2} E^2\right) - \operatorname{grad} P = 0 \tag{13}$$

which immediately leads to the relation

$$\int \frac{d}{dn}\left(\frac{P}{kT}\right) \frac{dn}{n} = \frac{\alpha E^2}{2kT} \tag{14}$$

Now it has often been shown that the formula

$$P = nkT[1 + Bn] \tag{15}$$

with an experimental constant B is a good approximation to the actual behavior of the osmotic pressure. By substituting this relation in equation (14) and performing the integration, we arrive at the new relation

$$\ln \frac{n}{n_0} + 2B(n - n_0) = \frac{\alpha E^2}{2kT} \tag{16}$$

in which n_0 is the number of solute molecules per cubic centimeter at a place where $E = 0$. In the limit for small effects this reduces to

$$\frac{n - n_0}{n_0} = \frac{\alpha E^2}{2kT} \frac{1}{1 + 2Bn_0} \tag{16a}$$

At higher concentrations the actual effect of the electrical field is therefore a good deal smaller than the effect calculated for ideal solutions. The change in concentration $(n - n_0)$ is proportional to the concentration only in the limit for small concentrations. With increasing concentrations and according to (16a) the effect should reach a limit. This is the same kind of behavior as observed for the intensity of the scattered light. The constant B becomes smaller in poorer solvents. This is why, in some of our experiments, cyclohexane was chosen as a solvent for polystyrene.

DISTURBANCES DUE TO HEATING

Any electric conductivity of the liquid filling the condenser will cause local heating and therefore expansion. Coupled with the expansion is a decrease of the dielectric constant, so we have another reason for a change in the capacity. As we saw, the concentration effect is proportional to E^2. The same is true for the heating effect. It therefore becomes necessary to determine how high the specific resistance of the liquid should be in order to eliminate the heating effect.

We shall be considering the most unfavorable case if we assume that the heat is carried away by heat conductivity only and that heat cannot escape through the inner wire but only through the outside cylinder.

In this case, the temperature difference τ measured against the temperature of the outer cylinder has to obey the equation

$$\frac{1}{r}\frac{d}{dr}r\frac{d\tau}{dr} + \frac{q}{\lambda} = 0 \tag{17}$$

in which q is the heat in calories produced per cubic centimeter per second and λ is the heat conductivity in calories per centimeter per second.

If the electric field strength E is expressed in volts per centimeter, and the specific resistance ρ of the liquid in ohm-centimeters, we have

$$q = \frac{E^2}{4.19\rho}$$

On the other hand we know that

$$E = E_0\frac{a}{r}$$

when E_0 is the field strength at the surface of the wire. It follows that

$$q = q_0\frac{a^2}{r^2} \tag{18}$$

with

$$q_0 = \frac{E_0^2}{4.19\rho} \tag{18a}$$

The boundary conditions for τ in equation (17) are

$$\tau = 0 \text{ for } r = A; \quad \frac{d\tau}{dr} = 0 \text{ for } r = a \tag{19}$$

The solution is

$$\tau = \frac{q_0 a^2}{2\lambda}\left[\left(\ln\frac{A}{a}\right)^2 - \left(\ln\frac{r}{a}\right)^2\right] \qquad (20)$$

In the case discussed before we had $E_0 = 225{,}000$ volts/cm. Taking for the heat conductivity that of benzene, $\lambda = 3.33 \times 10^{-4}$ cal/cm. sec, and substituting, we arrive at the temperature τ_0 at the surface of the wire

$$\tau_0 = \frac{q_0 a^2}{2\lambda}\left(\ln\frac{A}{a}\right)^2 = \frac{1.75 \times 10^{10}}{\rho} \qquad (21)$$

From the Clausius-Mosotti equation we know that $(\epsilon - 1)/(\epsilon + 2)$ is proportional to the density. For nonpolar liquids this is as good a base as any to calculate the temperature coefficient of the dielectric constant. If we denote the expansion coefficient of the liquid by β and write as before

$$\epsilon = \bar{\epsilon}(1 + \sigma)$$

it follows that at the surface of the wire

$$\sigma = \sigma_0 = -\frac{(\epsilon - 1)(\epsilon + 2)}{3\epsilon}\beta\tau_0 \qquad (22)$$

With $\beta = 1.2 \times 10^{-3}$, $\epsilon = 2.25$, and the value of τ_0 from equation (21), this gives

$$\sigma_0 = -\frac{1.65 \times 10^7}{\rho} \qquad (22a)$$

Now we saw before that the change in capacity due to local variations of the dielectric constant can be calculated from the relation

$$\frac{\Delta C}{C} = \frac{1}{\ln\dfrac{A}{a}}\int_a^A \sigma\,\frac{dr}{r}$$

Since at a distance r

$$\sigma = \sigma_0\left[1 - \left(\frac{\ln\dfrac{r}{a}}{\ln\dfrac{A}{a}}\right)^2\right]$$

we finally come to the conclusion, by performing the integration, that the heating effect results in a capacity change to be calculated in our case, in which we supposed that 7000 volts were applied to the condenser, from the relation

$$\frac{\Delta C}{C} = \frac{2}{3}\,\sigma_0 = -\,\frac{1.1 \times 10^7}{\rho} \qquad (23)$$

It was seen above that the concentration effect under the same circumstances was

$$\frac{\Delta C}{C} = 3 \times 10^{-5}$$

It is evident that in order to eliminate practically the heating effect we should strive to obtain a specific resistance of the liquid which exceeds $\rho = 10^{13}$ ohm-cm. In our experiments the electric conductivity has always been lower. Sometimes a specific resistance of up to 5×10^{15} ohm-cm has been obtained by our electric cleaning method.

EFFECT OF ELECTROSTRICTION AND ELECTRIC DOUBLE REFRACTION

A strong electric field can cause changes of the dielectric constant even in a liquid of one component. Where there is a gradient of the electric energy density, a force exists acting on every element of volume in the direction of increasing E^2. As a result of this force the pressure in the liquid varies from point to point. Since the liquid is compressible, pressure changes are accompanied by density changes and consequently by changes in the dielectric constant. At every point where the field strength is E we have an excess pressure

$$p = \frac{\kappa}{2}\,E^2 \quad (p \text{ in dynes/cm}^2\ E \text{ in esu}) \qquad (24)$$

a relation in which κ is the dielectric susceptibility defined as

$$\kappa = \frac{\epsilon - 1}{4\pi} \qquad (24a)$$

In our example, with a field of 225,000 volts/cm at the surface of the wire, the excess pressure at this point calculates to

$$p = 2.8 \times 10^4 \text{ dynes/cm}^2 = 2.8 \times 10^{-2} \text{ atm}$$

The compressibility of benzene is $\gamma = 10^{-4}$ atm^{-1}. At the innermost point we now have a relative change of density equal to $\gamma p = 2.8 \times 10^{-6}$, and, in analogy to equation (22), the corresponding fractional change of the dielectric constant will be

$$\sigma_0 = \frac{(\epsilon - 1)(\epsilon + 2)}{3\epsilon}\,\gamma\,\frac{\kappa}{2}\,E^2 = 2.2 \times 10^{-6} \qquad (25)$$

For a point at distance r the change will be

$$\sigma = \sigma_0 \frac{a^2}{r^2} = 2.2 \times 10^{-6} \frac{a^2}{r^2} \qquad (25)$$

Since the dependence of σ on the distance r is the same as in the case of concentration changes, formula (12) holds and we find

$$\frac{\Delta C}{C} = \frac{\sigma_0}{2 \ln \dfrac{A}{a}} = 1.8 \times 10^{-7} \qquad (26)$$

This is about 160 times smaller than the capacity change calculated (assuming ideal solutions) as due to concentration changes, in our example in which 7000 volts were applied.

The above estimates hold for nonpolar solvents. Should the solvent be polar, we would have to take account of the saturation effect.[c]

Finally there is still another reason why the dielectric constant changes in a strong field, called the Kerr effect. This change is due to an orientation of the molecules. Different changes occur in the direction of the field and perpendicular to it. In the effect detected by Kerr these changes are demonstrated by observing phase differences between light vibrating in the direction and perpendicular to the direction of the field, which passes through the liquid in a direction perpendicular to the field direction. It may suffice to say that according to observational values for this double refraction, the effect on the capacity is in our case many times smaller than the electrostriction effect.

DEPENDENCE ON TIME

All our considerations so far have been based on the equilibrium case. This equilibrium cannot be reached instantaneously. It will be established very fast in the electrostriction case, but where concentration changes are involved we shall have to transport solute molecules, and this will take an appreciable time. As a matter of fact it takes several minutes in our experimental arrangement before a final number of beats per second is counted. No detailed calculation of the time dependence of the capacity changes has yet been made. However, it is easy to make an estimate of what can be expected.

[c] This interesting effect is fully discussed in the book of G. J. F. Bottcher, "Theory of Electric Polarisation," p. 193. Elsevier, New York, 1952. The only experimental verification I know of is by F. Kautzsch. *Physik. Z.* **29**, 105 (1928).

If a molecule of effective polarizability α is subjected to an inhomogeneous field, the force F acting on the molecule is

$$F = \text{grad}\left(\frac{\alpha}{2} E^2\right)$$

This force will drive the solute molecules to the wire. At the same time a concentration gradient is set up and solute molecules will begin to diffuse back into the liquid. When the material currents due to both these motions are opposite and equal, we shall have reached the equilibrium which was discussed before.

In our case we have

$$F = -\alpha \frac{E_0^2}{a} \frac{a^3}{r^3} \tag{27}$$

Substituting $E_0 = 225,000$ volt/cm $= 750$ esu, $\alpha = 4 \times 10^{-20}$ cm^3, and $a = 5 \times 10^{-3}$, we have at the surface of the wire

$$F = F_0 = 4.5 \times 10^{-12} \text{ dynes}$$

This is of the same order of magnitude as the force on a univalent ion in an electric field of 1 volt/cm, which is 1.6×10^{-12} dynes. Under the influence of this force a sodium ion moves in water with a velocity of 5.2×10^{-4} cm/sec. However, the frictional constant[d] for our polymers is much larger. For a Na$^+$ ion the values just given correspond to a frictional constant $f = 0.31 \times 10^{-8}$ gm/sec. On the other hand we find in the literature[e] that, according to Beckman and Rosenberg, a polystyrene molecule of molecular weight 240,000 has a diffusion constant $D = 3.6 \times 10^{-7}$ cm^2/sec in toluene. Since the Einstein relation

$$D = \frac{kT}{f}$$

is general, this means that $f = 1.1 \times 10^{-7}$ gm/sec. This is 35 times larger than the frictional constant of a Na$^+$ ion in water. At the same time the molecular weight is 240,000 and not 1,000,000 as it was in our example. In our arrangement, with 7000 volts applied, the driving force then is 0.24 times F_0 as calculated above, which makes it 1.1×10^{-12} dynes. Such a molecule would therefore move with a velocity of 10^{-5}

---

[d] The frictional constant is defined as the factor by which the velocity has to be multiplied in order to obtain the frictional force opposing the driving force.

[e] R. H. Boundy and R. F. Boyer, "Styrene," p. 389. Reinhold, New York, 1952.

cm/sec in our arrangement. This means that it would take 500 sec to move over a distance equal to the radius of the central wire.

In view of this estimate it seems reasonable to expect that the establishment of the final change in capacity will be of the order of several minutes.

These considerations are intimately connected with an interesting possibility. The driving force in our experiments is proportional to the polarizability and this is, in our polymers, proportional to the molecular weight. On the other hand it is well known that the frictional constant for such polymers increases more slowly with increasing molecular weight (approximately represented by the square root of the molecular weight for high molecular weights). This means that, if we are dealing with a mixture of different molecular weights, we can expect that a curve representing the number of beats per second observed at consecutive time-spots during the establishment of the equilibrium will have features revealing details of the molecular weight distribution. After all, what we are dealing with here is a perfect analogy to sedimentation in an ultracentrifuge. This also makes it clear that we can expect this method of analysis to be effective only when solutions are employed which are dilute enough to eliminate too strong an interaction between the solute molecules.

FIELD INDUCED DIFFRACTION

In 1932 it was shown that supersonic waves traveling through a liquid can act like a diffraction grating.[f] If a parallel beam of light is passed through the liquid perpendicular to the direction of propagation of the sound waves, diffraction spectra can easily be observed. The angles at which these spectra appear are determined by the grating constant, which in this case is the wavelength of the supersonic waves in the liquid. This effect demonstrates that only relatively small changes of the refractive index of the liquid are necessary in order to produce relatively large intensities of the diffraction spectra. This is clear since the periodic changes of the refractive index in the liquid, which are the ultimate reason for the grating effect, are caused by the small periodic density variations of the liquid in the path of the sound wave.

In the "Letter to the Editor" of the Journal of Chemical Physics,

[f] P. Debye and F. W. Sears, *Proc. Natl. Acad. Sci. U. S.* **18**, 409 (1932); *Physik. Z.* **33**, 849 (1932).

R. Lucas and P. Biquard, *Comptes. rend.* **194**, 2132 (1932); *J. phys. radium* [VII] **3**, 464 (1932).

already mentioned,[a] experiments are described in which a similar grating effect is produced with the help of an arrangement by which a periodic accumulation of electric energy density is projected into a liquid. This is done by a pack of razor blades fixed at constant mutual distances and with their edges parallel to a plate. A voltage difference applied to the pack and plate arrangement produces the desired field distribution in the liquid in which this arrangement is immersed. Here I only wish to clarify why the arrangement as described is a very sensitive tool for detecting very small changes in the refractive index.

The number of light waves in a path parallel to a razor blade edge is about 10^5. The diffraction effect is due to the phase difference between a light ray passing underneath an edge and another light ray passing underneath the middle of the space between two edges. If a phase difference of even only one-tenth of a wavelength can be produced between these two rays, the intensity of the first-order spectrum becomes quite appreciable. Theoretically this intensity should be about 2.5% of the intensity of the central image. Taking again our case of a 1% solution of a polystyrene of molecular weight 1,000,000 in benzene, we know that a change in the index of refraction of 0.001 is produced by making the 1% solution. In order to obtain a phase difference of 0.1 wavelength on a path of 10^5 wavelengths it is necessary to change the refractive index only by one part in 10^6. This can be done by changing the concentration by 1 part in 10^3. In order to do this we need

$$\frac{\alpha E^2}{2kT} = 10^{-3}$$

with $\alpha = 4 \times 10^{-20}$ cm^3 and $kT = 4 \times 10^{-14}$ ergs this relation yields

$$E = 45 \text{ esu} = 13,500 \text{ volts/cm}$$

As a matter of fact, in our arrangement it is the difference in E^2 below the edge and at the same height below the middle of the gap between two edges which is important. However, it is evident that observable diffraction can be produced with relatively small applied potentials.

Author Index

287

Subject Index

Accumulation of specific ions, 70
Adsorbability, of ions, 182
Acetylcholine, 65, 116
  effect on membrane permeability, 39, 48
  electrogenic action, 46
  metabolic pathways, 42
  pharmacological action, 39
  receptor, 48
  synthesis, 46
Acetylcholinesterase, 17, 39, 65
  anionic site, 53, 54, 56
  binding forces, 50, 52
  concentration, 43
  Coulombic forces, 50
  difference with receptor, 62
  essentiality in nerve conduction, 40
  esteratic site, 53, 54, 56
  hydrolytic process, 57
  irreversible inhibitors, 41
  localization, 39
  specificity, 39
  turnover number, 39
Acidity of tubular urine, 81
Action potential, 116
Activation of membranes, by poly-electrolytes, 148
Active transport, 6, 13, 18
Activity coefficient, of dipolar ion, 221, 224
Adrenal hormones, 84, 89
Albumin dimer, dissociation by cyanide, 240, 241
Alcohol, in protein fractionation, 225
Alkyl phosphates, 41
  mechanism of esterase inhibition, 58
  pH dependence, 58
  reversal of inhibitory action, 59
Alternating electric potential, 125
Ammonia, 81
Anaerobic glycolysis, 19

Anions, binding by proteins, 251, 264
  by serum albumin, 226
  effects on solubility of metal-protein complexes, 261
Anomalous osmosis, 150, 151, 158–163
  rates of, 162
Anticholinesterases, 17
ATP, and bioelectric potential, 45
Atropin, 15
Availability of groups for metal ions, 250
Axon, membrane, 23

Back diffusion, 18
Beat method, 277
Bernstein theory of nerve potential, 25
Bi-ionic potentials, 137, 175–185
Bimolecular layers, 73
Binding of ions, 189, 206
Bioelectric potentials, 35
  action of acetylcholine, 39, 47
  change in permeability, 38
  energy sources, 44
  impedance changes, 36
  ion movements, 36
  membrane theory, 36
  sodium permeability, 36
Boltzmann's relation, 274
Boundary, Henderson, 133
  Planck, 133

Calcium ion, binding by serum proteins, 246
Carbon dioxide, 17
Carbonic anhydrase, 17, 37, 81, 82, 85, 94
Carboxyl group, binding of metals, 247
Cardiac output, 78
Carrier, 11, 20
  from substrate, 12
Casein-zinc complex, 266

293